OFF OUT

OFF OUT

by Gill Adams

WARNER CHAPPELL PLAYS

LONDON

A Time Warner Company

OFF OUT first published in 1994
by Warner Chappell Plays Ltd
129 Park Street, London W1Y 3FA

Copyright © 1994 by Gill Adams

The author asserts her moral right to be identified as the author of the work.

ISBN 0 85676 173 7

Printed by Commercial Colour Press, London E7

For my Mam and Dad
who taught me never to give up

OFF OUT was first presented by Hull Truck Theatre Company at the Assembly Rooms, Edinburgh, as part of the Edinburgh Fringe Festival on 15th August, 1994. After winning a Scotsman *Fringe First* Award, the play transferred to the Hull Truck Theatre, Hull in September, 1994 and the Riverside Studios, London in November, 1994. The cast was as follows:

JUNE	Sarah Parks
MAC	Tim Dantay
MAY	Emma Morgan
DANNY	Darren Tighe

Directed by Damien Cruden
Designed by Liam Doona
Lighting Design by Niall Black

The play is set in Hull, in the present, but could be set in any typical Northern town.

FOREWORD

When I first decided to write a play based on prostitution, all I knew was that I didn't want it to be just another documentary about the business. What appealed to me most was the other side, the women themselves and their home life. I also didn't want the play to be totally salacious, because I didn't want a lot of dirty old men in Macs turning up expecting to be titillated by women cavorting around in suspenders and high heels. Street life is very different. It's hard and often brutal.

Just before Christmas 1993, I started researching prostitution in Hull. I spent some time going out with the Hull Vice Department, and met with the women on the streets and in their homes. Mostly the women were keen to talk, even straight after 'doing business'. It was no big deal to them. Just a job.

Most women learn very quickly ways of detaching themselves from 'the job'. They also have to often be able to rise above what people say. Neighbours, friends, families and even partners can often turn against them because of what they do, not who they are. They cannot afford to be too emotional or soft, they have to learn how to look after themselves. When you're parked down a deserted back street miles from anywhere, who's going to hear you scream? Who really cares?

Above all I wanted an audience to realise that every night women like June and May are working the streets, not only in Hull but in most cities, selling their bodies and often risking their lives for one reason only . . . for money.

On the same day we celebrated winning the Fringe First Award in Edinburgh, one of the girls who had helped me with my research was found murdered in Hull. She was 31 and saving to get married.

Gill Adams
October, 1994

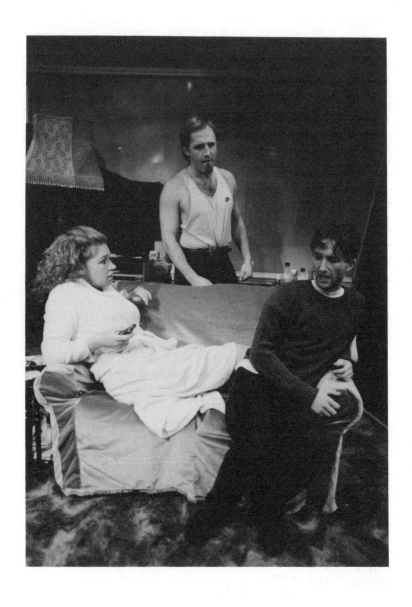

Photograph by Lamplight-Wakefield from the Hull Truck
Theatre Company production of *Off Out*

ACT ONE

Scene One

The setting is the living room and through-kitchen of June's *mother's house. Old-fashioned, dull, dark furniture except for a drinks trolley, record player, a small stacking table set and* June's *personal clutter. A drab, covered settee centre stage. To one side a large, ugly dresser/sideboard unit, with a "praying hands" statue on it, and an empty fruit bowl. A mirror is suspended above it. The room is a shell — off balance, cage-like. Outside the house is wasteland and street, which forms part of the playing area.*

It is 40 days before Christmas. June *sits sorting out which nail varnish to put on. Her son* Danny *is watching telly. She looks at the window thoughtfully.*

JUNE   It's nearly dark. I 'ate Winter. Them nets allus
          remind me of weddin's . . .

DANNY   Well, get rid of 'em then.

JUNE   I never said I didn't like 'em, I do. I said they
          remind me of weddin's, that's all. I do like 'em . . .
          they remind me of what I've never 'ad.

DANNY   That's why I watch *The Waltons* . . .

JUNE   I'll do a roast on Sunday, eh?

DANNY   If you like . . .

JUNE   Lamb?

DANNY   If you like . . .

JUNE   I'll get some fruit for that fruit bowl an' all.
          There's nothing worse than an empty fruit bowl
          . . . I can't stand to see an empty fruit bowl . . .
          it's like bein' a kid again. Fruit bowls are just
          ornaments to me.

DANNY   You don't eat fruit . . .

JUNE   So . . . it looks nice . . .

DANNY   Not when it goes rotten, and it allus goes rotten in this 'ouse, it's such a waste . . .

JUNE   (*sarcastic*) I know . . . 'ere, shall we put on a sad song and 'ave a good weep?

DANNY   No, *Home 'n Away*'s on in a minute . . .

JUNE   Do you like this colour? (*The nail varnish.*)

DANNY   No . . .

JUNE   What about this one? It's nice is this one . . . do you like this one? . . . I do . . . I think . . .

DANNY   What you wearing?

JUNE   Blue . . .

DANNY   It'll clash . . .

JUNE   What, with blue? . . . Nowt clashes with blue, does it? . . . Are you sure? Oh I don't friggin' know . . . are you sure?

DANNY   It'll clash. Wear red.

JUNE   What sort of red.

DANNY   Red red . . .

JUNE   Red? Are you sure?

DANNY   You can't go wrong with red. Unless you're wearin' orange of course . . .

JUNE   Now oranges look nice. They last an' all do oranges. I like them little 'uns . . . they allus remind me of Christmas.

DANNY   Satsumas, Tangerines or Clementines?

JUNE   Russets do an' all. I'll get some Russets . . . 'Ere, we could 'ave turkey?

DANNY   If you like . . .

JUNE   And a nice bunch of grapes.

DANNY   Grapes remind me of me Granny. Before she went she practically lived on grapes . . . Mind you she'd only eat seedless. She'd go barmy if I got 'er the other ones, said they were bad for you. Bad for your kidneys, give you stones.

JUNE   If you ask me it was probably the seedless ones that killed 'er.

DANNY   It was 'er heart . . .

JUNE   She never 'ad an 'eart. Now pomegranates allus remind me of Hull Fair . . . what do ya think about bananas?

DANNY   I'd rather not. Anyway they soon go rotten and stink . . .

JUNE   True. I used to like plums once. I did, I knew a fella that grew 'em, big 'uns an' all . . . in't it funny how you go off things . . . 'Ere, what about this colour?

DANNY   What's it called?

JUNE   Flame summat or other . . . red I think, yeah, flame red. It's from Woolworths in Scarborough . . . I got it last year, do ya remember? We wiped 'em out. That basket near the check-out all at half price. Robbin' bastards. Do ya remember? They'd all dried up, but this one was alright . . . I think . . . I'd 'ave played up 'ell if we 'an't 'ave been on our way to the bus. (*Pause.*) Flame red. I've a lipstick to match . . . I think.

        (*Pause.*)

DANNY   We could 'ave pork . . .

JUNE   No, I'll stick with lamb, it makes lovely gravy . . .
'Ere, do ya remember me on that donkey?

DANNY   How could I forget . . .

JUNE   I think it's awful the way they treat them
animals, don't you?

DANNY   They're fed regular . . .

JUNE   I suppose I could get a bit of beef, mind you I'm
allus unlucky with beef . . . They see me coming
with beef . . . It's allus tough is mine . . .

DANNY   You cook it all wrong. Anyway, donkeys don't
know any different.

JUNE   It's still not right though is it? I mean, to think
Jesus was sat on one of them once, and is this
what they've come down to? Poor buggers,
traipsin' up and down bloody beaches all day. It's
not right . . .

(*Pause.*)

DANNY   They 'ave their photo taken a lot . . .

JUNE   'Aye, with fat old ladies squashin' 'em . . . it's
rotten it is — it's mean . . . 'Ere — pour your
mother a gin. (*He does, she starts to paint her
nails.*) Danny, will you do me right 'and for us, I
can never do me right 'and . . . I'm useless with
me left. Do ya know, if I broke me right 'and I'd
be buggered . . . mind you me nerves are bad . . .
just look at that. (*Holds up her hands.*) At this
rate I'll probably mess the left 'un up an' all.
Where's that gin? . . . steady me nerves . . .

DANNY   (*looks at her, brings her the drink*) Oh come 'ere,
I'll do 'em for you . . . (*Moves closer.*) Your nails
are in a shockin' state . . .

JUNE   I know, it's shovin' false 'uns on all the time. I
think they sort of die underneath.

DANNY	I always thought you'd have nice hands.
JUNE	Age does cruel things to a woman . . .
DANNY	It's not age, it's neglect . . . Keep still . . .
JUNE	I can't afford to pamper myself . . .
DANNY	A bit of hand cream won't 'urt . . .
JUNE	It never stops there. Chemists are so up-market these days. It's all money.
DANNY	Well, you're gonna have to seek professional advice. These are shocking!
JUNE	I know, I'm ashamed.
DANNY	And this one, look at it . . . where's it gone?
JUNE	It dropped off . . .
DANNY	I thought the whole idea of false nails were that they're convenient?
JUNE	Well they are if they stay on . . . but once they drop off that's it. I'm not really in the right job for perfect nails . . . nails and stockings are a nightmare for me.
DANNY	You should buy in bulk. Stick to one make and buy in bulk.
JUNE	I know, you're right . . . I will . . .
DANNY	So what are you doing with your little finger?
JUNE	No one'll notice . . .
DANNY	Do ya want me to do this or not?
JUNE	Yeah . . .
DANNY	Well if I'm doin' it, I'm doing it properly, unlike you Mother, I'm a perfectionist . . .

JUNE   I don't care what you are, you're still my son. (*Kisses his forehead playfully.*)

DANNY   Stop fidgeting . . . I can't perform miracles. Ten fingers . . . and eight and a half nails. Jesus would 'ave 'ad a field day with this lot . . .

JUNE   Aye, sod the fish . . . reduce me bust, and give me hands like the Virgin Mary . . .

DANNY   'Course they'd love the likes of you, you're such a religious challenge . . .

JUNE   Says who?

DANNY   God.

JUNE   Says your bloody Granny . . .

DANNY   Same thing.

JUNE   Don't sit there spouting religion Danny, you're no bloody saint.

DANNY   'Ave you got a spare one somewhere? For your little finger.

JUNE   No. Look, can't you just paint 'em and 'ave done with it . . .

DANNY   You never do a job properly . . .

JUNE   I do . . .

DANNY   You don't. Keep still . . .

JUNE   We're missin' *Home 'n Away* you know . . .

DANNY   It won't hurt . . .

JUNE   I knew I should 'ave put a record on . . .

DANNY   Your music makes you depressed . . . .

JUNE   Everything makes me depressed.

DANNY	It's the life you lead.
JUNE	It's you sat there looking at me with your Granny's bleedin' eyes. I know . . .
DANNY	Don't worry Mam, guilt's steadily going out of fashion. Devil worship's in vogue now.
JUNE	True, it's like Arma-bloody-geddon down the Social . . .
DANNY	I mean, in times of trouble, who reaches for the Bible these days?
JUNE	Danny, let it drop.
DANNY	No, let's face it, it's much more likely to be Freemans Catalogue.
JUNE	'Aye, or Avon. (*Beat.*) Does me hair look like it needs washing?
DANNY	You mean to say you 'an't washed it yet?
JUNE	I forgot . . .
DANNY	See, you never do a job properly . . .
JUNE	Shall I not bother?
DANNY	No . . . I'll do it . . . (JUNE *smiles.*) I sometimes think you deliberately forget things . . .
JUNE	I know, it's me age. 'Ere, shove a record on, one we both like.
DANNY	Oh, alright then . . . 'Ere, blow on them, gently, else they'll come off . . .
JUNE	Danny?
DANNY	What?
JUNE	Put Al Jolson on . . .

(DANNY *puts on Al Jolson. It is the song*
'Mammy'. He pours her a tall drink with all the
works. She blows her nails. He sits by her and
lights her a cigarette then holds it for her 'til her
nails dry.)

DANNY   They'll need another coat . . .

JUNE   They're smashing now . . .

DANNY   Another layer and I'll be happy . . .

          (*She holds out her hand.*)

JUNE   What are you up to tonight?

DANNY   I'm cutting me nails and I've a week's worth of
          Emmerdale on tape.

JUNE   Why don't you meet me after?

DANNY   You never turn up . . .

JUNE   We can 'ave an Indian or summat . . .

DANNY   I don't eat after six o'clock . . .

JUNE   You're too thin, you are . . .

DANNY   I like bein' thin . . .

JUNE   You should pump some of that iron — like Mac.

DANNY   I like bein' thin . . .

JUNE   Mac's got lovely muscles . . .

DANNY   . . . and no brain.

JUNE   Do ya know, when I put me lipstick on it spreads
          very slowly into the creases round me mouth . . .
          In't that terrible?

DANNY   They're laugh lines, everyone's got laugh lines.
          Even if you don't laugh you get laugh lines.

JUNE   Even when I pencil round 'em . . . me smile sort of slips . . . I use to 'ave such lovely lips . . . sensual . . . like Marilyn Monroe. (*Pouts.*)

DANNY   You do exaggerate . . .

JUNE   I did . . . it was before you were born . . .

DANNY   The things you had and did before I was born . . . 'onestly, you do romance . . . don't fiddle, you'll smudge 'em . . .

JUNE   I blame the wind . . .

DANNY   You've hardly touched your drink. Is it too weak?

JUNE   It's all that standing around in the cold. They get chapped. Do ya know, last winter when I was caught in that hail storm, I swear it aged me a year. I do. I hate the cold. Me eyes go puffy, me nose runs and me lips crack. I wish I could wear gloves but they irritate me. I've even been known to go deaf with the pain in me ears . . . headscarf, and no one'll look at ya . . . you can't win. The only advantage in winter is the dark nights . . . and I hate dark nights.

DANNY   I know, it's a hard life. Still look on the bright side. There's only forty nights left to Christmas. Right, your nails are done, now let's tackle that hair. (*Feeling the ends of her hair.*) It's very dry. The ends are terrible.

JUNE   It's fucked.

DANNY   It just needs some T.L.C.

JUNE   I've been using washing-up liquid.

DANNY   I know . . . you're so lazy . . .

JUNE   Well it's like the Arctic in that bathroom, at least in the kitchen you can put the oven on. I'd kill for central heating.

DANNY   You walk around half naked . . . (*He runs his
             fingers through her hair with great difficulty.*)
             Well if you're gonna wash your hair in the
             kitchen you could at least bring the shampoo
             down.

JUNE   (*sarcastic*) So what's this T.L.C. stuff, have we
             got some?

DANNY   Surprisingly, yes. Come on then, let's sort you
             out . . . just watch them nails.

JUNE   (*looks at her nails*) It's a nice colour, in't it?

DANNY   Near perfection . . .

             (*The lights fade.*)

                            Scene Two

The street. Sound of loud thunder and rain. MAC *runs directly
towards the audience shouting in a rage as if running down
the street after a punter driving off.* MAY *runs on behind
holding her face. She is bleeding. Both are soaked through.*

MAC   You fucker! Get 'ere! (*Turns back to* MAY.) Come
             on, get up.

MAY   Am I bleeding . . . Mac . . . am I?

MAC   Shut up!

MAY   But am I?

MAC   NO.

MAY   Bastard liar, I am . . . look I am, I'm bleeding. I
             think I'm gonna need stitching . . .

MAC   (*on edge*) I'm trying to think.

MAY   Will you take me down casualty?

MAC   You're bleedin' stupid.

MAY	I know . . . but will ya?
MAC	Did ya know 'im . . . did ya know 'im?
MAY	Will ya Mac?
MAC	*Did ya know 'im?*
MAY	No . . . (*Obviously now in some pain, holding her face.*) Shit . . .
MAC	Fuck.
MAY	Will ya?
MAC	Idiot.
MAY	Me belly's killin' me . . . I feel sick.
MAC	Brilliant.
MAY	But I do . . .
MAC	This . . . is . . . it . . .
MAY	Me face is killing me.
MAC	Well what do ya think it's doing to me?
MAY	I feel horrible . . . ugh, I feel horrible.
MAC	Well 'urry up and be sick.
MAY	I can't.
MAC	If you want a lift 'urry up. (MAC *strides off.*)
MAY	(*running behind him, weakly*) I'm alright now.
MAC	I don't want me car in a state.
MAY	Do ya think I'm gonna need stitching?
MAC	Get a fuckin' move on.
MAY	God I hate stitches. (*Whining, childlike.*) Is it still bleeding?

MAC   (*turns suddenly, pushing* MAY *in front of him*) Get
               in the fucking car!

               (*They exit into the darkness.*)

                            Scene Three

DANNY *is hoovering up. The fruit bowl has been filled with
fruit.* JUNE *walks in and collapses on the settee.* DANNY *turns
the hoover off and looks at her.*

DANNY   You're early . . .

JUNE   I'm badly . . .

DANNY   Can you see double?

JUNE   No . . . well I don't think so. (*Playful.*) Who's
               that?

DANNY   Where?

JUNE   Stood next to ya . . . 'Ere, cheeky bugger's just
               winked at me!

DANNY   Shoes off . . . (*Helps her take her shoes off.*)

JUNE   Me ingrowing toenail's playing me up again . . .
               'Ere, kiss it better for me . . . come 'ere . . . come
               on, give ya Mam a kiss.

DANNY   You haven't even noticed 'ave yer?

JUNE   Give ya Mam a big kiss . . . (*Pouts.*)

DANNY   I don't know why I bother . . . I don't. (*Sulking.*)
               Look. (*Points to the fruit bowl.*) Halfway into
               town I had to go to get that lot . . .

JUNE   It's fruit . . .

DANNY   'Course it's fruit! It's in a fruit bowl.

JUNE   I don't eat fruit . . . It gives me the runs.

DANNY   It's not to eat, it's to look at . . .

JUNE   'Ere, is there a film on?

DANNY   (*picks her shoes up*) You've trod in something disgusting . . .

JUNE   You don't know the half of it. I'm knackered . . .

DANNY   (*looking at her heels*) Your heels are on the way out . . .

JUNE   Well tell 'em to use the doormat this time . . . dirty bastards . . .

DANNY   I wish you wouldn't swear like that. No wonder we 'ave no luck.

JUNE   It's you, you was born in a thunderstorm.

DANNY   No wonder I've got chronic asthma . . . I was conceived in the fog and born in a storm . . .

JUNE   You're just highly strung . . .

DANNY   It comes from havin' a mother who drinks . . .

JUNE   I drink because of you.

DANNY   You drink because you want to . . .

JUNE   'Cos I'm miserable . . .

DANNY   A few large gins and you're a monster.

JUNE   It's not the gin.

DANNY   (*quiet*) No . . . well we're savin' for a rainy day, remember?

JUNE   It's allus bloody rainin' . . .

DANNY   A sunny day then.

JUNE   I'm sick of it . . . I'm not bloody double jointed, not at my age. I'm wrecked . . . me back's killin' me, me hot flushes are getting ridiculous and me balance is all to cock.

DANNY   It's your shoes, they need heeling.

JUNE   Maybe I'm dying — me tongue feels disgusting.

DANNY   It's probably rubber fatigue.

JUNE   Do I look old? I do, don't I? Do ya know I was sat on the lav' the other day and I swear I pulled out an 'air on me chin that was nearly an inch long. You could 'ave told me.

DANNY   You look your age. There's no shame in that. Look at Pat Phoenix. She made a living out of it. It's just your outfits that deceive people.

JUNE   What's wrong with this?

DANNY   It's a size twelve . . .

JUNE   So?

DANNY   And you're a sixteen . . .

JUNE   Ah, shurrup!

(JUNE *drinks her gin.*)

DANNY   Your innards must be pickled . . .

JUNE   So's me outers . . . me tit's 'ave dropped. 'Onest to God, it's like dragging a ton weight around. I daren't teck me brassiere off, I'd put some poor sod's eyes out. I would.

DANNY   The joys of womanhood . . .

JUNE   My arse . . . if I ever 'ad to run agen I'd be buggered.

(*She stares into space, smoking.* DANNY *makes the tea and then brings* JUNE *her slippers and dressing gown.*)

DANNY   Another bad night?

JUNE   Shurrup . . .

DANNY   Shall I run you a bath?

JUNE   . . . And hold me head under . . .

DANNY   'Ave a good soak . . . you allus feel better after a
             good soak. I tell you what, I'll put some of them
             Dead Sea Crystals in it, that'll revive you . . . ten
             minutes and you'll feel like a new woman, eh?
             What do ya say?

JUNE   I 'an't been clean for years, look at me, me eyes
             are poking out a bag of nothin', me whole body's
             hanging . . . I drag it round like a sack of rotten
             fish, I do.

DANNY   Here we go . . .

JUNE   I stand next to other women and they gag . . .

DANNY   (sighs) 'Course they do . . .

JUNE   When I die they'll smoke me, hang me by me legs
             to dry out . . . They 'ate me round 'ere, dodge
             between parked cars, kids gob at me, or grab me.
             "Gi's a screw missus, feel of your tits" . . . They
             all know, new nets at me winda, best frock . . .
             taxi's late at night. It's all mucky money to them.
             What they don't know is money's all the same,
             dun't matter how you earn it, without it your
             buggered . . . I'm going for a bath . . . (Looks at
             him. Sarcastic.) . . . I'll do it meself.

DANNY   I'll do it . . .

JUNE   I said I'll do it meself . . . Me belly's killin' me,
             do ya know I'm half tempted to have it all taken
             away. I am. What's the use of a shrivelled up bag
             of nothing?

DANNY   Mother, I'm not listening . . .

JUNE	Women's insides are torture to live with. I'm in a killing mood agen.
DANNY	I'll pass you a razor then, shall I?
JUNE	It's no joke.
DANNY	You should take your Evening Primrose . . .
JUNE	I should take an evening off . . .
DANNY	No one's stopping you.
JUNE	No. Danny . . . (*Sighs.*)
DANNY	Shall I run you a bath?
JUNE	No . . . I'll do it meself . . .
DANNY	Fine do it yourself then . . .
JUNE	I will. (*Pause.*) Do I look badly to you? (DANNY *ignores her.*) Danny do I? Do I look badly to you?
DANNY	Yes.
JUNE	No, really . . .
DANNY	*Yes.*
JUNE	You're not just saying that to be rotten.
DANNY	No, you look dreadful . . . 'ave an early night.
JUNE	Pass us an aspirin . . .
DANNY	Aspirin's no good. You never learn . . .
JUNE	Oh belt up . . .
DANNY	See?
JUNE	(*bickering, not angry*) Well I'm sick of you allus on at me . . .
DANNY	Fine . . .
JUNE	Then you start that . . .

DANNY	What?
JUNE	That sulkin'. No wonder I never wanna come 'ome . . .
DANNY	What?
JUNE	You heard . . . why do ya think I'm allus out?
DANNY	You're just bein' spiteful . . .
JUNE	It's you. You friggin' depress the shit out of me.
DANNY	Everything depresses you . . .
JUNE	I gave birth to a beautiful baby boy . . . that grew into Doris flamin' Day . . .
DANNY	It's hard to believe I survived long enough to grow into anything.
JUNE	You're allus looking down your friggin' nose at me . . . thinking you're so bloody special . . . well you're not special, you're the same as everyone else in this bloody family. Screwed up.
DANNY	No, you're wrong. I just want more that's all . . .
JUNE	There's no such thing . . .
DANNY	For you maybe . . .
JUNE	Oh . . . I think I might be sick in a minute . . . I feel 'orrible . . .
DANNY	It's your badness coming out . . .
JUNE	Oh Shurr up . . .
DANNY	It's probably trapped wind. 'Ave some Milk of Magnesia . . . or shall I make you some toast, eh? Mam, shall I make you something?
JUNE	Aye, a bloody coffin . . . it's your fault, you're allus on at me . . .

DANNY   Shall I go for a Chinese?

JUNE   No. I don't like you wandering about this time of
           night.

DANNY   It's alright, I'll run.

JUNE   You don't know how to run. I blame your Granny.

DANNY   You'd be surprised. I came over Anlaby Road
           flyover like a whirlwind yesterday.

JUNE   Oh go on then. 'Ere, you choose, surprise me . . .

DANNY   Right. I'm off . . . 'Ere I'll get some prawn
           crackers an' all.

JUNE   Run there and back, luv . . .

DANNY   Yeah . . .

           (DANNY *exits.* JUNE *sits smoking and drinking.*
           MAC *enters, walks up slowly behind her.*)

MAC   (*sarcastic*) Ah . . . She's all alone . . .

JUNE   (*startled*) What you 'ere for?

MAC   I'm the answer to your prayers, June. The man of
           your dreams . . .

JUNE   Nightmares . . .

MAC   Flattery'll get you nowhere . . .

JUNE   I'm not in the mood, Mac . . .

MAC   Ok, so you look like shit . . . Eh! Am I
           complainin'?

JUNE   Thanks . . .

MAC   I speak me mind. I'm like you June, I know what
           I want, and I always get it . . .

JUNE	Aye, that's why we're both 'ere and not in the Caribbean . . .
MAC	You should look after yourself.
JUNE	Don't worry, I'm checkin' into a health farm next week . . .
MAC	Lay off the booze a bit . . .
JUNE	What's this?
MAC	I'm concerned, that's all.
JUNE	Oh aye?
MAC	You should eat more red meat . . .
JUNE	Really . . .
MAC	Yeh — Fish 'n that . . .
JUNE	You'll be wanting to 'ave a look at me teeth next . . . well they're in a glass in the bathroom.
MAC	I like my girls fit . . .
JUNE	I'm not yours and I'm no girl . . .
MAC	'Lady' then . . .
JUNE	And I'm no fuckin' lady . . .
MAC	Where's Danny boy? Ironing your frocks or are they 'is own?
JUNE	He's gone to get me a Chinese . . .
MAC	It must be nice to 'ave a slave . . .
JUNE	Where's May? Locked in the coal house?
MAC	Funny . . . no, you are a *very* funny lady . . . it's true. You make me laugh. You do. I like a sense of humour in a woman. I do.

JUNE	Aye, don't ya know I'm a bloody comedian.
MAC	Well you make me laugh . . .
JUNE	What do ya want Mac?
MAC	Just a friendly chat . . . that's all. There's no harm in that . . . is there?
JUNE	Look, I'm knackered . . .
MAC	You shouldn't be so popular, June . . .
JUNE	How would you know?
MAC	Good news travels fast . . .
JUNE	And I'm good news, am I?
MAC	Definitely . . .
JUNE	Funny, 'cos I've heard you're *bad* news, Mac . . . Trouble . . . you're off your bloody rocker . . .
MAC	I just protect my interests June, that's all . . . it's a big bad world out there . . .
JUNE	Probably 'cos you're still breathing . . .
MAC	I'd like to protect you June . . .
JUNE	What, with a baseball bat, or a sledgehammer?
MAC	Whatever it takes . . .
JUNE	Better bring in the army . . .
MAC	I like you June. I do. You remind me. (*Pause.*) Of me . . .
JUNE	You was doin' alright 'til then.
MAC	You take what you want . . .
JUNE	No Mac, you're wrong. I earn my money taking a lot of crap I can do without. I also don't like sharing. What I earn is mine . . .

MAC	And Danny's . . . you can't forget Danny boy, June.
JUNE	That's nowt to do with you . . .
MAC	Well you see June, I like to share. I do. I've a very generous nature see . . . and when I decide to share my life with a woman, I expect them to be as equally generous . . . and I know that deep down June, you are a very generous woman . . .

(*He moves closer and kisses and caresses her inside her blouse and between her thighs — she does not immediately respond — but he gradually wins her over.*)

JUNE	Are you sure I don't look a mess?
MAC	Come 'ere . . .

(*He kisses her.* DANNY *walks in.*)

DANNY	Mam . . . Mam?
JUNE	(*pulls back*) . . . Danny . . .
MAC	Evening . . .
DANNY	I've got you a special . . .
MAC	I think it's leaked.
DANNY	'Ave you got the plates warming? Mam?
JUNE	(*puts lipstick on*) I'm going for summat to eat with Mac, luv . . . you have mine. Right, I'm ready when you are. Don't wait up — leave the chain off the door . . .
DANNY	I don't mind waiting up . . .
MAC	'Ave an early night Danny — you look like ya need one. Say tara to your Ma' . . . (*He walks behind* JUNE, *looking at her behind.*) . . . very . . .

nice . . . (*Smacks it.*) You are one sexy lady June
. . . sex-y . . .

(*They exit. A spotlight rises on* MAY *in the street,
on her way to* JUNE'*s house. She's anxious and
slightly disorientated.*)

MAY   When I was twelve me 'Uncle', that was no
           friggin' relation to us, said he'd give me twenty
           cigs if I felt 'im a bit. Two hours later he let me
           go. I cried all the way to me gran's. He'd 'urt me
           that bad that by the time I stood in 'er kitchen . . .
           safe, me legs were covered in blood. I could 'ear
           her sat in the next room watching the *Two
           Ronnies*, so I stood outside and washed meself
           down under the back yard tap. It was February
           and the water was like ice . . . but to me it was
           the best feeling in the world . . .

(*Blackout.*)

Scene Four

Later that night. DANNY *is asleep on the settee. TV on,
untuned channel static only.* MAY *enters.*

MAY   (*shaking him*) Danny.

DANNY   Mam . . .

MAY   It's me . . . May.

DANNY   Where's me Mam?

MAY   I dunno. I 'an't seen 'er.

DANNY   You been out though?

MAY   A bit.

DANNY   You off your 'ead on summat?

MAY   A bit. I've had stitches.

DANNY   Aw. Does it hurt?

MAY   Yeah. I was sick. 'Ave you got any cigs?

DANNY   No, and me mother'll freak if she finds you 'ere.

MAY   I'm looking for Mac. I thought he might be here, has he been? I didn't know where else to go.

DANNY   Why didn't you go 'ome?

MAY   'Cos there's no one there. I hate bein' on me own.

DANNY   How did you get in?

MAY   Door's open.

DANNY   It's not!

MAY   'Tis.

DANNY   That's me mother . . . shit, I've been in all night with the door open.

MAY   Do you get frightened an' all?

DANNY   No . . . well, only if I've watched summat frightening on the telly, you know like *Crime Watch* or summat . . .

MAY   So Mac's been then?

DANNY   (*concerned*) Unfortunately.

MAY   He left me ya know . . . in the 'ospital, bastard. I walked 'ere. I hate hospitals. They know me in there, ya know. I tell you, I've been stitched up more times than that Frank bleedin' Bruno. It's true. Kicked . . . nutted . . . punched. I should 'ave been a boxer. Trouble is I can't be bothered to fight back.

DANNY   Who did it?

MAY   Some bloke that reckons he can get away with it . . .

DANNY   Well he 'as, 'an't he?

MAY   Suppose so . . .

DANNY   He's probably at 'ome with his wife and kids now.

MAY   Yeah, what a twat, eh? 'Ere, is there owt good on
          the telly?

DANNY   I don't know why she had to go out with 'im . . .
          we was gonna have a night in . . . have a Chinese
          an' that.

MAY   He likes June, I know he does.

DANNY   Well she dun't like 'im . . .

MAY   'Course she does . . .

DANNY   She doesn't, she's just humouring him. She does
          it with all men. She hates him really.

MAY   'Course she does . . .

DANNY   She'll be home soon.

MAY   Ya reckon?

DANNY   Without 'im . . . I know she will . . .

MAY   Yeah . . . dream on . . .

DANNY   It's true, she hates all men.

MAY   Don't we all — 'ere, can I 'ave a drink of
          summat cold?

DANNY   Water?

MAY   You got owt stronger?

DANNY   I can't give ya me mother's gin, she'll go barmy
          . . . Is sherry alright?

MAY   Owt'll do . . . ta . . .

DANNY It's not bad. I drink it all the time. It's advertised on the telly, not just at Christmas either . . . 'Ere. (*Pours her a glass and gives it to her.*) Cheers! Me Granny drank this stuff . . . or was it Pony . . . the little drink with the big kick.

MAY Does me face look a mess?

DANNY I've seen worse . . . is it still raining?

MAY (*pause*) I hope so. (*Drinks.*) I like sherry, it makes me warm inside. Mind you, so does vinegar.

DANNY (*pause*) Sherry allus remind me of weddings . . . (*Sips it.*) I don't know why, I've never been to one.

MAY I wanna get married . . .

DANNY To Mac?

MAY To anybody that'll 'ave me . . . well no, that's not true. I'd like to marry someone nice, 'ad a job an' that . . . got on with me bairns and made a fuss over me. Not just jealous . . . really liked me. Proper.

DANNY 'Ere, do ya fancy a Snowball?

MAY Oooh, yeah!

DANNY (*fixing them a Snowball each*) Seventeen-point-two volume you know, thank God me mother thinks it tastes like cold custard . . .

MAY I like drinks that taste of medicine, don't you?

DANNY I don't know, it's all the same to me. Let's face it, it's the cure for everything in this house . . .

MAY Mac confuses me . . .

DANNY I didn't realise he was that clever . . .

MAY (*trying to work it out herself as she speaks*) He says, "Take this . . ." So I do. He says, "How do

ya like it?" I say it's alright. He says, "Try this
. . ." So I do. He says, "How do ya feel?" I say
like shit. He says, "Take some more . . ." So I do.
He says, "How do you feel?" I say I don't, so he
gets mad on me. So I take more and more. Then
he stops asking . . . and he stops giving me stuff.
So I ask him to get me summat to 'elp a bit . . . to
make me feel summat more than miserable . . .
and he says . . . "No, get your own . . ." (*Pause.*)
You got any chocolate?

DANNY   No . . .

MAY   If we drank the whole bottle would we be sick?

DANNY   Probably . . .

MAY   And would it be yellow?

DANNY   Probably . . .

MAY   'Ave you ever 'ad red sick before, like blood?

DANNY   No, 'ave you?

MAY   Yeah, it stained the kitchen floor . . .

DANNY   Did you try Star Drops?

MAY   It's not as good as they reckon . . .

DANNY   Personally I prefer Ajax . . .

MAY   I've never had that . . .

DANNY   Oh. (*In thought.*) 'Ave you ever read that story
            about the acorn that fell on the little chick's
            head?

MAY   I don't read that much . . .

DANNY   He thinks it's the sky falling in . . . I feel like
            that chick sometimes . . .

MAY   I suppose I should really . . .

DANNY   'Cept I know it's not the sky . . . I just want it to
         be . . .

MAY   I just can't be bothered . . .

DANNY   I've tried warning me mother . . . tellin' 'er to
         watch out . . . that the wolf's at the door . . .

MAY   I flick through the odd magazine . . . very odd . . .

DANNY   Howlin' through the letter box . . .

MAY   (*laughs*) Bloody filthy actually.

DANNY   Laughing in the dark . . .

MAY   Who is?

DANNY   The big bad wolf . . .

MAY   Oh. Any more Snowballs left?

DANNY   Yep. (*He jumps up and makes her another.*)

MAY   Nice in't it?

DANNY   Sickly but nice . . .

MAY   Does your tongue feel funny?

DANNY   Mac's up to something, I can feel it . . .

MAY   Mine does . . . do ya know I 'ave to scrape it
         sometimes. In't that 'orrible? Sometimes it feels
         so disgusting I could cut it out. 'Onestly I could.
         I could gag on it. Can you imagine dying like that
         eh? Some people do, don't they?

DANNY   I mean why the sudden interest in me mother?

MAY   You know when they say someone died
         swallowing their tongue, does it come off?

DANNY   I don't trust him. For a start he should pluck his
         eyebrows . . .

MAY   Can you imagine a mouth without a tongue?

DANNY   Eh?

MAY   Do ya really talk with your tongue? (*Pulls at
          hers.*) 'Cos I mean it won't keep still will it? Can
          you imagine a tongue without a face? Just two
          eyes, a nose and this long wagging tongue . . .

DANNY   That's disgusting . . .

MAY   I know . . . I'll 'ave nightmares tonight. If you
          ask me you're obsessed with him . . .

DANNY   Who?

MAY   Mac . . . do ya fancy him?

DANNY   I despise the man . . .

MAY   Do ya know I allus think dog's tongues look like
          a slice of ham . . .

DANNY   That's disgusting . . .

MAY   Horrible, but true . . .

          (*Blackout.*)

                        Scene Five

Lights rise on JUNE, *in the street.*

JUNE   When I was little I wanted to be a nurse, and well
          I've a been a nurse, and a nun, teacher, traffic
          warden, lollipop lady, policewoman, Nell Gwynn,
          Bet Lynch, Madonna, Mary Queen of Scots, Mary
          bleedin' Magdalene, Mary 'ad a little lamb, The
          Virgin Mary . . . I've whipped Hitler in drag, and
          Thatcher in bondage. I've been nanny to judges
          and mother to bin men . . . I've been French,
          German, Russian, Chinese, Japanese and several
          farm animals. Aye, I'm very rarely me. When I
          retire I'm gonna open a shop. I am. I'm gonna
          call it 'Working Late'. Then when they say they

are, they're not lying, are they? . . . I'll stock
whips and chains, chainsaws and blow torches,
sledgehammers and tweezers and cheese graters
and tar and feathers and coal . . . I'll do school
uniforms, baby dolls, ballet dancers, choirboys,
naughty boys, nappies and frocks and stocks, and
bright red stiletto heels —up to size thirteen —
I'll keep Nazi uniforms and helmets, jack boots
and bin liners. Wigs and masks and make-up . . .
and a fuckin' great skip out the back . . . for them
. . . that like it . . . MUCKY . . . (*Makes a
sheep's bleating noise.*) Baaaaaaaaa . . .

Scene Six

*In the living room a new flowery settee has replaced the old
one.* [NB: *The same settee should be used, but with the cover
removed during the previous scene.*] JUNE *is sat on it posing
in different ways.* DANNY *walks in and goes to the kitchen.*
JUNE *jumps up, excited like a kid with a new toy.*

JUNE   Danny? Wait there. (*She rushes to him, puts her
           hands over his eyes and guides him over to the
           settee. With a flourish she removes her hands.*)
           Da-daa! Look what Mac's got us . . . in't it
           beautiful!

DANNY   (*unimpressed*) It's got flowers on it . . .

JUNE   'Course it's got flowers on it. It's class is this . . .
           real class . . . I'll 'ave you know Mac went to a
           lot of trouble to get us this . . .

DANNY   Caught it from a speeding lorry did he?

JUNE   Eh?

DANNY   It fell off the back of a bleedin' lorry!

JUNE   I don't care if it fell from the bloody sky, and
           since when did you bloody swear?

DANNY   Since you took up with a con-man . . .

JUNE   (*sitting back*) Eh Danny, look — you can lose yourself in it . . .

DANNY   You might 'ave to when the police arrive . . .

JUNE   'Ere come and try it, it's for both of us you know . . .

DANNY   I liked the old one . . .

JUNE   It was old-fashioned . . .

DANNY   It suited us . . .

JUNE   You maybe . . . no, I'm after the best me . . .

DANNY   The best? Since when?

JUNE   Look if you like the old 'un so much friggin' well 'ave it . . . go on, it's in the yard, sit on it all night for all I care . . . this one's stayin' 'ere. I'm gonna get curtains to match . . .

DANNY   Match what?

JUNE   Me new settee stupid, match the flowers an' that. Oh aye, I can see 'em now. 'Ere, and some of them tie-back things, oh yeah they're dead posh are them . . . I'll be then envy of the whole street with them. I'll get a new carpet an' all . . . the best. 'Ere, I'll get bloody shag-pile!

DANNY   Very appropriate . . .

JUNE   In cream . . .

DANNY   Really?

JUNE   Nice and thick . . .

DANNY   I'm sure . . .

JUNE   Oh I can feel it now . . . (*Rubs her foot along the carpet.*) 'Ere, an there'll be no more shoes . . .

DANNY   What?

JUNE   On me new carpet . . . I'm gonna look after it, I am, and I'm really gonna look after this. (*Stroking the settee.*)

DANNY   Mother you're not capable of looking after anything. Well, not for long. You lose interest. Look at me . . .

JUNE   I love this settee . . . I'm gonna teck real good care of it . . .

DANNY   You don't care about anything in this house. I thought you hated this house?

JUNE   I do. Well I did, but now I'm getting rid of the old and in with the new.

DANNY   You're not very good with settees though are ya?

JUNE   I don't know what ya mean.

DANNY   You was allus chuckin' up and over the old one.

JUNE   Only 'cos it was 'ers.

DANNY   Peein' on it . . .

JUNE   So?

DANNY   Amongst things . . .

JUNE   That's what settee's are for . . .

DANNY   I've been brought up with the old one. I like it. Don't chuck it out Mam . . . this one's 'orrible.

JUNE   Why don't you shut your flamin' face, eh? You don't want to me 'ave owt nice . . .

DANNY   It dun't suit you . . .

JUNE   Well I'm tellin' ya straight, there's gonna be some changes round 'ere and if you don't bloody like it . . . tough! You can bloody lump it!

DANNY   What's new?

JUNE   I tell you what else I'm gettin' an' all . . .

DANNY   Dafter . . .

JUNE   A coffee table . . . for just 'ere. (*Indicating in front of her, dramatically.*) Yeah, just 'ere . . . in glass, yeah . . . smoked glass . . .

DANNY   Until you come 'ome pissed one night, fall on it and decapitate yaself . . .

JUNE   'Ere and I can put that big ashtray on it. You know, the one I got from the Royal Hotel in Harrogate . . .

DANNY   Off the reception desk . . .

JUNE   No, it's gonna be a completely different room is this . . . dead posh . . . dead stylish . . .

DANNY   Why? You never sittin' in 'ere agen?

JUNE   And you can't 'ave your tea in 'ere no more . . .

DANNY   So where do I eat it? . . . Out the pan?

JUNE   In the kitchen . . .

DANNY   And where do I sit . . . on the fridge?

JUNE   Look Danny, I mean it. This room's for best . . .

DANNY   Mother, best rooms are great, if you've got another one . . .

JUNE   You 'ave . . .

DANNY   Where?

JUNE   Your bedroom . . . you can stay up there. I'll get you a little portable telly . . .

DANNY   Oh I see . . . what did you say this room is for agen?

JUNE   Best . . .

DANNY   Best what?

JUNE   (*ignores him*) 'Ere, come and try it . . . Danny
            come on, it's ever so comfy . . . oh, I could just
            fall asleep in it . . .

DANNY   Well that's not gonna be very profitable, is it?

JUNE   'Ere I tell you what else I'm gonna get for you . . .

DANNY   What?

JUNE   A bloody big zip for your filthy mouth! (*Clouts
            him.*)

            (JUNE *lays back on her settee, smoking, doing her
            best to look sophisticated.* DANNY *pulls a pouffe
            up and perches on it uncomfortably. There is an
            awkward silence.* DANNY *stands up to leave, as if
            going to bed.*)

JUNE   This is Mac, in't it? You can't stand to see me
            bloody 'appy with someone can you?

DANNY   'Cos you never are. You just pretend.

JUNE   Danny, get out there and get a life . . .

DANNY   Like you 'ave?

JUNE   You're like a bloody old woman . . .

DANNY   And I wonder why?

JUNE   You've always been bloody soft . . .

DANNY   Well maybe I should act more like Mac . . .

JUNE   I blame ya Granny I do . . .

DANNY   He'll 'ave you on drugs next . . .

JUNE   Sitting round kitchen tables drinking tea all day . . .

DANNY	At least I want on me own.
JUNE	Oh shurr-up . . .
DANNY	I'm allus on me own these days. You're never in.
JUNE	And I wonder why . . .
DANNY	I get scared on me own.
JUNE	It's this house, it's bloody haunted.
DANNY	Don't say that.
JUNE	Everywhere you look she's stood there bloody tutting . . . well I've had enough . . .
DANNY	She'd hate this settee.
JUNE	Good.
DANNY	And 'im.
JUNE	Good . . .
DANNY	So do I.
JUNE	Good.
DANNY	Well if he moves in 'ere . . .
JUNE	What!
DANNY	Eh?
JUNE	If he moves in 'ere, *what*?
DANNY	(*on edge now*) I'll make a fresh pot . . . don't look at me like that . . . alright, I take it all back. The settee is lovely. No, it is . . . Mam come on, don't look at me like that . . . I'm sorry . . . I am 'onestly . . . I had three asthma attacks in Asda yesterday. Three . . . I'm sorry. All I'm saying is . . . I just can't stand to see you heartbroken. New settees are fine, but I know you're giving him money . . .

JUNE   It's mine!

DANNY   I know . . . but come Christmas Mam it'll still be
            just us hanging up them trimmings . . . you know
            it's true.

JUNE   He thinks I'm sexy . . .

DANNY   Sexy's not everything . . . I'll put the kettle on.

            (DANNY *exits. Pause.*)

JUNE   Tis . . . (*She stares thoughtfully into space,
            stroking the settee.*)

                        Scene Seven

JUNE's *living room. Later.* DANNY *watching TV.* MAC *enters.*

MAC   Where's June?

DANNY   Since when 'ave you 'ad a key?

MAC   Since I decided I wanted one . . . where is she?

DANNY   Out . . .

MAC   Out where?

DANNY   Well you should know . . .

MAC   I said I'd pick 'er up at ten . . .

DANNY   So?

MAC   So where is she?

DANNY   I've just told you, she's out . . . but perhaps I can
            help you . . . sit down . . . (*Sarcastic.*) Come on,
            sit down on our wonderful new settee . . . it's
            ever so big . . . and comfy . . .

MAC   Eh?

DANNY   There's plenty of room for two . . .

MAC	What time's she back?
DANNY	Who knows. Tomorra maybe?
MAC	Tomorra?
DANNY	Or the day after . . . who cares . . .
MAC	Where did you say she was?
DANNY	I didn't . . .
MAC	I've got summat in me pocket you might be interested in . . . summat I carry for protection. A long . . . sharp . . . knife. Don't you want to see it? . . . It's fuckin' massive . . .
DANNY	I'm sure it is.
MAC	I think you need teachin' a lesson . . .
DANNY	I think you've been watching too many gangster films . . .
MAC	I never watch, I like to be where the action is see, do the job meself . . . so, where's your mother?
DANNY	(*casually*) Blackpool . . .
MAC	Blackpool?
DANNY	To see the lights . . .
MAC	What fuckin' lights?
DANNY	The Golden Mile . . .
MAC	The golden what?
DANNY	She said she'd bring you back a stick of rock . . .
MAC	Who's she with?
DANNY	It's very famous is Blackpool rock . . .
MAC	Who's she with?

DANNY   She might even bring you a bronze miniature Blackpool Tower.

MAC   Who the fuck is she with?

DANNY   They'll be collectors items one day . . .

MAC   WHO'S SHE GONE WITH?

DANNY   I don't know his name . . .

MAC   His? . . . Who? . . . Who's she with?

DANNY   Look I don't know his name . . . but I do remember his car. What car do you drive again?

MAC   A Ford Cortina . . . Mark Four . . .

DANNY   A Ford Cortina . . . er, no it was definitely not a Ford Cortina . . . no . . . it was . . . a BMW. Yes, a big black BMW.

MAC   She's in deep shit . . .

DANNY   No, she's in Blackpool . . .

(MAC *takes his knife and slashes the settee.* [NB: *The reverse side of the settee cushions are tacked — but already slashed — and turned over during the furious attack.*] *Blackout.*)

Scene Eight

The next evening. JUNE *is sat on the new settee. She has been crying. Her mascara's run — she looks wrecked. The settee has been slashed.*

JUNE   How's he know?

DANNY   Calm down . . .

JUNE   How the fuck did he know?

DANNY   Calm down Mam, it's not worth upsettin' yourself over . . .

JUNE   I loved this settee . . .

DANNY   It could 'ave been worse . . .

JUNE   How? It's ruined . . .

DANNY   It could 'ave been you . . . or me . . . it could 'ave been me instead.

JUNE   I WISH IT HAD BEEN! . . . I was gonna get curtains to match . . .

DANNY   Don't shout Mam . . . cig? (*Gives her one of her own and lights it for her.*)

JUNE   Well I was . . .

DANNY   Well the old 'uns match, well now they do . . .

JUNE   It's ruined, no one wants me to 'ave owt nice . . .

DANNY   I do . . . anyway you 'ave . . . drink? (*Fixes her a drink.*)

JUNE   What? . . . What the 'ell 'ave I got?

DANNY   You've got some fabulous outfits . . . and me . . . You've got me.

JUNE   I loved this settee, I was gonna get a coffee table and everything . . .

DANNY   Well you still can, we can mend it . . . I'll 'elp you.

JUNE   Oh yeah how? Look at it, all the stuffin's 'angin' out of it, how the 'ell can you mend this?

DANNY   Well maybe we could get some stretch covers, you know, some nice ones with flowers on . . .

JUNE   I 'ate fuckin' stretch covers . . .

DANNY   You can get nice ones these days . . .

JUNE   Put stretch covers on it and it'll look 'orrible, it'll look disgusting. In stretch covers it'll just be a shape.

DANNY   Yeah, but it's a nice shape . . .

JUNE   What's that got to do with it? . . . A nice shape in stretch covers still looks like shit! . . . I should friggin' know . . . 'ere, I wonder if I can get it insured? . . . I know loads of insurance men . . .

DANNY   Well people usually insure things before they 'ave an accident Mam. Anyway it'd be a bit 'ard explainin' this, I mean you could hardly say you slipped with the nail scissors . . .

JUNE   I wanted me mates to see it an' all. May was comin' round after . . .

DANNY   Well listen, why don't we do this . . . chuck a white sheet over it and say that we're in the middle of decoratin' . . . eh?

JUNE   But I was only askin' 'er round to see me new settee . . .

Scene Nine

MAC *walks on, cocky but with an edge.* JUNE *ignores him.* DANNY *looks nervously towards her.*

MAC   June, Danny, lovely weather we're 'avin' for the time of year don't you agree? Mind you I 'ad heard it was pissin' it down in Blackpool.

JUNE   Get lost.

MAC   You heard your mother Danny, get lost.

JUNE   Stay where you are.

DANNY   Shall I make a drink?

MAC   Yeah, he's a good lad in't he June? Very well
           trained . . . (*To* DANNY.) Well, go on then.

JUNE   Just stay where you are Danny.

DANNY   (*stands*) I don't mind, 'onest . . .

JUNE   I SAID SIT THERE!

MAC   SIT! STAY! GOOD BOY! You should enter 'im
           for Crufts, June.

DANNY   I think me Mam wants you to leave.

MAC   I think your Mam's wanted you to leave for years.

JUNE   I've nowt to say to ya, Mac.

MAC   That's alright . . . (*Sits on the settee.*) Owt good
           on telly?

JUNE   Danny, make a drink.

DANNY   No you're alright. I'll say 'ere with you.

JUNE   I said make a drink.

DANNY   Mac, me Mam wants you out of 'ere.

MAC   I don't think so Danny, she wants to me say and
           you to piss off. In't that right June?

DANNY   You don't, do ya Mam?

MAC   (*sarcastic*) MAM . . . MAM . . .

DANNY   Mam? You don't do ya?

JUNE   Don't whine, Danny.

DANNY   But you don't, do ya?

MAC   There's a good boy Danny . . . shift your arse.

DANNY   Mam . . . Mam? Tell 'im.

JUNE   Go on Danny, make a drink.

MAC	Well go on then, do as you're told, earn your keep!
JUNE	Leave 'im alone you.
DANNY	Shall I ring the police?
JUNE	Shurr-up daft. Look Mac, I don't want any bother alright?
MAC	As if, June.
DANNY	So just go then.
JUNE	Danny just keep out of it . . . go an' make me a drink son.
DANNY	He dun't bother me . . .
MAC	So how ya been keeping then June? You look a bit under the weather to me, funny that 'cos I 'ad 'eard you 'ad a bit of an 'oliday by the sea. I thought sea air was good for you, for your complexion an' that . . . you know, puts a bit colour in your cheeks. (*Turns her face around.*) You can't 'ave taken much in . . . sea air that is. You look like shit June, knackered, you look shagged . . . well shagged . . . you look like you've been over-doing it to me . . . burning the candle at both ends, eh? What you been doing June, overtime?
JUNE	Danny . . .
MAC	(*beat*) Don't you think so Danny, don't you think your Mam looks like she's been up all night?
DANNY	Ignore 'im Mam.
JUNE	I won't tell you again Danny.
MAC	Danny boy can't ya see you're upsetting ya Mother.

DANNY   It's not me it's you, why don't you just clear off?
          Can't you see we don't want you 'ere?

MAC   Put 'im straight, June . . .

DANNY   Mam?

JUNE   Mac, don't start.

MAC   Tell 'im.

DANNY   Tell 'im what?

JUNE   Leave it.

DANNY   What?

JUNE   Ignore 'im Danny, he's just winding you up . . .
          go and make a drink . . . go on. I'm alright,
          Mac's not staying.

          (DANNY *leaves*.)

DANNY   If you need me just shout, I'll be right near the
          knife drawer . . .

MAC   He's gotta be a joke. Where did you go wrong
          June?

JUNE   Before you start Mac, I'm warning you it won't
          work, I'm off out in a bit and I've got someone
          picking me up, so you might as well just go.

MAC   I'm gutted June, I thought we 'ad summat going.

JUNE   Bull . . . shit.

MAC   Don't swear at me June, it's not lady-like.

JUNE   What would you know.

MAC   You see I allus thought you was different from
          the rest, 'ad a bit of pride an' that. Not just some
          old slag out to make a bit of extra, know what
          I'm saying?

JUNE   What's it to you what I am?

MAC   You might never know . . . (*Stands.*) Shame that.
              Could 'ave been good . . . could 'ave been very
              good.

JUNE   You're full of it, you are.

MAC   See ya around . . .

JUNE   Mac?

MAC   See ya . . .

JUNE   You mean it?

MAC   Like I said, see ya around . . . and June, do
              yourself a favour — dump the kid, start to live a
              bit.

              (MAC *leaves.* JUNE *sits a while in thought.* DANNY
              enters flustered, mouth open ten-to-the-dozen.)

DANNY   Thank God he's gone. You should 'ave let me
              ring the police, I don't know who he thinks he is
              coming round 'ere. Why did you give 'im a key?
              We should get them locks changed. I'll do it
              tommorra, we should change our phone number
              agen an' all . . . 'ere, I've sweetened your tea
              with honey, we've ran out of sugar . . .

JUNE   I can't drink that.

DANNY   It's better for you.

JUNE   Don't you tell me what's good for me!

DANNY   Well it is.

JUNE   Well I don't want it. Where's me red shoes?

DANNY   Why?

JUNE   'Cos I want 'em that's why.

DANNY   I thought you was staying in?

JUNE   Well I'm not.

DANNY   I've got a video . . .

JUNE   Where the 'ell are they?

DANNY   *Poltergeist II.*

JUNE   I've seen it, you've seen it, why the 'ell do you
        allus get videos we've seen? Anyway what did
        you get that for, you know it frightens you.

DANNY   Not when I'm with you . . . stay in Mam, stay in
        and watch it with me.

JUNE   And listen to you screaming all night? No Danny,
        I'm fed up, I'm going out.

DANNY   With Mac?

JUNE   No. To work, to keep you in bloody videos you've
        seen thousands of times . . . where's me red
        shoes?

DANNY   They're at the cobblers.

JUNE   What the 'ell are they doing there?

DANNY   Visiting relatives.

JUNE   Funny . . .

DANNY   What do ya think they're doing there? I'm getting
        'em heeled for you.

JUNE   I didn't want 'em heeling!

DANNY   You did.

JUNE   I didn't!

DANNY   You did. They made you walk lopsided.

JUNE   SO? Maybe I like walking lopsided . . . I wish
        you'd bloody well leave my stuff alone, you're

allus touching me things . . . why don't you mind your own bloody business!

DANNY   Right. I will. (*Stands up.*)

JUNE   Where are you going now?

DANNY   To mind me own business. I'll start by taking your smalls out from soak, then I'll chuck all your frocks back in a ball on your bedroom floor shall I?

JUNE   Oh just shut up will you . . . where's that packet of cigs you got me? (DANNY *ignores her.*) Danny, where's me bloody cigs?

DANNY   They're of no concern to me.

JUNE   Stop trying to be bloody clever . . . where are they?

DANNY   Mac probably pocketed 'em whilst your back was turned.

JUNE   The trouble with you lad is you've got nowt else to think about . . .

DANNY   The trouble with you is you only think about yourself . . .

JUNE   That's right . . . carry on Danny.

DANNY   Well it's true.

JUNE   I've gone. (*She starts to walk out.*)

DANNY   Mam . . .

JUNE   I want you in bed when I get in, I'm 'avin company.

DANNY   Mam? . . .

JUNE   And tidy round a bit, the kitchen's like a bomb sight.

DANNY   (*sternly*) You got summat?

JUNE   (*surprised*) What?

DANNY   Protection.

JUNE   Oh 'aye. I've got Starsky and bleedin' Hutch wi'
             me.

DANNY   Ave ya . . . ?

JUNE   Yes . . . yes! I tell you I've got that many
             different flavours by the time I get in tonight I'll
             smell like a bleedin' fruit cocktail . . . (*Suddenly
             serious.*) Why don't you watch one of the other
             films, eh? *Sound of Music* or summat . . . see you
             son . . . well come on, give your Mam a kiss.

DANNY   Make loads of noise when you get in so I know
             you're back safe . . .

             (JUNE *exits. Blackout.*)

                          Scene Ten

Lights rise on JUNE, *on the street.*

JUNE   Some blokes never want sex. Take Trevor. He just
             shouts a lot. Apparently when he was little he
             wasn't allowed to talk. Well, not without
             permission. But with me he can shout 'til his
             heart's content. We both do. Sometimes for
             several hours. But then I 'ave to punish 'im . . .
             and he 'as a little cry. I wash 'is 'ands and face,
             and he's off agen . . . to face the world in silence.
             You'd think he'd work in a library wun't ya? He
             dun't, he's a Master Butcher. Sometimes he
             brings me a pig's heart, or an ox tail, or some
             chicken livers . . . next week he's promised me
             some tripe.

             (*Blackout.*)

Scene Eleven

Later the same night. MAY *and* DANNY *in* JUNE's *living room.*

MAY   Yeah he's a bastard 'in't he, oh he told me you
           know, yeah he came round and told me, said your
           Mam 'ad fucked off to Blackpool with some
           ponce so he slashed 'er new settee. He did that to
           me once 'cept mine weren't new, and anyway I'd
           only gone to Bingo . . . I think he must really like
           June.

DANNY   But I thought he lived with you?

MAY   He dun't know how to live anywhere . . . anyway
           I don't want him, I only want me kids now . . .
           I'm getting 'em back you know . . . I'm sortin'
           the back yard out . . . it's full of dog shit. Mac's
           bloody dog. I 'ate the thing but at least it barks if
           it hears someone coming up the back passage.
           Your Mam'll go barmy if she knew I was here.

DANNY   Yeah . . . do ya 'ave to go?

MAY   I'm a hardworking girl, me. Some of us 'an't got
           mothers that give us everything.

DANNY   It's gonna rain.

MAY   Good . . . look, I gotta go . . .

DANNY   Can't you stay a bit longer?

MAY   Time's money . . .

DANNY   I'll make you some toast, cheese on toast.

MAY   Cheese?

DANNY   Beans then.

MAY   What time's your Mam back?

DANNY   Dunno . . . and I don't care. I'm meant to be
         cleaning up . . .

MAY   She'll go mad . . .

DANNY   I know. Eh, we could 'ave a walk across park . . .

MAY   I'm after another house you know, one with a
         garden for me kids. I'm gonna get 'em a swing
         an' that . . . I like swings, don't you?

DANNY   They always made me sick. I was followed in
         park once by a man in a duffel coat, I had to hide
         in the flower beds.

MAY   Only once?

DANNY   Me mother hates flowers. They're banned from
         the house, give 'em a day or two and she starts
         going on about 'em smelling of death.

MAY   Did he catch you up?

DANNY   Who?

MAY   The man in the duffel coat?

         (*A loud clap of thunder is heard.*)

DANNY   You should have a coat on you know . . . was that
         thunder? (*Pause.*) Yes he did. There's gonna be
         such a storm you know. Are you frightened of
         lightening?

MAY   Only if I am stood under a tree . . .

DANNY   Or behind a bush . . . anywhere outdoors really.
         You're not safe . . . not even in Wellies . . .

MAY   I wish I was a kid again don't you?

DANNY   Apparently I was born old . . . where you going?

MAY   I better get off . . . I need twenty quid by ten . . .
           I'll see you.

DANNY   Can I come with you?

MAY   Stay in Danny . . . stay in and wait for your mam,
           tell her you're frightened of the lightening . . .

DANNY   When I was little me Granny use to say that the
           thunder was God in a rage. Black clouds were
           man's evil thoughts, and the rain was all the
           mothers in heaven, crying over their fallen
           children. I asked once . . . what lightening was,
           she said it was God warning us that his power is
           greater than any living man's.

           (*They stare out of the window as the lights fade.
           End of Act One.*)

ACT TWO

Scene One

DANNY *is watching telly.* MAC *walks on. He's had a bath and is wearing a towel around his waist.* DANNY *does his best to ignore him.* MAC *admires his reflection in the mirror. He begins lifting weights, and has obviously made himself well at home — which should make* DANNY *very uneasy, not only at the cheek of* MAC *helping himself, but also the fact that he has a skimpy towel on.* MAC *is obviously aware of this and is enjoying it.*

MAC   It's no good, your mother's gonna 'ave to get some bigger towels. 'Ere Danny boy, will you iron this for us? (*Throws a shirt at him.*)

DANNY   No.

MAC   Go on. Your summat of an expert with an iron.

DANNY   I'm watching telly.

MAC   Watching telly? A young lad like you, you should be out there Danny . . . chasing arse and downing a few . . .

DANNY   Really.

MAC   Game of pool, laugh with the lads.

DANNY   Don't let me stop you.

MAC   A lad of your age should be out all night.

DANNY   I'm happy here thanks.

MAC   Clubbing it.

DANNY   Tecking drugs?

MAC   Living a bit.

DANNY   Like you?

MAC   Like all lads your age.

DANNY   And you'd know would you?

MAC   Stuck in 'ere every night.

DANNY   I like it 'ere thank you. Well, when you're not 'ere.

MAC   Ah but I am, aren't I? So what about it then? You iron me shirt and I'll give you a lift.

DANNY   A lift, to where?

MAC   To meet your mates, you 'ave got mates, 'an't you?

DANNY   I'm trying to concentrate on this if you don't mind . . . (*Meaning the telly.*)

MAC   Come on . . . name the pub and I'll drop you off.

DANNY   I'm staying in . . . 'ere, wear it creased, it'll suit you better. (*Throws it weakly.*)

MAC   (*picks it up slowly*) Please yourself . . . but I better warn you, if you want a peaceful night go and spend it in your room . . . know what I'm saying?

DANNY   I'll stay where I am.

MAC   Yeah?

DANNY   Yeah . . . you can't tell me what to do.

MAC   Who can, your Mam?

DANNY   Mind your own business.

MAC   Ah, but it is my business . . . your mother does as she's told, Danny . . . she does what I tell 'er . . . and do you know why? . . . 'cos she needs me. She doesn't want to lose me. (*Drops towel.*)

DANNY   She's a good liar my Mam . . .

MAC   So like I said if you want a peaceful night . . . be
            a good boy, stay in your room out of the way . . .
            alright?

            (*Blackout.*)

                          Scene Two

A street. JUNE *and* MAY, *doing business.*

MAY   I'm freezing me bloody tits off 'ere . . .

JUNE   Come on . . . gerr on with it . . .

MAY   Shit. I can't remember if I turned the bloody iron
            off!

JUNE   'Is 'ands are like bloody icebergs . . .

MAY   Christ! What if it bursts into flames?

JUNE   At last . . . oh brilliant! He's a bloody asthmatic!

MAY   It'll burn the bloody 'ouse down . . . 'ere, does
            your flamin' heater work or what?

JUNE   Well which pocket is it in?

MAY   Christ, I'm not insured . . .

JUNE   I can't find it . . .

MAY   What do ya mean your battery'll go flat?

JUNE   I can't understand a word you're sayin' . . . .
            Teck deep breaths . . .

MAY   'Ere, you're not an insurance man are ya?

JUNE   Will a paper bag do?

MAY   Can't you go faster? I think I've burned me 'ouse
            down . . .

JUNE	Next time bring your pump, alright?
MAY	Well I'm not surprised, it's like the shittin' North Pole in 'ere . . .
JUNE	I need a drink . . .
MAY	I need some insurance . . .
JUNE	What agen? . . . It weren't my bloody fault . . .
MAY	You just need a bit of friction . . .
JUNE	What you done that for?
MAY	It's not my bloody fault . . .
JUNE	If you don't let go of me, I'll scream me bloody 'ead off . . .
MAY	Gerr off! . . . what you doin'? I said gerr off me!
JUNE	Vice'll 'ave your number you know, they was parked up down the street . . .
MAY	Stupid dick 'ead, let me out . . .
JUNE	'Ere, teck your flamin' money. Just let me go . . .
MAY	Don't hurt me, I've got kids . . .

(*Blackout.*)

Scene Three

Lights rise on the living room. JUNE *rushes into living room and stands in front of the fire, obviously distressed.* DANNY *walks in.*

DANNY	You're late Mam, you alright? Mam?
	(*He goes to put his arm round her but she recoils.*)
JUNE	Yeah, just tired.

DANNY   Why don't you have a lie down, eh? I tell you
what, put your feet up and I'll wrap you up.

JUNE   Ta luv . . . you're a good lad . . .

DANNY   I'll get me reward in Heaven . . .

JUNE   Aye, send me a postcard . . .

DANNY   Shall I turn the telly off?

JUNE   Put Al Jolson on . . .

DANNY   'Toot Toot Tootsie'?

JUNE   No. 'I'm Sitting On Top of the World' . . . I need
a lift.

DANNY   Do you want to sit up and sway? It's what I use to
do to cheer meself up when I was little . . .

JUNE   (*looking through newspaper*) No . . . put the telly
on instead . . .

(DANNY *puts the telly on.*)

JUNE   Bugger me, we've missed it. Shit Danny, it was
about them on Death Row. Is this yesterday's
paper? 'Ere, what time's *This Is Your Life* on?

DANNY   (*beat*) You've missed it, it was on last night . . .

JUNE   Story of my bleedin' life that. I miss out on
everything. (*There is a knock on the door, off.*)
Answer that door . . .

DANNY   It's May, Mam . . .

JUNE   Brilliant. That's all I bloody need.

(MAY *enters.*)

DANNY   (*to* MAY) Be warned, she's not in a good mood . . .

MAY   Is she ever? I've not come to see her. I need Mac
          — is he in?

JUNE   No . . .

MAY   Can I wait for 'im?

JUNE   I don't know how long he'll be . . .

MAY   I don't mind waitin' . . .

JUNE   Well I do . . .

DANNY   I'll make a drink . . .

MAY   Ta . . . I've got some catalogue money for you
          Danny . . . a fiver . . .

JUNE   You 'an't paid owt for weeks . . .

MAY   I know, I 'ad to get the bairns shoes an' that.

JUNE   They aren't even livin' with you . . .

MAY   I'm doing the house up. Then they can come
          'ome . . . decoratin' and that. Council's been and
          sorted the damp in the bedrooms . . . it looks
          nice.

JUNE   Good, I'm pleased for you . . .

MAY   You got a cig?

JUNE   'Ere . . . (*Gives her one, reluctantly.*) Look I
          don't know how long he'll be, he might go
          straight out. If I see 'im I'll tell 'im you wanna
          see 'im . . .

MAY   It's just that I've still got 'is dog. I can't afford
          to be feeding it. He never comes to teck it out. I
          don't even like the thing. It stinks the place out.
          I'm gonna get a settee like this, only better, a
          sofa bed . . . Mac's sortin' it for us . . .

JUNE   Like I said, I'll tell 'im . . .

MAY   Don't be like that with me June, we was allus mates, wan't we?

JUNE   May, go 'ome . . .

MAY   I don't mind waiting . . .

JUNE   Mac won't be back for ages. Anyway he's pissed off with you, you never pay 'im what you owe . . .

MAY   I'm keeping 'is bloody dog, aren't I? . . . bastard thing shits all over the yard.

JUNE   You better pay 'im back, that's all.

MAY   What's it got to do with you?

JUNE   Don't get clever lady . . . you know where the door is, and don't think our Danny's a soft touch either, 'cos he's not.

MAY   That's not what Mac says . . .

JUNE   Eh?

MAY   'Cept my settee's gonna be brand new . . .

JUNE   What you on about?

DANNY   (*entering with two cups of tea*) Right, milk, two sugars (JUNE.) . . . black, five (MAY.) . . . watch out, it's a bit hot . . .

MAY   Thanks . . . Social's assessed me 'an everything. The 'ouse'll be sorted by Christmas. I'm getting 'em anything they want, me kids . . . I'm gonna save up.

JUNE   Don't spill it on me rug, it's new . . .

MAY   It's nice. It nearly matches the settee.

DANNY   It's not cream, it's oatmeal. It's got very tiny specks in it. When the sun shines it looks smashing.

MAY   Yeah, it's nice, but I bet it dun't 'alf get mucky
          quick . . .

DANNY   You're looking well . . . in't she Mam?

JUNE   (*sarcastic*) Today . . .

MAY   'Onest to God, I'm sorting everything . . . I've
          got some smashing paper for their bedrooms.

DANNY   That's lovely, in't it Mam?

JUNE   (*sarcastic*) Aye . . . lovely . . .

MAY   I'm giving up smoking next. By Christmas I'll be
          sorted. I'm off the streets, the lot . . . I'll do a
          few weeks before for a bit extra, for the bairns
          an' that, but then I'm getting a proper job. Me
          cousin's gettin' me it, cleaning offices an' that . . .
          I'll put a word in for you if you like Danny.

JUNE   He's got enough to do 'ere. (MAC *enters.*) Shit . . .

MAY   Yeah. I'm getting a proppa job while I'm still
          young enough to . . . oh hiya, Mac. I've come to
          see you . . . I need a word.

MAC   (*on edge*) I'm not stoppin' . . . Jesus, did you
          move a Jackson's carrier bag?

MAY   I'm doin' the 'ouse up . . . aren't I Danny?

DANNY   Er . . . yeah . . .

JUNE   (*to* DANNY) Shurr-up stupid . . . (*To* MAC.) It was
          in the back of your car . . . alright?

MAC   Right . . . ta . . . you got a cig? . . . See you . . .

MAY   Mac, the dog's missin' yer . . .

MAC   I'm comin' for it Wednesday.

MAY   It's allus barking and that . . .

MAC	Why, have you been kicking it?
MAY	NO!
JUNE	Bloody 'ell . . .
DANNY	Don't you think she looks well . . . eh? Mac?
JUNE	Shurr-up . . . idiot . . .
DANNY	Well she does . . .
JUNE	See you after then . . . Mac?
MAC	You been feedin' it 'an't ya?
MAY	Yeah . . .
MAC	I left plenty of food . . .
JUNE	She's probably 'et it . . .
MAY	I need to talk to yer . . .
JUNE	You just 'ave . . . now it's time you was going . . . (*Jumps up, stands* MAY *up.*)
DANNY	Mother . . .
MAY	Alright . . . June, I'm going. (*She kicks cup over as* JUNE *pulls at her.*) Now look what you've made me do . . .
DANNY	Oh shit . . .
MAC	Bloody 'ell . . . right then . . . I'm . . .
JUNE	You little cow, you did that on purpose!
MAY	You made me . . .
JUNE	DANNY, GET A CLOTH QUICK! If this stains I'll bloody swing for you . . .
MAY .	Oh aye?

JUNE   GET OUT. GO ON . . . GET 'ER OUT, MAC!

MAC   Get 'er out yourself, it's nowt to do with me . . .
          Mad cows. (*Starts to leave.*)

MAY   Wait, I'll come with ya . . .

JUNE   You won't . . .

MAY   Will you give us a lift?

JUNE   NO! He won't. Mac, stay 'ere 'til she's gone . . .

MAC   Eh?

JUNE   You 'eard . . .

MAC   Shurr-up June, you're off your 'ead . . .

MAY   Give us a lift 'ome and you can see the dog . . .

MAC   That's true . . .

MAY   I'll do you some tea . . .

JUNE   Don't push it lady . . .

DANNY   Come on May, I'll see you out . . .

MAY   MAC, COME ON, GIVE US A LIFT!

JUNE   Mac, don't you dare, shut up and sit down!

MAC   Who are you talkin' to?

JUNE   YOU!

MAY   Come on Mac, she's a stupid old cow.

JUNE   You what?

DANNY   Mam, leave 'er, that's what she wants . . . May,
          why don't you just go?

MAY   Why?

DANNY   You're not proving anything by staying 'ere . . .

MAY   Whose turn is it tonight? The son or the mother . . .

JUNE   That's it . . . I'll smash 'er bleedin' face in . . .

             (MAC *grabs her.*)

MAC   Leave it June . . . Danny, get 'er out . . .

JUNE   Filthy rotten little . . . (DANNY *pulls at* JUNE, *too.*) Gerroff me . . . what's she tryin' to do, eh? Comin' 'ere . . . if that carpet's ruined . . . I'll kill 'er . . .

DANNY   May . . . Please . . . just go . . .

MAY   Well? . . . you still an't answered me question? Is it your turn tonight Danny?

DANNY   (*slaps her face*) . . . You little trollop!

JUNE   Fist 'er Danny!

MAC   (*laughing*) Fuckin' 'ell . . .

MAY   *No*, he'll leave that for you Mac. (*Starts to walk out.*) Oh and Mac, don't bother picking the dog up, I'll 'ave it brought round . . . (*She exits as the lights fade.*)

             (MAY, *on the street, dragging the dead dog in a sack.*)

MAY   I'm just a doll me, not one of them dolls little lasses love . . . I'm a living, breathing version of one of them rubber things. The ones nobody lets on they 'ave . . . the ones nobody 'ad teck 'ome to meet their mother. Three holes, two tits and no voice. You can grab it, push it, pull it, smack and kick it, you can mess it up any way you want to, and it'll never complain . . . it'll just spring back into position and look at you with them big painted on eyes . . . you can even deflate it when the relatives come around, shove it in a drawer . . . and it'll say nothing, and when you want it back agen . . . all you have to do is blow it up . . . the . . . kiss . . . of life.

Scene Four

MAC, JUNE *and* DANNY *are watching telly.* MAC *is on edge.*

MAC	Do we have to watch this rubbish?
DANNY	No, *you* don't. Leave.
JUNE	Turn it over Danny.
DANNY	No . . .
JUNE	Do as you're told.
DANNY	Just 'cos he dun't want to watch it.
JUNE	Just do it . . .
DANNY	It's not fair.
MAC	Forget it . . . (*Jumps up.*)
JUNE	Oh . . . 'ere. (*Flicks the remote control.*) . . . Mac . . . 'ere look it's football . . .
MAC	You moved the keys?
JUNE	I've just turned it over . . .
MAC	I said 'ave you moved the keys? (*To* DANNY.) You, 'ave you 'ad 'em?
DANNY	Why — you going out?
MAC	'Ave you moved 'em?
JUNE	Mac, what you doing?
DANNY	There, in the fruit bowl . . .
MAC	What they doing in there?
DANNY	Hiding between two rotten plums?
MAC	Just leave my stuff alone, alright?

JUNE   Mac don't go . . . our Danny's goin' to pictures
            after . . .

DANNY   I aren't . . .

JUNE   You're doing as you're told . . . Mac?

DANNY   I'm not going out . . . let him go out. There's a
            good film on after . . . a weepy . . .

JUNE   Oh bloody shurr-up, stupid . . . Mac, stay in . . .

MAC   I'm off out . . . so just leave it, alright?

JUNE   But . . .

MAC   I SAID SHUT IT!

DANNY   Don't talk to my Mam like that . . .

MAC   I'm off . . .

DANNY   Good . . .

JUNE   Danny! Keep your bloody mouth shut! Where you
            going? . . . Mac?

MAC   Out . . .

JUNE   Where?

MAC   Just out . . .

JUNE   If you wait, I'll come with ya . . .

DANNY   You'll miss the film . . .

JUNE   Mac!

MAC   What!

JUNE   I said I'll come with ya . . .

MAC   I heard . . .

DANNY   It's a good one Mam . . .

JUNE   Well?

MAC   I don't want you with me . . . seen me shoes?

DANNY   Near the door . . .

JUNE   What do you mean?

MAC   What I said . . . I'm going out on me own . . .

JUNE   You're gonna May's aren't ya?

DANNY   Don't start all that Mam . . . 'ere look, there's a
           choice of two on . . .

JUNE   SHE SHOT YOUR BLOODY DOG!

MAC   I know . . . she misses me . . .

JUNE   You're not going back to 'er are ya? You are
           aren't ya? Christ! I don't believe you. You could
           be next. Mac, she's off 'er 'ead. She's already
           scarred you for life. You know what she's like.
           You'll end up killin' 'er just to shut 'er up . . .
           Mac?

DANNY   Mam . . . (*Quietly.*) Don't beg Mam, it don't 'elp.
           He'll be back.

JUNE   Shurr-up you . . . Mac, she's bloody mad!

MAC   (*grins*) You're all mad . . . she loves me, can I
           'elp it?

JUNE   Go back then . . . go, but teck another look at that
           dog in the yard first, 'cos if that's lovin' someone
           you might as well climb in that sack with it!

MAC   It used to stink . . .

JUNE   Oh so shoot it? You're as bad as 'er . . . Danny
           fetch me shoes down, me red 'uns.

MAC   For fuck's sake, it's only a bloody dog!

JUNE   Don't go . . . teck me . . . Mac! I can be ready in
            five minutes . . .

DANNY   Your hair's all over . . .

JUNE   GET ME ME FRIGGIN' SHOES WILL YA!

MAC   The best thing she ever did was shoot that dog.
            I'm glad. I should've done it years ago. I should.
            What kind of life did it 'ave any road? Chained
            up all day. Fed on crap. It shitted all over the
            bleedin' yard. Pathetic it was, crying all the time,
            like a friggin' wild animal. Howlin' all night.
            Not 'cos it was 'ungry, not 'cos it was cold . . .
            'cos it wanted to be free, aye free from me bloody
            boot. It used to make me sick to look at it, it did,
            it used to look at me sometimes, right in the eyes,
            as if to say . . . do it, put me out me misery . . . I
            should've done it years ago. It's the best thing
            she could 'ave done. She was doin' me a favour.

JUNE   She should've blown 'er own bleedin' 'ead off . . .

MAC   I'll burn it tomorra . . .

JUNE   She's not fit to be a mother . . .

DANNY   Aye, well it's a bloody good job you didn't keep
            an 'orse!

JUNE   Shurr-up, stupid . . . look, wait for us . . . I'll get
            me own bloody shoes. (*She exits.*)

            (MAC, *cocky and on edge, paces up and down the
            room.* DANNY *sits unmoved.*)

MAC   The thing about women is they think they know it
            all . . . do you know what I mean? . . . All gob.
            Now take June, if she kept 'er mouth shut she
            wun't be bad . . . bit wrecked an' that, but she's
            alright . . . if she kept it shut . . . but does she?
            Does she 'ell. It's non stop bloody garbage with
            'er in't it? Gob all bloody mighty. Tis. She's
            never off me back. I do everything for that
            woman . . . but is that enough? . . . NO . . . the

thing about women is they're never bloody
satisfied. Can't be 'appy with what they've got.
They allus want more. A bloke's 'appy with . . .
money in his pocket, decent car, game a pool, bit
of blow and a good game on the telly. Alright, so
I get rat-arsed . . . who dun't . . . I like a good
time, and why not? What the fuck else is there?
It's the bloody women that turn everything into a
bloody punch up . . . and why? . . . 'Cos they
won't keep this shut. Ok, so I like to live a bit
dangerously . . . nowt serious, bit of pinching, bit
of dealing . . . I keep me hand in . . . I'm known.
A bloke needs a bit of respect, a bit of friggin'
appreciation . . . women don't see it, do they?
They just can't bloody see it. I tell you, some
women only shut it when you're shaggin' 'em,
it's true. I reckon that's why blokes want it so
much. Na, I can do with June, I can. If she'd just
get it right. Gob shut, legs open.

DANNY   May'll be waiting . . .

MAC   So's your mother . . .

DANNY   I don't think so . . . don't you realise she just
          uses men . . .

MAC   Well maybe I like bein' used. Maybe it makes me
          feel wanted . . . like I count. Know what I mean,
          eh Danny?

DANNY   Uses 'em till she gets bored . . .

MAC   I'm well gone by then . . . you got any cans?

DANNY   Have you replaced the ones you've 'ad already?

MAC   Who buys 'em, eh? . . . Who puts food in your
          belly?

DANNY   I do my share . . .

MAC   Your mother sweats blood for you . . .

DANNY   I know . . . I don't need you tellin' me . . . I
         know already . . .

MAC   Out every night . . .

DANNY   I do my share, we was alright before you showed
         up . . .

MAC   Stinkin' of old fella's toss . . .

DANNY   I think you better leave . . .

MAC   Just so you can sit on your wet little arse and
         watch telly all day.

DANNY   She'd be lost without me . . .

MAC   'Ave you seen the state of some of 'er regulars?

DANNY   We don't discuss her work. She won't allow it.

MAC   The sort of blokes that live with their mothers
         until they're too friggin' soft to get any woman . . .

DANNY   I'll check the fridge. I think there's a light ale in
         it somewhere.

MAC   The sort of blokes that can't get it up without
         bein' smacked or whipped or pissed on . . .

DANNY   I don't know what you're trying . . .

MAC   The sort of blokes that cry like a like a little kid
         begging your Mam not to 'urt 'em but she does —
         yeah she does 'cos they pay her to. So Danny boy,
         next time you're out and you pass some old git in
         the street, teck a fuckin' good luck at 'im, 'cos
         he's the bloke that's been keepin' ya . . . Tucked
         up safe and warm in your mother's house . . .
         Tell 'er I've gone.

         (MAC *exits.*)

Scene Five

The wasteland. MAY *is held tightly by* MAC's *full body weight behind her. Her hair in his grasp, she is too weak to struggle.*

MAY   Is it 'cos of the dog? . . . Is it? I'm sorry Mac, 'onest . . . I'll get you another . . .

MAC   It's not the dog . . .

MAY   What then?

MAC   (*nicely*) What do you think it is May?

MAY   I've no money. I ain't been working . . . I've been badly . . . 'onest I feel crap . . .

MAC   You look it . . .

MAY   I know, I feel it . . .

MAC   But that's alright, I didn't come to look at your face . . .

MAY   I can't, 'onest Mac, I feel crap . . . can't you just give us summat . . . I'll pay you back . . .

MAC   Oh I know you will . . .

MAY   I've been badly . . .

MAC   Well I'm your miracle cure . . .

MAY   I've no strength . . .

MAC   I'm not asking for a fight . . . I've been standin' in line, it's my turn . . .

MAY   What do ya mean?

MAC   I want it all . . .

MAY   I can't . . . (*She starts to panic and struggle.*)

MAC   Oh you *can* . . .

MAY   Come back tomorra . . . I'll be better by tomorra.

MAC   There is no tomorra . . . (*He unzips his fly.*)

MAY   I 'ant been out, I've told you I'm badly . . . look Mac 'onest I'll pay you back . . . I'm off out tomorra . . . 'onest.

(*She struggles as* MAC *thrusts himself forward into her. Blackout.*)

Scene Six

Spotlight rises on JUNE.

JUNE   Sex? Sex is like going to the lav to them, 'tis. They don't feel owt. They don't feel owt but bunged up, bunged up with summat hard, summat bad that's rottin' their insides. They just want it out that's all. Out and over with. They go about their lives topping up the badness, pushing it down, ignoring the ache. Sitting behind their desks in their grey little offices and topping up the badness . . . and waiting for the exit . . . watching the clock. Clock in . . . clock out . . . eight hours of waiting. Eight hours of sitting on their tight little arses organising people's lives. But allus with an edge, 'cos of an ache . . . 'cos of the waiting. One eye on the clock, one eye on the form, the paper work, the in tray, the out tray, the fucking up someone's life tray. You've seen 'em, they're everywhere. Everywhere and nowhere. Mr Fuckin' Grey Suit shuffling the shit. Mr Big Car. Mr Appointment Only. Mr Sweaty-arsed Whip Me In Me Mother's Night Dress . . . make me cry . . . make me remember to feel summat, summat more than the ache, Mr Dripping Dick, sad in the corner, sad in his suit . . . stained his car seat but not his life. Mr Can't Look You In The Eye, can't take the long journey home. They've got to get it out, see. The dull ache, the big pain . . . so they stop off and see me. I'm everything they need. I've got two legs, two hands and one very big mouth that never says their name . . . and they want it all, every bit of me that's flesh. 'Cos my body's a laxative, a plunger, can opener, cork screw . . . I've an arse like a stick of dynamite. Oh aye, I can unblock anything me . . . best fucking plummer in town.

(*Blackout.*)

Scene Seven

Ten days before Christmas. DANNY *is lying down on the settee surrounded by paper chains. Only the Christmas lights are on.* MAY *enters from the back way — quietly whispers to* DANNY *— she is in a drugged state.*

MAY   Danny . . . *Danny* . . .

DANNY   Mam?

MAY   Mam!

DANNY   Mam is that you?

MAY   Mam is that you?

DANNY   May?

MAY   Don't put the lights on . . .

DANNY   But I can't see you . . .

MAY   I don't want you to . . .

DANNY   What you been doing?

MAY   Dunno . . .

DANNY   Where you been?

MAY   Dunno.

DANNY   I've been making paper chains . . .

MAY   'Ave yer?

DANNY   Yeah . . . I feel a bit sick now. I think it's all that
               licking.

MAY   So do I . . .

DANNY   You alright?

MAY   Sometimes I wake up with such a feeling inside,
               like I'm homesick or summat . . . sort of lost in
               time, not a kid but not grown up . . . and I miss
               me Mam, and I miss a feeling that's gone now.
               Safe . . . but not safe . . . and it's 'ere, just in the
               pit of me stomach . . . sort of churnin' in time
               . . . and I feel so little, inside, outside . . . in this
               friggin' big town . . . like a speck of nothin'
               worth anything . . . like nobody no bugger wants
               . . . and I wanna know why . . . why I can't think
               no more . . . it's all gone wrong in me head . . .
               mixed up. Where am I?

DANNY   You're 'ere with me.

MAY   Is it dark?

DANNY   Yeah — shall I put the lights on?

MAY   I'm scared of the dark.

DANNY   Shall I put the lights on?

MAY   I like being scared, it reminds me of summat . . .

DANNY   It's nearly Christmas.

MAY   I hate Christmas.

DANNY   But I thought they let you see your kids at
               Christmas.

MAY   What kids?

DANNY   Your kids, remember?

MAY   No.

DANNY   'Course you do . . .

MAY   No . . . I don't anymore . . .

DANNY   Course you do, one's nearly two and the other's
           four . . . your son, remember? May — remember?

MAY   No I don't . . . why should I? . . .

DANNY   But I thought you wanted 'em back?

MAY   Don't put the light on . . .

DANNY   May? You do want 'em back don't ya?

MAY   I've stood on summat . . . what's all this? What's
           all this?

DANNY   Paper chains . . .

MAY   Paper chains . . . (*Laughs.*)

DANNY   You alright?

MAY   Dunno . . . I'm starfished . . .

DANNY   What's starfished?

MAY   Dunno . . .

DANNY   Do ya feel sick?

MAY   Star . . . fished . . .

DANNY   May?

MAY   Star . . . friggin' fished . . .

           (*Blackout.*)

Scene Eight

DANNY *is sat watching TV by the light of the Christmas tree*
and the fire. MAC *enters quietly, holding a bunch of flowers.*
He stands and watches DANNY *for awhile before speaking.*

MAC   (*quietly*) Danny boy . . .

DANNY   (*jumps in shock*) She's out . . .

MAC   I know she's out . . . (*He puts on the standard lamp.*)

DANNY   What's them then?

MAC   Flowers.

DANNY   I can see they're flowers.

MAC   For your Mam.

DANNY   She hates flowers.

MAC   Does she?

DANNY   They remind 'er of death.

MAC   They'll remind 'er of all the good times I've shown 'er . . .

DANNY   She's still got the bruises for that . . .

MAC   You're sharp Danny . . . you are, but not quite sharp enough . . .

DANNY   Unlike you . . .

MAC   Exactly . . .

DANNY   Well don't cough, you might cut your own throat.

MAC   You've got all the answers an't you Danny?

DANNY   Like I said she's not 'ere so you might as well leave — an' take your flowers with ya . . . put 'em on your dog's grave . . .

MAC   I'd rather give 'em to your mother . . . .

DANNY   I bet you knew May was gonna do that to your dog.

MAC   I know, silly cow . . . 'ave you seen me baseball bat?

DANNY   Do you actually care about anything?

MAC   Er . . . (*Long pause.*) No.

DANNY   God I feel sorry for you.

MAC   I know, sad in't it? (*Beat.*) Eh! I've just thought of summat I care about — This! (*Holds his groin.*) Yeah, I care about this! I see it's well looked after. Clean, fed, exercised . . . Why, is there summat wrong with that? Eh? Find that offensive do ya? Find that shockin'?

DANNY   Animal . . .

MAC   What?

DANNY   I said you was an animal. May should 'ave shot you. Put you out of your misery. Do the world a favour.

MAC   You think so do ya? (*He moves closer in a threatening manner.*)

DANNY   I only 'ave to scream and they'll be in from next door. The walls are like paper . . . I will, I'll scream.

MAC   Scream then.

DANNY   He's big is Betty's 'usband, ex-fisherman . . .

MAC   I'd like to meet 'im . . . go on then, scream . . .

DANNY   You're not proving anything . . .

MAC   Oh you're wrong Danny. You're very wrong. I'm proving what a wet little fucker you are . . . and I wanna hear you crying for your Mam . . . come on, it's not the first time is it?

DANNY   Just go . . .

MAC   Is it? I bet you was allus crying for your Mam when you was little . . . eh? Wan't ya? . . . Wan't ya? (*He grabs* DANNY'S *arm and starts to twist it.*)

DANNY	Get off . . .
MAC	But she want 'ere was she? . . . (*Tightening his grip*.) I said was she?
DANNY	No . . .
MAC	Just like she's not 'ere now. And why? . . . (*Softly spoken*.) Where is she Danny?
DANNY	Out . . .
MAC	Out where?
DANNY	Just out . . .
MAC	Out where?
DANNY	Get off . . .
MAC	OUT WHERE?
DANNY	Working . . .
MAC	(*holding him tighter*) Where?
DANNY	I don't know . . .
MAC	Oh you do . . . out where?
DANNY	NO . . . let go . . .
MAC	What's she doing Danny?
DANNY	I don't know . . . get off . . .
MAC	What's she doing? . . . What do you think your mother is doing right this minute?
DANNY	NO MAC, PLEASE . . .
MAC	Shall I tell you . . .
DANNY	NO . . .
MAC	(*moving his free hand slowly towards* DANNY's *groin*) Your mother is out there with some sad . . . old . . . (*Suddenly grabbing* DANNY's *groin*.) Git!
DANNY	I know.

MAC	Now I wanna hear you say it . . . come on Danny . . . "My mother is out there with some sad old git" . . . SAY IT!
DANNY	No . . . please Mac, let go . . .
MAC	Say it . . . "My Mam's out there with some sad . . . old . . . git."
DANNY	Please . . .
MAC	And what do you think she's doin' with 'im, eh?
DANNY	No . . .
MAC	Come on Danny, use your imagination . . . what do you think they're doin', eh?
DANNY	I don't know . . .
MAC	Oh you do . . .
DANNY	No . . .
MAC	Come on, I wanna hear you say it . . . "My mother is out there with some sad old git" . . . Doin' what?
DANNY	You're sick . . . you are . . . you're sick . . .

(MAC *throws* DANNY *to the floor.* DANNY *reaches for his asthma pump — he can hardly breathe.* MAC *places the flowers on him.*)

| MAC | It's a sick world, Danny. |

(MAC *exits. Blackout.*)

Scene Nine

Lights rise. DANNY *and* JUNE *are both sat on the settee.* DANNY *is being indifferent.* JUNE *is trying not to notice but is failing miserably.*

JUNE   Me guts ache . . .

DANNY   (*reading a book*) Really . . .

JUNE   (*looking at a hand morror and pulling hairs out of her chin*) I haven't been sleepin' . . .

DANNY   I wonder why . . .

JUNE   I keep burping up sick . . .

DANNY   Perks of the job . . .

JUNE   I nearly collapsed on this poor old bloke the other night . . .

DANNY   Mmmm . . .

JUNE   Good job he was a vet . . .

DANNY   You should 'ave asked 'im to put you down . . .

JUNE   Mac's comin' round after . . .

DANNY   Why don't you go and see a proper doctor . . .

JUNE   They can't be trusted . . .

DANNY   Stay in . . .

JUNE   And live on fresh air?

DANNY   It's chucking it down . . .

JUNE   What's new . . . 'ave you seen me bag?

DANNY   You're sat on it . . . I don't want to be on me own . . .

JUNE   You're just bein' dramatic. Tidy up a bit, the toilet's a disgrace . . . I'll bring you a Chinese in. (*There is a long silence.* JUNE *tries to ignore it, but is on edge. She gets up and pours herself a drink.*) No, you're alright Danny, I'll get meself a drink . . . you just sit there . . . reading

... what you reading for? Put the telly on ... if
you're doing this to annoy me it won't work ...
(*Sits back down on the setee.*) What you reading?

DANNY The Bible.

JUNE (*gives him a look*) I worry about you sometimes
... what do you think about this colour? ... Oh
there's only a bit left ... Danny, do ya reckon
this'll stretch to nine? (*Holds an empty bottle of
nail varnish up.*)

DANNY Where's the tenth?

JUNE God knows ... it's no good, I'm gonna 'ave to
stock up on some decent colours ... .'ere Danny,
did you put any nail varnishes in the Christmas
box? ... Next time you see that Avon woman,
pin 'er down will ya? I might even treat us both
to some luxury items. Apparently their Rolled
Gold is smashing ... .

DANNY Then he said to them ... watch out, be on your
guard against all kinds of greed; a man's life
does not consist in the abundance of his
possessions. (*He closes the book, sighs.*)

JUNE 'Ere, did you iron me best frock? Sod it, I'm
going the whole hog, 'ere I might even wear
tinsel in me hair ... come on Danny, liven up a
bit will you? There's only four days left to
Christmas. If you carry on like this Sunshine,
you'll end up with a sack of bloody cinders ...
do you 'ear me? Do ya know I was just thinking
that things are on the 'up' tonight ... I was.
(*Pause.*) You're not gonna put me in a bad mood
... (DANNY *just sits, sulking.*) Carry on Danny,
carry on. You know you'll regret it. (*Beat.*) Oh,
for fuck's sake, what's wrong with ya?

DANNY You haven't even asked 'bout May ...

JUNE ... 'Ave you moved the TV Times?

DANNY   Well?

JUNE   It's the only time they put owt decent on the telly
           . . . I want summat taping . . . mind you they're
           all repeats . . .

DANNY   Thankfully she's still alive . . .

JUNE   Pity . . .

DANNY   No thanks to you or Mac . . .

JUNE   It's not the first time, she's allus doin' it . . .
           she's barmy . . .

DANNY   I told you what he's like. He gave 'er it you know.

JUNE   She'll 'ave begged 'im for it . . .

DANNY   She could 'ave died . . .

JUNE   Why do you think she's on the streets?

DANNY   I'm not listening to any of your lies.

JUNE   . . . Well 'ave you moved the TV Times or what?

DANNY   (*throws her the TV Times*) Oh 'ere . . . it's
           frightening, especially when you've got no one to
           look after you . . .

JUNE   So will you tape us summat or what?

DANNY   And she misses 'er kids . . .

JUNE   (*sarcastic*) 'Course she does . . . (*Looking in the
           magazine.*) Oh . . . I've seen it sixteen bloody
           times . . . I wish we 'ad Sky you know.

DANNY   She loves them kids . . .

JUNE   'Course she does . . .

DANNY   You're just jealous . . .

JUNE   Grow up, Danny . . .

DANNY   'Cos she's my friend . . .

JUNE   You been lending 'er money?

DANNY   No . . . well not much . . .

JUNE   Well keep on doing it and she'll be your friend forever . . .

DANNY   I said not much . . . any way . . . that's my business . . . you give Mac money all the time.

JUNE   That's nowt to do with you . . .

DANNY   So he's not using you then in't he?

JUNE   Don't push your luck, Sunshine . . .

DANNY   No, I wanna know why you think you're better? I would 'ave thought you 'ad a lot in common with May . . . let's face it you share the same man, and the same job. The only difference is you give him money and he gives it to May.

JUNE   He dun't give 'er it, he lends 'er it. Well he use' to. He in't any more . . .

DANNY   But of course she's a lot younger than you . . .

JUNE   Danny, keep out of what you don't know . . .

DANNY   No, tell me . . . I wanna know . . .

JUNE   I said shut it . . .

DANNY   No . . .

JUNE   Look Danny . . . she's a rip-off merchant . . . she tecks their money and runs. There's loads of scraggy little lasses like 'er. Sixty, seventy quid a day on shit. They've no bloody morals. They'd rip their own fathers off . . . they go down there on a night in their pairs, like daft little school kids. They're pathetic the bloody lot of 'em.

Some can hardly speak they're so drugged up.
There's nowt on 'em. They're all skin and bone
. . . and May's just as bad, 'er head's gone —
she's given up. Telling you, she's doing it for her
kids. She's allus done it — she dun't know no
different. The only good thing she ever did for 'er
kids, was letting 'em go. Poor little bastards . . .
she'll end up killing 'erself, everyone's warned
'er. Vice are sick of 'er. Even Mac won't get 'er
owt no more. She owes money all over the bloody
place. She gives the business a bad name. She's
asking for trouble.

DANNY   Why don't you stay in tonight? I'll give you one
        of my special facials . . . Mam?

JUNE   No. If we want turkey on Christmas Day, then
        I've got to work.

DANNY   I can get a job . . .

JUNE   What, with your chest?

DANNY   Stay in Mam, just tonight . . .

JUNE   Don't be soft . . . I'll see you after . . .

DANNY   I'll come with ya . . . .

JUNE   You're just bein' daft now . . .

DANNY   I'll look after you, write their numbers down . . .

JUNE   Hold me 'and?

DANNY   Please Mam, let me . . . I'll watch out for ya . . .

        (MAC *walks in from the back way.*)

MAC   Er . . . I think your mother's big enough and daft
        enough to look after 'erself — don't you June?

JUNE   Right then . . . 'er shoes . . . (*Looks for her
        shoes, quickly.*)

MAC   'Urry up June . . .

DANNY   Mam, can I just have a quick word with you . . .
           in private . . .

MAC   (*grinning*) In what?

JUNE   Don't be soft Danny . . . right, I'm ready . . . is it
           still bloody snowing? Will I need me brolly? 'Ave
           you seen me brolly?

DANNY   Mam . . .

MAC   (*mocking*) Mam . . .

JUNE   Danny, calm down, you'll set yourself off if
           you're not careful — you got your asthma pump
           on you?

MAC   Come on June . . .

DANNY   Mam please . . .

MAC   Mam please . . .

JUNE   I said I'm ready . . .

MAC   See ya Danny boy . . .

DANNY   She's not going!

JUNE   Shut it Danny . . . come on then.

DANNY   Mam! . . . stay in . . . please.

MAC   Why? Do ya want someone to sing you to sleep?

JUNE   (*to* MAC) I thought you was in a hurry?

MAC   See ya Danny. (JUNE *sprays herself with perfume*.)
           June, you've got enough of that shit on already,
           you smell like a bloody whore. (*He takes the
           perfume from her and sprays* DANNY.) There you
           are Danny, you won't miss your Mam now 'cos
           you've still got 'er smell with ya . . . and later on
           you can 'ave a kipper for your supper and pretend
           she's home already!

JUNE	(*to* MAC) You're such a shit sometimes . . . ignore 'im Danny, he's only trying to wind you up . . . well, come on then.
MAC	Don't forget to lock all the windows and doors, there's some dodgy characters around these days . . .
DANNY	Mam?
JUNE	What?
DANNY	Be careful . . .
JUNE	Yeah . . . night son . . .

Scene Ten

Later the same evening. DANNY *and* MAY *are sat on the settee.* DANNY *is painting* MAY'S *fingernails.*

MAY	Me mam always 'ad disgusting nails, she bit 'em all the time. (*She smells the nail varnish.*)
DANNY	Keep still, they'll smudge . . .
MAY	Do you think you can get high on the smell of nail varnish?
DANNY	Probably, but it gives you brain damage . . .
MAY	You're clever with words, aren't ya?
DANNY	'Ave you ever considered false ones?
MAY	Tits?
DANNY	Nails.
MAY	I'd 'ave false tits . . . them implants. I'd get massive ones . . . would you?
DANNY	I'm not sure about this colour . . . an't you got little hands.

MAY	Yeah . . . and tits.
DANNY	Now look what you've made me do . . . oh, I'll have to start again now . . . pass that bottle . . . (*Cleans her nails off with the remover.*)
MAY	'An't you got long eyelashes.
DANNY	May, keep still.
MAY	I'm fed up now . . . do you like holding me hand?
DANNY	Keep still.
MAY	Do you put gel on your hair?
DANNY	No, mousse . . .
MAY	(*strokes his hair*) It's nice . . .
DANNY	If these nails are still wet, you'll stick to me.
MAY	I'd like that . . .
DANNY	I'll give up in a minute . . .
MAY	Don't stop . . . I like you holding me hand, I've allus got cold hands you know . . .
DANNY	Cold hands, warm . . . (*She takes his hand and puts in on her breast.*) Heart . . .
MAY	Can you feel me heart?
DANNY	Shall I do you some toast?
MAY	Can you feel me tit?
DANNY	We've got some nice lemon curd.
MAY	I like you Danny.
DANNY	(*starts to panic*) Oh God . . .
MAY	I'll do it for nowt . . . are you a virgin? I bet you are. What do ya say Danny — shall we?

DANNY   If me mother comes 'ome May, she'll hack you to
        death . . . with her bare hands . . . and then kill
        me an' all . . . (*With increasing panic now.*) How
        about some Bovril, that'll warm you up . . . you
        look freezing . . .

MAY   You can keep me warm . . .

DANNY   I'll put another bar on the fire, me Mam'll go
        barmy but I'll tell 'er you're not well . . .

MAY   (*enjoying* DANNY'S *discomfort*) Come on Danny,
        I'll make a man of you . . .

DANNY   I don't want to be a man!

MAY   'Course you do . . . you like that don't you
        Danny?

DANNY   Why did you kill Mac's dog?

MAY   Eh?

DANNY   Why? It wasn't a very nice thing to do . . . was
        it?

MAY   It wanted me to. Feel. I've got two you know.
        (*Moves his hands.*) . . . one . . . two . . .

DANNY   Stop it May . . .

MAY   Why . . . you getting a hard-on Danny?

        (JUNE *walks in with* MAC. DANNY *pulls back but*
        MAY *hangs on to his hands. She lunges forward
        quickly. It all happens very quickly. But* JUNE *can
        only see* MAY *on top of* DANNY *on the settee.* MAC
        *is off his head, pissed and doped-up. He is
        grinning.*)

JUNE   (*as she enters*) I'm nithered, knackered and in
        need of a very large . . . what the 'ell . . . DANNY!

DANNY   (*jumps up, pushing* MAY *back, but she is trying to resist him*) . . . Mam!

MAY   (*cocky, pulling her top down, grinning*) June . . . Hiya . . .

DANNY   You're early . . .

         (MAC *is laughing*.)

MAC   Fuckin' 'ell . . . Danny boy . . . eh! When the cat's away!

JUNE   I think you better leave . . .

MAY   Who?

JUNE   YOU!

MAC   Come on June let's leave 'em to it . . . 'ave an early night . . .

JUNE   AND YOU!

MAC   EH?

JUNE   You heard! The pair of you get out!

DANNY   Mam, I can explain — it's not what you think . . .

MAC   (*squeals*) This is fuckin' brilliant!

JUNE   I said out!!!

DANNY   But Mam . . .

JUNE   Shut it . . . May, get out . . .

MAC   June, let the boy say his piece . . . come on Danny, you was just saying . . .

DANNY   Get lost . . . (*Beat.*) Mam . . .

MAY   Leave it Danny. I'll go. (*Kisses him.*) And Danny — thanks . . . see you around . . .

JUNE   Don't bank on it lady. Mac, I want you out an'
              all.

MAC   I think you're over-reacting a bit 'ere, June . . .

JUNE   Get out!

MAC   June, I don't know who you think you're talking
              to darlin' but I'm getting a bit sick of it . . .
              alright? . . . (*Grins*.) You should be happy June,
              you should be celebrating. (*Grins*.) Your Danny's
              not as wet as he looks . . .

JUNE   (*pushes him*) Get out . . . go on . . . get out of my
              house . . .

MAC   (*laughs*) You're off your head woman!

DANNY   Just go Mac . . .

MAC   (*suddenly changes*) Danny boy . . . I think you've
              offended your mother 'ere, son . . . I think you
              owe 'er an explanation, don't you? Better think of
              some answers . . . quick.

DANNY   Get lost.

MAC   (*laughs*) Eh, just out of interest Danny . . . how
              much was she asking?

JUNE   (*sitting quietly, staring into space and smoking*)
              Arsehole . . . get out . . .

              (MAC *leaves. But just before his exit he turns
              back to* DANNY.)

MAC   Eh . . . Danny . . . next time ask me son, I can
              sort you out with summat decent. A nice bit of
              mature arse maybe? . . . Alright? (*He winks, and
              exits. An awkward silence*.)

DANNY   Mam . . .

JUNE   Don't 'Mam' me.

DANNY   It's not what it looked like, honestly . . . nowt
         was going on. I was doing her nails.

JUNE   Shut up.

DANNY   But it's true . . . honestly. She was just mucking
         about . . .

JUNE   You must think I was born yesterday . . .

DANNY   Honestly Mam, it's true.

         (JUNE *fixes herself a drink.*)

JUNE   Have you been at this lot an' all? I hope you 'an't
         been giving it to May . . . it's nearly all gone!

DANNY   I havn't been giving it to anyone, I made a trifle
         didn't I, ready for Christmas Eve. Mam . . .
         (*Panicking.*) You've got to believe me. I wasn't
         doing anything, honestly . . . it was just . . .

JUNE   ALRIGHT! Let it drop . . . you taped me owt?

DANNY   May was just mucking about . . . you know what
         she's like.

JUNE   Fine . . .

DANNY   She was just winding me up . . .

JUNE   'Ave you seen me slippers?

DANNY   That's all . . .

JUNE   (*shouts*) I said drop it! . . . I don't care.

DANNY   You do.

JUNE   So 'ave you taped me a film or what?

DANNY   No.

JUNE   Brilliant. TOO BLOODY BUSY I SUPPOSE!

DANNY	See. You're mad with me still. Mam I wasn't . . . doing *anything* with May . . . honest to God, cross my heart and hope to die . . .
JUNE	Get to bed.
DANNY	'Ere we go . . . no.
JUNE	I've nowt to say to you Danny. Do as you're told go on. I'm too bloody tired tonight.
DANNY	No. Not until you say you believe me.
JUNE	She's a bloody drug addict!
DANNY	So.
JUNE	And a little slag.
DANNY	And you arn't?
JUNE	It's time you sorted yourself out lad . . .
DANNY	Like you have?
JUNE	Did you give her money?
DANNY	I don't believe this. NO! I did not give her money I did not do anything with May. I was painting her nails. Which actually was impossible because she hasn't got any. Nails. (*He starts to leave.*) I'm going to bed.
JUNE	Good. Get out me sight.
DANNY	(*quickly coming back*) And even if I was, what's it got to do with you anyway?
JUNE	Are you drunk?
DANNY	(*laughs*) No . . .
JUNE	Has May been giving you summat?
DANNY	I'm going to bed.
JUNE	'Ave you drunk that sherry? You have 'an't ya?

DANNY	So what if I have . . .
JUNE	That's it. When I go out this booze gets locked up. I don't go out to work so you can sit in behaving like your bloody Granny all night . . .
DANNY	She didn't drink sherry.
JUNE	Danny, she'd drink vinegar if you let 'er.
DANNY	And I wonder why.
JUNE	Probably because she was a miserable old cow.
DANNY	With you for a daughter . . .
JUNE	God, you get more like 'er every day.
DANNY	Good . . .
JUNE	Evil old cow . . .
DANNY	That's my Granny you're talking about . . .
JUNE	(*half laughs*) Stupid . . . I don't know who you think you are . . .
DANNY	And you do?
JUNE	Get to bed.
DANNY	No. I'm gonna 'ave another drink . . .
JUNE	You aren't. (*They fight over the sherry bottle.*)
DANNY	KEEP IT . . . I don't want it, I don't want anything from you!
JUNE	Get out me sight . . .
DANNY	Don't worry, I am . . .
JUNE	For good!
DANNY	Why? So you can put a sign on the door . . . open twenty-four hours a day?

JUNE　　　　How dare you talk to me like that!

DANNY　　　Like what? . . . It's true.

JUNE　　　　I've worked hard for everything decent in this house . . .

DANNY　　　I know, I know but you did take this off Mac.

JUNE　　　　I teck a lot of things off a lot of people.

DANNY　　　I know . . . I just wish you didn't.

JUNE　　　　Why? In't it good enough for you any more?

DANNY　　　It's not that . . . you know it's not that . . .

JUNE　　　　Well you 'an't done bad out of me so far, Sunshine.

DANNY　　　I don't want anything from you!

JUNE　　　　GET OUT!

DANNY　　　Mam . . .

JUNE　　　　You heard me — get out!

DANNY　　　But . . .

JUNE　　　　YOU UNGRATEFUL LITTLE SOD! I come home knackered and you do this to me . . .

DANNY　　　MAM . . . you don't understand, it's not that . . . it's . . . I'm sorry . . .

JUNE　　　　Well sorry's not enough, get out me sight . . . go on, get out!

DANNY　　　But it's snowing . . .

JUNE　　　　Well get wet. I do most nights.

DANNY　　　Don't say that Mam . . . I'm sorry, 'onest I am . . . I'll replace the sherry . . .

JUNE　　　　Just go . . .

DANNY   Please Mam, let's not argue, it's nearly
Christmas . . . I'm sorry, I am. I'm ashamed.

JUNE   What do ya want from me, eh? . . . WHAT?

DANNY   Nothing . . .

JUNE   Nearly every friggin' night I am out there.

DANNY   I know . . . don't . . . don't get upset . . .

JUNE   And why?

DANNY   I know why . . .

JUNE   'Cos of money that's why . . . money, ha! That's
a joke . . . 'ere. (*She gropes around in her bag,
pulls out some money.*) 'Ere, that's what I'm
worth . . . count it. Go on, it won't take you long.

DANNY   No Mam, don't . . .

JUNE   Count it.

DANNY   No.

JUNE   Go on — count it!

DANNY   No. Please don't do this to me . . . I'm sorry.

JUNE   I'll tell you how much there is, shall I? Forty
eight quid . . . that's it . . . that's what I'm worth
tonight . . . but you never know, tomorra I might
be worth fifty . . . or even sixty, then we can go
mad and have meat 'til January . . .

DANNY   Don't say that.

JUNE   What a woman, eh?

DANNY   Shall I make a drink?

JUNE   If I die tomorra, that's what I leave behind . . .
well it's all yours . . . 'ere, you might as well
'ave it now.

DANNY   I don't care about money.

JUNE   You make me sick.

DANNY   It's only money.

JUNE   Yeah . . .

DANNY   That's all . . .

JUNE   Yeah . . . that's all . . .

DANNY   There's more important things than money.

JUNE   You reckon, do ya . . .

DANNY   'Course there is . . .

JUNE   My money means nothing to you then?

DANNY   People are more important.

JUNE   (*tries to laugh but is obviously hurt*) People . . .

DANNY   Yeah people . . .

JUNE   Pick it up. (*Meaning the money.*)

DANNY   No . . .

JUNE   Pick it up, go on 'ave a good look at it Danny,
             'cos even though it means nothing to you . . .
             that's how much I'm worth.

DANNY   No . . .

JUNE   Why, is it mucky?

DANNY   No . . . don't Mam, I feel a bit breathless . . .

JUNE   Gutless you mean. You are, you're gutless. Pick it
             up and 'ave a good look at it . . . or does it stink
             too much, eh?

DANNY   Don't say that Mam, I can hardly breathe.

JUNE   'Course it stinks Danny, it's mine . . .

DANNY   That's not true . . .

JUNE   Course it is . . . but it's only money, in't it?
What does it matter . . . easy come, easy go . . .
and it's easy money, in't it? Course it is . . .
given to me by all those grateful punters . . . all
two of 'em . . . a fat twat and a stinking ponce.

DANNY   I can't breathe . . . 'onest, I'm not well . . .

JUNE   Against the wall and on me knees . . .

DANNY   No . . .

JUNE   'Ave it . . . the one's that call me beautiful are
allus the ugliest . . .

DANNY   You are beautiful.

JUNE   Not even on the inside . . .

DANNY   You are, to me you are . . .

JUNE   Get out me sight . . .

DANNY   Don't say that . . .

JUNE   Go on . . .

DANNY   Don't say that . . . how can you say that?

JUNE   Easy . . . I mean it . . .

DANNY   No . . .

JUNE   You ungrateful little bastard . . .

DANNY   Why?

JUNE   I've nowt to say to you, Danny . . .

DANNY   Why, 'cos I don't want your money? Nearly all
my life, you wasn't there for me — and now you
expect me to be grateful — 'cos the only way you
can earn a living is by opening your legs . . .

JUNE   (*suddenly slaps him*) How *dare* you speak to me
        like that! How dare you . . . this is her fault.

DANNY   It's not . . . it's yours. You're the one who left
        me. All me Granny did was look after me and try
        and protect me from what people were saying . . .

JUNE   What?

DANNY   What do you think? (*Pause. He sits nearer.*)

JUNE   Get to bed.

DANNY   I want you, that's all . . .

JUNE   (*laughs*) That's all . . . that's all . . .

DANNY   Is that too much to ask? You are me mother.

JUNE   Oh and that makes it easy does it . . . well I'm
        sorry to disappoint you Sunshine, but this
        mother's 'ad enough, alright? I give up on you.
        You've ruined Christmas already . . .

DANNY   Given up on me? You never even tried . . .

JUNE   The trouble with you Danny, is you live in the
        past . . .

DANNY   I've only got the past. Why didn't you come and
        get me? Every Christmas, I thought you would.
        Instead of sending a present.

JUNE   The sooner you bloody grow up, the better . . .

DANNY   Grow up?

JUNE   Yes, grow up — get out there and get a life . . .

DANNY   You want me to grow up?

JUNE   Yes I do . . .

DANNY   Why?

JUNE   What do you mean why? Are you barmy? 'Cos
        I'm sick and bloody tired of all this — that's why.

DANNY   All this, all this what? All this truth. Didn't you ever, just once, hold me and want to keep me?

JUNE   Don't be bloody soft Danny . . . you know nothing . . .

(She moves away to the dresser.)

DANNY   Did you ever want me in the first place?

JUNE   You know nothing . . .

DANNY   Why didn't you just get rid of me?

JUNE   Carry on Danny, dragging up the bloody past . . .

DANNY   She allus said you'd come back for me . . .

JUNE   *(surprised)* Me mother?

DANNY   She said one day you'd come back for good . . .

JUNE   She said that . . . when?

DANNY   She allus said it . . . but you was probably having too much of a good time to want me. You only came back 'cos she was dead . . .

JUNE   Danny, you can't keep living in the past luv . . .

DANNY   I can't help it . . . why didn't you want me?

JUNE   *(it looks as if she is almost going to put her arms around* DANNY *. . . but just cannot do it)* I did . . . *(Walks to the bar and as she speaks she makes herself a tall drink.)* First time you was one, two days after your birthday. I bought you a bike — ooh, it was too big — but I knew you'd grow into it.

DANNY   She didn't let me . . .

JUNE   No . . . I know. I never saw you play on it . . . 'Cos I did see you . . . playing top of terrace . . .

> with your push-along dog . . . that was your
> favourite, wan't it?

DANNY   Yeah, You knew?

JUNE   I knew, oh yeah . . . I knew. First time I came
          back was when you was three. I stood over there
          near the winda and begged 'er to let me see you.
          She said 'no' . . . to come back in the morning,
          that it was late, it was. I'd been in the pub all
          night, dutch courage an' that. But I knew she
          meant no, not ever. I left and went up town
          dancing, later that night I put a brick through her
          winda.

DANNY   You broke her praying hands.

JUNE   Should 'ave been 'er neck. (*Pause.*) I came back
          nearly every year . . . Can I just see him? I'd say
          . . . play with him for a bit . . . he's settled, we
          don't want him upset. You get yourself nicely
          sorted first . . . nicely sorted. (*Laughs.*) Oh, I was
          already nicely sorted thank you. Every fella's
          good time. She knew, 'course she knew. Let's
          face it, who didn't. (*Laughs.*) Trouble was she
          was right. The old cow was allus right. I must
          'ave been barmy . . . stood in front of her . . .
          dead smart, dead posh. But the smarter I tried to
          look . . . the dirtier she made me feel. Oh yeah. I
          'ad years and years of bloody marvellous times,
          begging to that old cow.

DANNY   Why did she tell me you'd come back for me?

JUNE   'Cos she knew I wouldn't. She knew I'd give up,
          you was better off without me. What could I give
          you? I 'ad no love. I made meself do without. I
          stopped wanting. Except when she died. (*Pause.*)
          Then I wanted this house. I was gonna burn it
          down . . . but no . . . no, that was too easy . . .
          just me living in it's enough. Every time I fuck
          someone in this house, I'm paying her back . . .

DANNY   What about me?

JUNE   What about you?

DANNY   How did I fit in?

JUNE   Fixtures and fittings . . .

DANNY   No, you don't mean that.

JUNE   Don't I . . . why? What did you expect, an' 'appy
          ending? Well this isn't *The Waltons* Danny, we
          don't love in this house, we just exist. Face it
          darlin' you can't forgive me anymore than I can
          forgive 'er. But I tell you Danny, people think
          running away's easy. It's not. Staying's easy.
          Carrying on's easy. Running away takes guts.
          'Cos you know that the longer you go for the
          harder it is to come back. The longer you stay
          away, the harder it is to lie to yourself and
          everyone else. I didn't come back for you Danny
          'cos I didn't want you any more. I'd stopped
          being your mother the day I walked out that door
          . . . and nowt's changed.

DANNY   You don't mean that . . .

JUNE   Don't I?

DANNY   Do you?

JUNE   If she was rotten to you Danny, I'm sorry . . . if
          she wasn't, then you're lucky, she was an old cow
          to me.

          (JUNE *leaves.* DANNY, *shocked, stands in thought
          for awhile then quickly puts his shoes on, collects
          his coat and the Bible. Shirley Bassey's 'Moon
          River' plays.* DANNY *looks around the room
          slowly, then leaves. As the music continues to
          play, the lights fade to half, and the light from
          the TV glows as* MAC *enters, followed by* JUNE *and*
          MAY. MAC *sprawls on the settee, drinking from a
          can and watching TV with the remote control in
          his hand.* JUNE *silently puts the finishing touches
          on her make-up in front of the mirror as* MAY

warms herself by the fire. After a short while
JUNE *crosses to* MAC, *kisses him, then turns to*
MAY, *showing her nails. They then both exit.* MAC
watches them leave, looks back to the TV, and
using the remote control quickly turns it off.
Blackout.)

THE END

DANGEROUS ENGAGEMENT

CHARLOTTE BYRD

Copyright © 2020 by Charlotte Byrd, LLC.

Proofreaders:

Renee Waring, Guardian Proofreading Services, https://www. facebook.com/GuardianProofreadingServices

Julie Deaton, Deaton Author Services, https://www. facebook.com/jdproofs/

Cover Design: Charlotte Byrd

Visit my website at www.charlotte-byrd.com

Identifiers

ISBN (e-book): 978-1-63225-109-1

ISBN (paperback): 978-1-63225-110-7

❀ Created with Vellum

ABOUT DANGEROUS ENGAGEMENT (WEDLOCKED TRILOGY BOOK 1)

Not long ago, there was nothing I couldn't have. Now, I don't even have the choice of whom to marry.

To save my father's life and our family's legacy, I have to marry a cruel man who wants me only as a trophy.

Henry Asher was just supposed to be a summer fling, but we fell in love. We thought we would be together forever, but life got in the way. After we broke up, I vowed to never tell Henry the truth about my engagement.

What happens when the lies that were supposed to save me start to drown me?

Henry Asher

I didn't always have wealth or power. There was even a time when I didn't want any of that.

Then I met her: Aurora Tate is an heiress to a billion-dollar fortune. She grew up on Park Avenue, had a house in the Hamptons, and skied in Aspen. Our first summer together was magical. We were naive enough to think that love was going to be enough.

Now, she's forced to marry a man she hates to save her father's life.

To get her back and to make her my wife, I need to become the man she needs me to be.

Can I do it in time?

Read the FIRST book to the addictive

WEDLOCKED series by bestselling author Charlotte Byrd.

What readers are saying about Charlotte Byrd:

"Extremely captivating, sexy, steamy, intriguing, and intense!" ★★★★★

"Addictive and impossible to put down." ★★★★★

"I can't get enough of the turmoil, lust, love, drama and secrets!" ★★★★★

"Fast-paced romantic suspense filled twists and turns, danger, betrayal and so much more." ★★★★★

"Decadent, delicious, & dangerously addictive!" ★★★★★

begins it's exhilarating with that nail biting suspense that keeps you riding on the edge the whole series. You'll love it!" ★★★★★

"What is Love Worth. This is a great epic ending to this series. Nicholas and Olive have a deep connection and the mystery surrounding the deaths of the people he is accused of murdering is to be read. Olive is one strong woman with deep convictions. The twists, angst, confusion is all put together to make this worthwhile read."
★★★★★

"Fast-paced romantic suspense filled with twists and turns, danger, betrayal, and so much more." ★★★★★

"Decadent, delicious, & dangerously addictive!" - Amazon Review ★★★★★

"Titillation so masterfully woven, no reader can resist its pull. A MUST-BUY!" - Bobbi Koe, Amazon Review ★★★★★

"Captivating!" - Crystal Jones, Amazon Review ★★★★★

"Sexy, secretive, pulsating chemistry…" - Mrs. K, Amazon Reviewer ★★★★★

"Charlotte Byrd is a brilliant writer. I've read loads and I've laughed and cried. She writes a balanced book with brilliant characters. Well done!" -Amazon Review ★★★★★

"Hot, steamy, and a great storyline." - Christine Reese ★★★★★

"My oh my....Charlotte has made me a fan for life." - JJ, Amazon Reviewer ★★★★★

"Wow. Just wow. Charlotte Byrd leaves me speechless and humble… It definitely kept me on the edge of my seat. Once you pick it up, you won't put it down." - Amazon Review ★★★★★

" Intrigue, lust, and great characters...what more could you ask for?!" - Dragonfly Lady ★★★★★

WANT TO BE THE FIRST TO KNOW ABOUT MY UPCOMING SALES, NEW RELEASES AND EXCLUSIVE GIVEAWAYS?

Sign up for my newsletter: https://www.subscribepage.com/byrdVIPList

Join my Facebook Group: https://www.facebook.com/groups/276340079439433/

Bonus Points: Follow me on BookBub and Goodreads!

ABOUT CHARLOTTE BYRD

Charlotte Byrd is the bestselling author of romantic suspense novels. She has sold over 600,000 books and has been translated into five languages.

She lives near Palm Springs, California with her husband, son, and a toy Australian Shepherd who hates water. Charlotte is addicted to books and Netflix and she loves hot weather and crystal blue water.

Write her here:
charlotte@charlotte-byrd.com
Check out her books here:
www.charlotte-byrd.com
Connect with her here:
www.facebook.com/charlottebyrdbooks
www.instagram.com/charlottebyrdbooks
www.twitter.com/byrdauthor

Want to hear about new releases, free books and get exclusive giveaways?

Sign up for my newsletter!

Sign up for my newsletter: https://www.
subscribepage.com/byrdVIPList

Join my Facebook Group: https://www.
facebook.com/groups/276340079439433/

Bonus Points: Follow me on BookBub and
Goodreads!

 facebook.com/charlottebyrdbooks

 twitter.com/byrdauthor

 instagram.com/charlottebyrdbooks

 bookbub.com/profile/charlotte-byrd

ALSO BY CHARLOTTE BYRD

All books are available at ALL major retailers! If you can't find it, please email me at charlotte@charlotte-byrd.com

Wedlocked Trilogy
Dangerous Engagement
Lethal Wedding
Fatal Wedding

Tell me Series
Tell Me to Stop
Tell Me to Go
Tell Me to Stay

Tell Me to Run
Tell Me to Fight
Tell Me to Lie

Tangled Series
Tangled up in Ice
Tangled up in Pain
Tangled up in Lace
Tangled up in Hate
Tangled up in Love

Black Series
Black Edge
Black Rules
Black Bounds
Black Contract
Black Limit

Lavish Trilogy
Lavish Lies
Lavish Betrayal
Lavish Obsession

Standalone Novels
Debt

Offer

Unknown

Dressing Mr. Dalton

1

AURORA

I watch him from afar. I know him even though I don't even know his name. He probably wants everything that's mine. He imagines that my life is wonderful and fun and full of possibilities that he could only dream of. What he doesn't know is how boring it can be or how isolating.

I have my parents, my friends, my parents extended social circle, and even my grandparents. But none of them really know me. I wish they did.

Not even my therapist knows me.

Everywhere I go, I wear a false face and it makes my life a farce.

My makeup and dress are my armor.

Thousand dollar shoes. Two thousand dollar bags. Three thousand dollar dresses.

My closet is as big as most one-bedroom apartments in New York City. I can buy anything and therefore, I want nothing.

My therapist thinks that I'm depressed. She diagnosed me with anxiety and post-traumatic stress disorder and prescribed meds that I don't want to take. Maybe I am depressed. But who wouldn't be? I'm in my mid-twenties and I can be anything I want. The only problem is that I don't want to do anything.

During the year I stay busy by going to school. The classes give me some structure to the day.

I take four each semester and between that, studying, the gym, and the weekly spa session, I manage to stay busy enough to forget how bored I am.

On the weekends, my girlfriends, the ones working sixty hours a week at non-paying internships for famous designers, artists, and gallery owners insist that I pull myself away from my books and my boring grad-school "friends" and hang with them instead. Their parties are usually two-day affairs that require helicopter rides and mansions in far-flung places. It's the stuff of dreams, or in my case, nightmares.

They say *friends* using quotation marks because they know that those people are not really my friends at all. They're just people I know. What my other friends don't know, however, is that they aren't really my friends either. They are just people I have known longer.

This guy with his hazel eyes, casual smile, and cheap clothes probably thinks the same thing of me as everyone else. That I'm just a spoiled little girl who has had everything handed to her, that I have never worked hard for anything, and I will never deserve anything I have.

I don't blame him. A part of me thinks the same way. What else can you think? My father owns a media empire and has dominated New York society ever since he came onto the scene in the 1980s. He owns hundreds of buildings and homes in New York and around the world. He's someone every businessman wants to be but can't because he will never step down.

I'm his oldest child and he wants to groom me to take over, but I know that that will never happen. He is not the type to retire. He's not the type to fade away. Besides, I have no interest in running an empire. I want to carve out my own place in this world, what that is exactly I do not know yet.

Neither of my parents understand this, even though they should. They both came from nothing and they both grew Tate Media into what it is today. My mother was not the type to stay at home. She is Tate's Chief Financial Officer and that's just scratching the surface of what she does there.

My parents are Tate Media. They have built it from scratch, buying up one distressed radio station at a time. They know the ins and outs of the whole business and, despite all of that, they have never made me feel welcome there.

I have spent one long and miserable summer there during my sophomore year with both of them looking over my shoulder and micro-managing my every move. After that, I said no more and promised myself that I would never work there again.

The guy glances at me. I sit back in the lounger and point my toes. I take a sip of my margarita, pursing my lips just so. I adjust my Chanel sunglasses and oversized floppy hat to both hide my gaze and to get a better look at him.

He's cute enough and probably witty, to a degree, but I wish that people weren't so predictable. I know exactly what he's going to say before he says it. I know exactly what he's going to compliment me on and what he's going to pay attention to. There is no surprise and without that, he will be just like a hundred others I've met who did not hold my interest.

He walks up to me slowly. I brace myself for a boring pick-up line. He looks deep into my eyes, so deeply in fact that I can't look away. I pull my sunglasses to the bridge of my nose and wait for him to open his mouth. His lips curl at the corners, but only slightly.

"Have you ever read Flannery O'Connor?"

I sit back in my seat, taken aback. Hmm…this is interesting.

"Of course," I say, raising one eyebrow.

"She's one of my favorite writers," he says, spreading his shoulders out widely. He holds a mop in one hand and with the other runs his fingers through his hair.

The confidence he exudes is overwhelming, and a little off-putting. "Why are you asking about her?"

"Well, I was just reading one of her stories this morning before work, *Good Country People*. You know it?"

I nod.

"Really?" he asks as if he doesn't believe me.

He is challenging me, which is not something that usually happens. No, let me amend that. That's not something that has *ever* happened.

"It's about Joy, a thirty-two-year-old atheist and a PhD student of philosophy who lives with her small-minded mother," I say, focusing my eyes directly on his. "Joy doesn't have a leg because she lost it in a childhood shooting accident. A Bible salesman comes to see them and her mother believes that he is good country people, as they say. Then he invites Joy out for a date and that's when things get, let's just say interesting."

He raises his eyebrows and takes a step away from me.

"Are you surprised?" I ask.

"Yes, to tell you the truth I am. Pleasantly."

"Why is that?" I ask.

"It's pretty obscure," he says with a pronounced shrug.

I fold my arms across my chest and raise my chin in the air in defiance.

"Did you bring it up to teach me a lesson?" I ask. "Maybe make me feel bad, or stupid even?"

He shakes his head. When I look into his eyes, I can't look away. There's something in them that pulls me in, even convincing me that he didn't mean it that way at all. It was a genuine attempt to make a connection.

"While they are on their date, the Bible

salesman persuades her to go up in the loft and to take off her prosthetic leg," he says. His words come out smoothly, naturally even. "He then shows her the inside of one of his Bibles that contains a bottle of whiskey, condoms, and cards with naked women on them."

"When she says no to his advance," I finish the story for him, "the Bible salesman tells her that he collects fake legs and takes off with hers."

"What do you like about the story?" he asks.

"Who said that I liked it?" I ask him.

He smiles.

"You have to."

"I have to?" I ask.

"You know it so intimately and innately that they must've made an imprint on your soul," he says.

I gaze into his eyes. I have lived for twenty-five years and not once have I ever spoken with another human being about the existence of a soul. Yet here is a stranger, a simple worker on my father's yacht, who speaks of it as if it's second nature, as if it's as real as gravity.

"I think what I like about it, and what I like about Flannery O'Connor's work in general is her sense of irony," I say. "It's comedic. The title of the story is G*ood Country People*, and that's exactly what her mother thinks the Bible salesman is. And yet he is the furthest thing from that. And even she, with her advanced degree, is someone who should know better, but she doesn't. It's almost funny. But then again, my own mother thinks I have a perverse sense of humor."

"I think we might have that in common," he says.

Our voices die down and all we are left with is a sweet silence that is both comforting and comfortable. I want to stay in this moment forever but we are quickly interrupted.

"Hey, you missed one hell of a lunch! Did you get some of that alone time you wanted?" Ellis Holte asks. She plops down on the lounger next to me and asks the guy who I've been talking to for a refill of her drink.

"No, he doesn't do that," I interject. But he just shrugs his shoulders and says he will get it for her anyway.

"Are you seriously at this point, already?" she asks.

"What are you talking about?"

"You know what I'm talking about," she says, pointing to her index finger adorned with a three-carat diamond ring in my face. It's not an engagement ring, it's a *just because* ring. "Are you already messing around with the *help*? I thought we would only be doing that when we are seven years into boring marriages, not while we are still single."

"I'm not messing around with anyone," I say sternly.

I don't even know his name I note to myself. I run my tongue over my lower lip and repress the desire to talk to him again. Why do I even care?

Why am I so interested all of a sudden?

He is one of the only people that, no correct that, he is *the* only person who I have met who hasn't bored me. I couldn't predict anything that was going to come out of his mouth and I want more of that.

Unfortunately, I don't see him again until later that night. His boss is watching his every move to make sure that he is doing a good job cleaning all of the decks of my father's boat. Of course, I could go up and talk to him myself, but I'm not quite ready to go that far out of my comfort zone.

After spending the whole day drinking, talking, and reading magazines, the girls are ready to shower, do their hair, and go out for a night on the town. Begrudgingly, I go through the motions as well. I finish before the rest and take a circle around the yacht, hoping to run into him again.

Him. The guy whose name I don't even know.

Though I don't see him, I do see the manager. Mr. Madsen is in his sixties and has worked on my father's boat, overseeing all personnel, for as long as I can remember.

"Mr. Madsen, do you happen to know where I can find the guy who was cleaning the decks earlier today?" I ask as casually as possible.

If he wants to give me a knowing smile, he doesn't. Mr. Madsen is the epitome of professionalism.

"We had a few people working that position today. Henry Asher, Tom Cedar, and Elliot Dickinson."

"Um, he was about six feet tall with broad shoulders and thick dark hair."

"Oh, yes, you're referring to Henry Asher. He is probably downstairs in the crew quarters."

"Thank you very much," I say, going straight to the staircase.

Appalled, Mr. Madsen rushes over to me and blocks my way.

"I will, of course, get him to come upstairs to see you, Miss Tate," he says quickly. "If you don't mind waiting in the living room."

I don't really want to wait, but I decide to go along with it. The guests are not supposed to go down to the crew quarters. It has been that way since the beginning of time. Besides, I don't really want my friends to see me going down there anyway.

Before I have the chance to glance at my

watch for the second time in five minutes, he appears in the doorway. He looks just as tall, dark, and handsome as he did earlier today, only this time the angles in his face and his muscles look even more defined as a result of the tan settling deeper into his skin.

"Hi," he says, hanging his head just a little, before turning his eyes up to mine.

"Hi," I say quietly.

"You wanted to see me?" His hair falls slightly into his face as he leans on the side of the wall like some sort of modern day James Dean.

What the hell do I say now? This is the first time I have ever even made an inkling of a first move on a guy. It feels foreign and unnatural and yet exciting at the same time.

"I was just wondering," I say slowly, "if you wanted to join me ashore tonight?"

He raises his eyebrows before smiling out of the corner of his mouth.

"Of course," he says confidently. "What did you have in mind?"

"Well, I was going to go out with my girlfriends. We'll probably go dancing or something like that. Nothing is set in stone."

Henry takes a few steps closer and sits down on the couch right next to me. I turn my body toward his so that our knees are nearly touching.

"Well, if it's not set in stone," he says, "what do you think about doing something else instead?"

"Like what?"

"How about dinner at one of my favorite taco stands? Followed by a few drinks at a shitty but incredibly fun dive bar?"

Anyone else in his position would try to impress me by taking me to some fancy five-star restaurant and fumble through the wine list. Anyone else would try to pretend that they were a lot more worldly than he is, even though we both know that he works crew on my father's boat.

But he doesn't.

I am intrigued and surprised by his audacity. He is a breath of fresh air that's so intoxicating, it leaves me disoriented.

2

HENRY

At first, I thought that she was just like the rest of them. Rich, spoiled, and completely disconnected from reality. I had no interest in talking to her. Yes, she is pretty, gorgeous even, but there's more to a woman than beauty, or there should be.

But as I watched her that morning, I saw that she was different from her friends. She didn't laugh as much, it was cursory at best. She smiled even less. It was like she was being forced to be there. It was like she was only complying with them.

But it's her boat, or rather it's her father's yacht. How different could she be? It's hard to explain what came over me that afternoon, when I saw her sitting there on the deck all by herself while her friends were inside nibbling on their salads, getting drunk on rosé, and taking selfies.

Why didn't she join them?

What is she reading on that tablet of hers?

It would have to be something stupid, right? There's no way she could know anything about *real* literature.

That's why I approached her in the first place; as a joke.

I wanted to say something meaningful and being who I am, Flannery O'Connor was the only thing that came to mind. And that's when things got interesting. An obscure 20th century short-story writer somehow opened the door for me to someone I didn't even have an interest in talking to.

After her friends came back, and Mr. Madsen gave me a stern lecture about interacting with the owner's daughter, especially in such a casual manner, he put me on downstairs duty cleaning all the bunk rooms, floors, toilets, and every other dirty job he could think of. I didn't see her again for the rest of the day until she called me upstairs and asked me to go out with her.

She asked me out on a date even though she did it in such a way that it wasn't supposed to look like a date. She asked me to go out with the whole group as if we were friends, and as if I could give a shit about anyone there besides her.

No, she is the only one that I am interested in. She is the only one that I want to get to know.

We take a dinghy over from the yacht to shore, and on the way, Ellis Holte whispers into Aurora's ear, occasionally glancing over at me. I can't really hear what she's saying over the sound of the boat splitting the waves and its roaring motor. I can only hope that she doesn't change her mind. When we get to shore, she takes a step toward me and grabs my hand. I text Lyft, a ride-share app, on my phone and leave Ellis and her other dumbfounded friends alone on the dock.

"So, is this your favorite place to eat?"

Aurora asks, looking at the outside of the place with a tilt to her head.

I laugh. "I know that it doesn't look like much but trust me, this is the place for the best fish tacos in the whole of the Hamptons."

She looks around the place, not exactly impressed. I do have to admit that Jack's Crab Shack has seen better days. They used to have a place to sit inside, but one of the big winter storms flooded the place and they never reopened that part to the public.

Now, the restaurant is something of a fast food joint. You order what you want through a glass window and pick up the food at another window. There are about ten wooden picnic tables out front where you can bury your feet in the sand and all of them are occupied. She doesn't know what to order, so I order for her.

By the time our tacos are ready one of the picnic tables clears out. Taking a sip of her Sprite, she looks up at me and shakes her head.

"What?" I ask, shrugging my shoulders.

She shakes her head again and bites into her fish taco.

As soon as she swallows, I can tell that I have converted her to my side.

"Are those delicious?" I ask. She nods vigorously and quickly takes one more bite and then another and another.

Once her taco disappears before my eyes, she reaches for mine. At first, I protest but she shakes her head and puts her index finger up to stop me and I quickly give in.

After she's done, she takes a few more sips of her drink and gets up. "Oh my God, I'm so sorry," she says. "I didn't mean to eat your whole dinner."

"Yes, you did." I smile. I nudge her and she nudges me back.

"Come on. Let me make it up to you."

I follow her to the back of the line, which has grown substantially since the last time we stood in it.

"I can't believe you just ate my dinner," I say, shaking my head. "What the hell was that about?"

"I was hungry," she says, tilting her head and smiling widely.

"Still, that's no excuse for lack of manners."

"Lack of manners?" she asks. "You just took me on a date to one of the dingiest places ever!"

"So what? It's delicious. You, me, and everyone in this line knows it. You ate both your dinner and mine in five bites."

"Yes, I'm not arguing with that," she says." All that I'm saying is that it's not the kind of first date that I'm usually used to."

"Did you ever eat like that on any of your other first dates?" I ask.

She shakes her head from side to side.

"And how many of those first dates resulted in second and third dates?" I ask.

She starts to laugh.

"What's so funny?" I ask.

"Well, you seem to be so certain that there is going to be a second date here."

"I am."

"And why is that?"

I don't have an answer. I just look into her eyes and lose myself there. She opens her mouth just a little bit to say something else and I can't help but reach for it.

I touch her lower lip with my thumb, parting her lips slightly. I move an inch closer. My hand runs down her neck and then up toward her hair. I tip my head toward hers and open my mouth.

When our lips touch, my tongue searches for hers. I bury my hands in her hair, tugging slightly.

She opens her mouth wider and kisses me again. I taste the salty air and the warmth of her body all at once. I wrap my arms around her waist and feel her fingers and nails digging into my back. She sends shivers down my spine that make my knees weak.

Who are you? I wonder. And where have you been all of my life?

3

AURORA

T he kiss takes me completely by surprise and yet it feels like the most natural thing in the world. The moment is just right. His lips are soft and effervescent. His hands are deliberate and knowing. Tugging at my hair, he runs his fingers softly down my neck. Each one of his moves makes my breath quicken just a little bit, following the beat of my heart.

"Who are you?" I ask him when we pull away from each other.

My eyes focus deeply on his. There are specks of green and yellow and blue in there and they all twinkle under the harsh fluorescent lights of the taco stand.

"What do you want to know?"

"Everything."

"I am Henry Asher. I am twenty-seven. I live in New York City. I grew up in Montauk, not too far from here, in a two-bedroom house with my mother. She still lives there. Montauk is a place that no one ever really leaves so moving to New York a few years ago is one of my proudest accomplishments. That and getting my short story published in the *New Yorker*. Your turn."

My mouth drops open. I stare at him in disbelief.

No one is this dishonest with a total stranger. Why isn't he trying to impress me like everyone else out there? What kind of game is he playing?

"Are you not gonna tell me who you are?" he asks.

"You already know, don't you?"

"I know some things, I guess."

"Like what?"

"Like your name is Aurora Penelope Tate and your parents started Tate Media. Your father owns that yacht we were floating on all day and you don't seem to like your friends very much."

I stare at him, cross my arms, and even take a step away. "What gave you that idea?" I ask, defensively.

He's not wrong, I'm just embarrassed by how obvious I had been when I thought that no one could know the truth.

"Just the way you were with them. Standoffish. It's like you are just tolerating their presence."

"They are a little bit too much sometimes, I guess," I admit. "But that doesn't mean that I don't like them."

He tilts his head, unconvinced.

What he just said is of course the truth, but he is a stranger and this is going too far.

"So is there anything else about you that I should know?" he asks.

We're almost at the window but the people in front of us place an order for twenty tacos so we're not as close as I had thought.

"Well, you seem to know everything already, I'm not sure what else I can share with you."

"I doubt that," he says, refusing to take his gaze off me.

His stare is so intense I can barely look away. When I try, I can't.

"Tell me something… True about you," he says.

This is not how first dates are supposed to go. There's supposed to be a lot of joking and laughing and talking about nothing in particular.

But Henry is so intense, and that intensity is completely disarming. I'm tempted to make light of this, but I don't wanna ruin the moment. He wants to know something about me. He's the first person in a very long time who has not seen me as an heiress, a trophy, or simply an extension of my parents. Why does this scare me so much?

"I know that I want to do something important with my life, but I don't know what that is," I finally say. "Everyone wants me to be somebody. My parents want me to be the perfect daughter and the perfect heir to their fortune. My friends want me to be the perfect girlfriend, someone who laughs at their jokes even when they're stupid, and drinks way too much and gossips about what everyone else is wearing. I try to be these things to the people in my life, but most of the time doing that just makes me sick to my stomach. And the more time that passes, the more afraid I get that they're going to find out the truth about me."

"Which is what?"

"That I'm not their perfect daughter or friend, and I'm not interested in running Tate Media."

"Let's say, that they do," Henry says. "What happens then?"

I shrug. He waits.

"I don't know," I whisper. "I just feel this enormous pressure on my shoulders all of the time to be this person for everyone else, this person that I am not really at all. I'm afraid to tell anyone any of this because the truth is that I don't really know who I am except that I'm not *her*."

"How can I help you?" the cashier asks through the glass.

"We're back," I say.

"It happens," she says, completely unfazed and unimpressed.

Henry orders two tacos each this time and refuses to let me pay.

"I may not have much money, Aurora. But I can certainly afford four dinners at Jack's Crab Shack." He smiles and I laugh.

"I wasn't insinuating that you couldn't, I was just trying to be nice."

"Well, you're on a date with me, why don't you let me worry about being nice. Besides, we're going to a bar after this, so you can cover that tab if you want."

He drapes his arm around my shoulder, pulling me closer to him. When I look up, his lips collide with mine. The people behind us have to physically nudge us to get us to move. A part of me is embarrassed at all of these public displays of affection, but another part of me could not care less. I want to kiss him as much as I want to and I want him to kiss me for as long as he wants to.

When our food is ready this time, we are not as lucky with finding a table so we take our tacos to the beach. The breeze coming off the water is soft and warm and the roaring ocean of only a few months ago is nothing but a memory. We walk past the grasses and bushes that scatter along the coastline and find a quiet dune where we can be alone.

I only manage to eat one taco this time, watching him polish off the other three. After we are both satiated, I lean against his shoulder and watch the waves break in front of us. They aren't very big today, nothing worthy of surfing, but that's what also makes them calm and relaxing.

"What are you doing working on my father's boat if you live in New York City?" I ask.

"Jobs for summer people pay quite well and I'm off anyway during this time. So, I figured I'd come home, spend some time with my mom, and make some money."

"Off from what?"

"I teach high school during the year."

"Why haven't I seen you before? Is this your first summer?"

"The job on your father's boat is temporary. I'm filling in for someone.

Normally, I work at the Southampton Yacht Club."

"What do you do there?" I ask.

"A little bit of everything, but mainly bartend. I've been working there since I was fifteen. So I get to bartend as much as I want."

"Is that the best thing to do?"

"Yes." He nods and laughs, probably at my naïveté.

"That's where you get all the tips. And summer people, the good ones anyway, tip pretty well."

Suddenly, I have an overwhelming urge to find out as much as possible about him. I want to know where he was born. I want to know what he was like growing up. I want to know if anyone has hurt him or broken his heart. I want to know about his mother.

But when I turn to face him and open my mouth to speak, he kisses me. The kiss is soft and airy, moving along with the waves. I curl up snugly into his armpit, noticing how nicely my body fits into his.

He wraps his arms around me and I intertwine my legs with his.

His fingers run down my side as his tongue finds mine. I arch my back against his strong lean stomach. I feel the bulge in his pants growing in size as I press my butt against it.

I'm about to say something when his hands start to make their way down my breasts. My nipples perk up as if they have been awakened from a deep sleep. My whole being gets energized. I arch my back again and again as his fingers start to massage me. His hands are soft yet firm and knowing. They're deliberate like the rest of him. He knows his way around my body as if he has done this a million times before. There is a strength in that and the feeling is completely disarming.

The sound of loud laughter interrupts our solace. It comes from the gaggle of teenagers rounding the dune and setting up their blankets right next to ours. All are too drunk to notice or care about our presence. One of them builds a fire and another one blasts house music from a speaker. The rest start to dance by swinging their hips and shoulders from side to side, in the same direction.

"How about we go somewhere else?" Henry asks.

I nod.

He holds out his hand to help me up to my feet. I want to go somewhere private, where we can be alone and together. I want to feel his hands all over me and me all over him, but he doesn't suggest a place like this. Instead he takes my arm and walks me around the corner to a rowdy, loud bar.

"This place makes cocktails as good as any of the ones I had in those craft bars in Manhattan. And they don't cost eighteen dollars a pop," he says.

I don't want to go inside because I want to keep him to myself. But it's too soon. We have just met. I look at the menu that the bartender hands me and quickly order the first thing I spot, a cucumber margarita.

The bar is busy but we manage to find a seat in a dark corner, somewhat away from the music that's blaring out of the speakers. Everyone else is straining to talk, screaming at the top of their lungs to barely make themselves heard.

But here, in our little space, the music is at just the right level. It sets the ambience without being overpowering or obnoxious. When our drinks arrive, I watch him take a sip of his Old-Fashioned before trying my margarita.

"Wow, this is really good," I say, nodding my head and noting that all of the ingredients are fresh. Nothing is prepackaged or processed.

"They make everything from scratch," he says.

"I am shocked that they have the time to do this given how busy this place is."

"A little known secret of the restaurant trade is that it's actually much cheaper to make things from scratch," he says with a shrug. "But it does take a little bit more time. I know the owner of this place, I went to high school with his son, and he's very old-school. That's why this place is as popular as it is."

We drink our drinks in silence for a few moments and he takes my hand in his. I like the way he runs his thumb over the back of it and I can't help but let my fingers intertwine with his, but our solitude doesn't last.

A guy with a cool haircut approaches and Henry quickly gets up to give him a hug. He quickly calls over three of his friends and they all embrace, exchanging complicated handshakes. Henry introduces me as Aurora Tate, but the name doesn't register. Instead, they ask him about the yacht club. I've never heard anyone talk like this about us before. They think of the rich as others might think of animals at the zoo; something exotic, something worthy of admiration but something completely different from them. The yacht club is the epicenter and they talk about it with a mix of envy, jealousy, and contempt wavering between hating the summer people and wanting to be them.

4

HENRY

I didn't particularly want to see my friends tonight, but there is no getting around it. At first, I think that they are going to recognize Aurora from the gossip magazines that she is often featured in, but they don't.

Instead, they just talk about themselves. Half an hour is all that I'm going to give them, I decide. That will be enough to not be rude, spend some time with them, and then cut things short since we are on our first date.

Taylor Portman, of course, dominates the conversation. He is tall and attractive and he knows it. He's finishing his last semester at city college and his dream is to make millions on Wall Street.

I met him in the neighborhood, but he is about four years younger than I am. Once, after more than a few drinks, I made a mistake and told him that I wanted to be a writer and ever since then he has been mercilessly making fun of me. The mocking got worse when I got my short story published in the New Yorker, the epitome of success, and got paid $320 for my efforts. At eight cents a word, the pay is significant for a literary magazine and yet paltry at the same time.

Tonight is no exception. As soon as Taylor has two beers in him, he goes off on me.

"You know what this guy does for a living, right?" he asks. When she doesn't respond, he covers his mouth and laughs. "Oh, shit, did I just blow your secret?"

"I know that he is a writer."

"Wait, is that what you are? Or are you just an *aspiring* writer?" he continues. "'Cause I think you have to at least pay the rent with your job if you're doing it for real."

I hate him for being this way; callous and cruel. I try to remember why we're friends at all.

"You talk about it like you think that there's something wrong with it," Aurora says to Taylor.

"Well, you have to admit it's a little bit silly. It's like wanting to be an astronaut."

"But you would agree," she challenges him, "that there are people who are astronauts."

"Yes, of course."

"So, what would be so wrong with wanting to be one?"

"It's just so…unrealistic. Actually, being an astronaut is probably a lot more realistic than being a writer. In this day and age. I mean, who the hell has time to read anymore? Am I right?"

"No," she says sternly. "You're wrong. There are a lot of people who like to read and there are a lot of people who make their living writing. What you don't know about it could fill the whole ocean out there."

Taylor narrows his eyes and stares daggers into her. But she doesn't waver.

Instead she broadens her shoulders and sits up.

"Sorry, I didn't mean to make everything so tense. Are you a writer, too?" he asks, taking a sip of his beer.

"No, I'm not," she says without wavering in her gaze. "I'm Aurora Tate, of the Tate Media empire. Perhaps you've heard of us?"

Taylor's mouth physically drops open. She leans in closer and flicks the bottom of his chin to shut it.

"What's the matter?" she asks. "Cat got your tongue?"

***

My friends don't stick around long after that. A group of attractive local girls come in and they drift away in search of a warm body to curl up to. Taylor hangs around the longest.

I'm not sure what he's waiting for but it certainly feels like he's waiting for something. Eventually, a pretty girl approaches him and he finally pulls away. Aurora finishes her margarita and asks for another one, with a glass of water.

"I need to stay hydrated," she says, "otherwise, all of this alcohol is going to go straight to my head."

"Of course," I say. "There's no need to explain."

I have already finished two Old-Fashioneds, and I'm working on my third one. I'm not big on alcohol but being here with *her* makes me nervous.

When our next round arrives, I turn to her and raise my glass.

"I want to thank you for something."

"For what?"

"I want to thank you for standing up to Taylor. He has an annoying habit of making fun of me for that. Perhaps I should have never told him the truth, but at one point I thought that we were actually friends. That's the only reason why he knows that I write."

"Do you usually not tell anyone?" she asks, surprised.

I shrug and look down at the table. "It's a difficult thing to talk about," I admit.

"Not everyone understands," I add. "I'm

not sure exactly why it's so difficult but somehow, telling people, it's like revealing this secret part of me."

"You had no problem telling me earlier today," Aurora points out. I shrug.

"You're a stranger and frankly, I wasn't sure if we were going to hit it off at all. I guess I didn't think I had anything to lose."

"How very valiant of you," she says with a smile, keenly aware of the fact that what I have just said is a lie.

I pick at a little speck of dirt on the table with my index finger. It doesn't come off. It's just a deformity, so I put my palm flatly against it to feel the indentation.

"So, you don't think I'm stupid for doing what I do?" I ask.

"No, not at all," she says, shaking her head. "In fact, I think you are very brave."

"Brave?"

"You're pursuing your dreams, what can be braver than that?"

I take her hand into mine, wondering if she is in fact real.

"Besides, it's actually very refreshing to

meet someone who isn't just after money," Aurora says.

"Yeah," I say, "I guess it's hard to find a man in New York City who isn't that singularly focused."

"You don't know how true that is." She laughs.

"What about your friends?" I ask.

"What about them?"

"What would they think if they had heard this about me?"

"They would think that I am dumber than they even knew," she says, rolling her eyes and taking another sip. It's meant to be a joke but the delivery falters.

"Is that okay with you?" I ask.

She shrugs and looks away.

"I don't really want to talk about my friends," she says. "Let's talk about something else."

5

HENRY

W e don't stay at the bar long because it gets louder and more rowdy with each passing hour. Instead, we go on a walk. I hold her hand as we meander up and down the empty streets of the small summer town where no one walks and everyone drives.

Surprisingly, the streets are welcoming to pedestrians and we enjoy the view of the large expanse of lawns and the weeping willows, along with a few thick oaks.

"Did you grow up in a house like this?" she asks, pointing to an enormous four-bedroom home that sits on two acres.

I stare at her and shake my head from

side to side. She tilts hers as if she has no idea what I'm talking about.

"Do you really think I would be poor if I grew up in a house like this?" I ask.

She looks at the house again.

"It's probably only three-thousand square feet," she says. "That's not very big. Not for a house in the country."

I want to laugh but I don't want to make her feel bad. Instead, I tell her that my own house is about seven-hundred square feet.

"Wait a second," she says, "but I thought you grew up in a two-bedroom?"

"I did." I nod.

"Well, that's not nearly big enough, right?"

I shrug.

"That's all my mom could afford. My dad left when I was two and I haven't seen him since then. She only has a high school diploma, so she wasn't qualified to get any job besides being a cashier at the local grocery store. That's what she did for years."

"How much does that pay?" Her asking this takes me by surprise and I shake my head no. I don't want to answer.

"I'm sorry," she apologizes. "I shouldn't have asked that. I didn't mean to pry. The thing is that I have never really talked to anyone who came from so little."

I shake my head again.

"That sounds terrible," she says.

"Yes, it does," I agree.

"I shouldn't have asked."

I think about that for a moment. "No, I'm glad you did. How about this? I'll tell you the details of my life and you tell me the details of yours. 'Cause I never really talked to anyone who came from so much either."

Aurora smiles, pushing her hair behind her ear, and shakes my extended hand.

"My mom made minimum wage for about twenty years."

"And a minimum wage is what exactly?" Aurora asks.

"It was around $7.15 when I was little and they raised it to $11.10."

"An hour?" she gasps and shakes her head. "And she works forty hours a week?"

"No, she usually works sixty hours a week. And it's still not enough. The rent is

$1300 and then there is food, utilities, and all of the medical bills."

I look away, suddenly a mountain of guilt covers me as if it were an avalanche. Maybe I should've been a better son. Maybe I should have paid more attention to money and not just been out there pursuing my senseless dreams.

But it was my mother who always encouraged me to go after what I want. She was the one who said it was okay to pursue whatever degree I wanted in college. She was the one I wanted to see my dreams come true.

Hell, that makes me feel even worse. Perhaps, I should've gotten a degree in finance and have spent the last five years working on Wall Street and sending every penny of that back home to make her life easier, but the truth is that she would never have had it that way.

She always said that the most unfair thing about not having enough is that you have to compromise your dreams. She always wanted better for me. I don't go into all of these details with Aurora, instead I steer the conversation back to her.

"What about you?" I ask. "How much does your father make?"

"Well, it's actually both my father and my mother. She's the CFO there."

I wait for her to answer my question. "Are you going to tell me how much they make?"

"It's hard to say," she says with a slight shrug. "But they are both individually featured in Forbes' richest people in the world list."

"What does that mean exactly?" I press her.

"I don't know what their exact net worth is because there are different ways of calculating that but it's billions. Many, many billions."

"That is so much money, it's actually difficult to comprehend," I admit.

"I know exactly what you mean," she says with a shrug. "It's stupid but I feel like no matter what I will do in my life, it will never be good enough. I will never be able to step from behind their shadow."

"And what is it that you want to do?" I ask. Shrugging, she looks down at the ground.

"That's the whole problem," she says. "I have no idea. I know what it is that *they* want me to do, but I'm not exactly sure if I can do that."

"What's that?"

"They want me to take over the company."

"You don't want to?"

"It's not that, it's more that I don't know if I can. It's their baby, more than I ever was, and they want me to raise it exactly as they would. They want me to run it exactly as they would run it."

"That's impossible."

"Yeah, tell that to them." Aurora laughs. "On top of that, they don't trust me to make any decisions."

"Do you even want to?"

"Not under these conditions, but I'm not sure if I'll have a choice."

"What do you mean?" I ask. She takes my hand in hers and gives me a weak smile.

"Let's not talk about this anymore. I don't have the energy."

Her wish is my command. I don't press her for anything more. Instead, I try to make her laugh. I do impressions, the ones that I taught myself how to do through YouTube and the ones that have always worked well on my mother.

President Obama. President Bush. Britney Spears. Cher. Madonna.

Aurora laughs so hard big tears stream down her cheeks. When we get to a quiet corner and she stops laughing so hard, I pull her closer to me and kiss her.

Our mouths now feel comfortable with each other. There was never any awkwardness, but now we belong to each other completely.

I want this moment to last as long as possible. I kiss her harder and harder. She presses her body against mine, kissing me back with the same intensity.

"Let's go somewhere," she says, pulling away from my mouth only briefly.

"Back to the boat?" I ask.

"No, absolutely not. I want to go somewhere private."

The only hotels around here are the kind that rent rooms by the hour. They're dark and gross and the sheets are barely changed and that's not where I want my first time with this goddess to be.

"I know this is gonna sound strange," I say. "But do you want to go to my house?"

"Isn't your mother there?" she asks.

"She's probably sleeping already."

"Would she mind?" Aurora asks.

"No." I shake my head. "I'm an adult, remember?"

"Yes, of course. I'm just being stupid," she says with a nervous laugh.

I open the ride-share app and a driver picks us up five minutes later. Montauk is half an hour away at the edge of Long Island.

"I've never been there," Aurora says.

"You haven't? Well, you're in for a treat. It's kind of a quaint little town that's full of charm, at least in the summertime. In the winter, it's pretty dead like the rest of the island."

When we get to my house, I take her inside through the back door and tell her to be very quiet. The house settles and creaks with each step, but she is careful not to make any noise. She's so committed to it that she even takes off her heels.

"I don't want your mother to wake up," she explains and follows me to my old room.

If I had known that I would have a visitor tonight, let alone Aurora Tate, I would've at least picked up some of the dirty clothes off the floor and

organized the books scattered all over the place. But she doesn't seem to mind.

Instead she just wraps her arms around my neck and stands up on her tiptoes, pressing her lips to mine. I take her into my arms and bury my hands in her hair. Her skin feels soft and full of life, and when I lick her, I taste the salt coming off the ocean.

Her shoulders broaden and contract with each breath as I slowly run my lips down her neck. She tilts her head back enjoying the moment. I linger for a moment around her collarbone before tugging at her dress. When the spaghetti straps slide down her arms, it falls to the floor.

She's not wearing a bra, only a pair of black lace panties. Her body is soft in all of the right places and she has curves that go on for miles. She's not overweight, but she is also not a stick figure.

I can tell that she's a little bit embarrassed by her nudity, but I get down on my knees and kiss her stomach to make up for it. She tries to bring me back up to a standing position, but I refuse. I want to kneel here and worship her.

Slowly, I pull down her panties and she opens her legs. She tucks her hands up by her breasts and waits for me to press my mouth to her.

6

AURORA

He touches me in every way a woman wants to be touched. His hands are firm and strong and they direct my body to maximize my pleasure. But instead of bending me to his will, he bends to mine. The only issue is that I don't know exactly what I want. I need him to show me.

Being naked in front of him is not like being naked in front of other people. My curves and my lumpy bits seem to only turn him on. In the past, I've had a boyfriend or three tell me that I would be prettier if I were just a little bit thinner.

It is hard to describe what it feels like to

have someone say the one thing that you are most terrified of that someone else is thinking.

But Henry revels in my body. He loves it. He buries his tongue and his fingers deep within me and it's all I can do to not scream out his name.

But I have a dirty little secret. I have never had an orgasm. Of course, I have moaned and yelled a guy's name and went through all of the motions to pretend like I was experiencing something epic, but it was all a show. Maybe, my secret is not so dirty after all.

Unfortunately, tonight is no different.

It's not Henry, he is hotter and sexier than any other guy I have ever been with. In addition to his hard as steel body, there's his personality and his way of being that makes me want to just rip off his clothes.

But tonight, I reach a plateau again. It has nothing to do with him.

It's all me. I'm in my head, and I can't get out of it.

Maybe it has something to do with me being self-conscious or just uncomfortable in a new environment, or maybe it's just the fact that I'm not lying on my back the way I do when I touch myself, but I can't let go.

I can't let him take me there, to that space where nothing else exists except for two of us.

He continues to go down on me and my knees start to grow weak. For a moment, I think that it might happen after all but then another one comes and my hopes evaporate.

I pull him up to his knees and lead him to his bed, a comically small twin-size bed, the kind that I have seen little kids have on television. My bed at home has been king-size ever since I can remember.

The smallness of this one brings us even closer together. There's nowhere to go except into each other's arms.

He drapes his body over mine as he climbs on top of me.

He kisses my neck.

He kisses my breasts. He goes all the way down to my stomach and then to my pelvic region. He wants to go south again, but I want something else. I ask him to flip over me. Moving his legs toward my face, he positions his own head in between mine. I wrap my hands around his large, thick cock and run my tongue up and down eventually taking it into my mouth.

Our movements become one as the ebb and flow of our kisses morph together. He starts to moan my name and I start to feel like I'm inching closer to the edge, but the minutes tick along and I don't get there.

Sometime later, he flips me onto my stomach and climbs on top. I push my butt up into the air as he finds that sweet spot in the middle of my core and thrusts himself inside. He opens me as wide as possible and I take him deeper and deeper inside with each thrust. We move in complete unison with even our breaths mimicking one another's.

Suddenly, a strange feeling comes over me. I begin to relax. Every muscle in my body gets infused with oxygen and somehow softens. But then Henry's movements speed up and he whispers my name over and over again into my ear.

When he moans, I moan along with him. I am not faking anything. This experience has been one of the most exciting and titillating of my life, and yet I know that I have not reached that epic point where I fall off the cliff. He yells my name into the pillow, muffling his voice, and I whisper "shh" over and over again to get him to be quieter.

Afterward, he holds me in his arms and I let myself drift off to sleep. For the first time, in a long time, I am completely at peace.

———

THE FOLLOWING MORNING, I wake up before him. I revel in the fact that we actually slept with our bodies intertwined with each other's. I thought that was only possible in the movies. But somehow I slept in the crook of his elbow and neither of us were uncomfortable or even crammed.

There is an old-fashioned alarm clock on the bedside table and it flashes 8 a.m.

Shit, I say to myself. I doubt that my friends are actually worried about me, but I am certain that Mr. Madsen is. We were supposed to come back that night, late, but not this late.

I climb out of bed slowly, quickly wrapping the sheet around my body. When I notice that the sheet is also wrapped tightly around Henry, I decide to let it go and not disturb him. Instead, I scramble around the room looking for my panties and my dress.

I find my phone next to my heels in the far corner of the room. I scroll through the messages as quickly as I can. They're all from Mr. Madsen and I quickly write him back.

Much to my surprise, Ellis has not contacted me and neither have any of the other girls. Mr. Madsen is not satisfied with a simple text and demands that I call him immediately so that he can make sure that I am actually safe.

I dial his number. If this were anyone else, I wouldn't bother. But Mr. Madsen and I have a special relationship, he has been like a favorite uncle of mine ever since I was a little girl. And while I suspect that my own father only pretends to worry about me, I know that Mr. Madsen actually does.

"Hi, I'm here… I'm fine," I whisper into the phone, trying to be as quiet as possible. "Why am I whispering?" I repeat his question. "I don't want to wake Henry."

His name escapes my lips before I can catch myself. I'm not sure if I should tell him who I'm with, and normally I wouldn't, but all of those margaritas have gone straight to my head.

"Henry Asher? You are with Henry Asher?" Mr. Madsen asks. I bite my lower lip, unsure what to do with his disapproving tone.

On one hand, it's none of his business who I sleep with. On the other hand, I have known him for so long that he is almost a father figure and someone I definitely don't want to disappoint.

"Henry Asher is an employee of yours," Mr. Madsen explains. "You have no business spending time with him…recreationally."

"I know that this is probably inappropriate," I say quickly. "But we really connected with each other, and he's not actually my employee. He just happens to work on a boat that my father owns."

"Well, that won't be the case for long," Mr. Madsen says.

"No, please, please don't take this out on him," I plead. "He didn't do anything wrong."

"He knew the rules," Mr. Madsen says. "He should not have been developing friendly relations with the guests."

This conversation is getting away from me. No, I need to stand my ground.

"But as you said yourself, I am not just a guest. I am my father's daughter and, as such, I ask you to please look the other way in this particular situation."

He doesn't answer me one way or another, and I don't push it anymore for now. Instead, I thank him for worrying about me and for checking in on me and apologize again for not telling him about my plans.

I know that his worries are not for no good reason. I am an heir to a huge fortune and if it were anyone else, they would probably only go outside with a bodyguard or two.

But that's just not how I can exist in the

world. I can't have anyone following me and tracking my every move. I feel like I am too much of a prisoner already.

When I sit back on the bed, I find Henry awake.

"He's going to fire me, isn't he?" he asks, leaning on one elbow.

"Not if I have anything to do with it," I insist.

"I think your powers are limited." He smiles. "This is Mr. Madsen that we're talking about."

I laugh, but I'm not so sure that I'm right. Mr. Madsen is in charge of all the help and his decisions are final. I worry that this night could have cost Henry his job, one that he so desperately depends on.

"OK, let's just forget about it," he says, reaching out and grabbing my arm.

He pulls me closer to him and kisses me again and again and again. Somehow my dress comes off again and we press our bodies to each other's, flesh to flesh.

But then he hears something in the hallway, right outside the door.

7

AURORA

"I t's my mom," Henry whispers into my
ear. "We better get up and join her for
breakfast."

He dresses quickly and I follow him
down a very small corridor, which is only
three steps across. Seeing this house in the
light of day, I am surprised by exactly how
small it is.

A long time ago, when my nanny was hit
by a car and was taken to the hospital, the
housekeeper took me to her house while my
parents were out at a party. I'd never seen
such a small house before, and it was about
five hundred square feet bigger than
this one.

Even though Henry's home is small, it's quant and inviting. The decorations are humble but tasteful. The cabinets in the kitchen have a fresh coat of paint and there are beautiful pictures of seascapes on the walls, giving the place the feel of a cottage by the sea.

"Mom, I want you to meet Aurora Tate," Henry says.

"It's very nice to meet you, Mrs. Asher," I say, extending my hand. Her skin is warm and soft to the touch.

"Please don't call me that," she says with a smile. "I'm Karen."

"Okay, Karen. It's very nice to meet you," I correct myself.

"Did you two have a nice evening?"

Henry nods and tells her that we went to the crab shack for dinner and then Tommy's.

"I have to tell you, or rather apologize to you for the fact that my son has such terrible taste in places to take a girl out on a date," Karen says, shaking her head.

"There's no need," I say quickly. "I've actually had a really good time."

"Then you must not get out much," Karen says and we both burst out laughing. I want to tell her that I'm a little tired of those high-end pretentious places that guys usually take me to but I sort of love the fact that she doesn't know who I really am.

"I made pancakes," Karen says, "Would you two like to have some?"

Henry and I exchange glances.

"Yes, please," I say quickly, "but only if I can help you."

Karen walks with a cane but gets around the kitchen very quickly. The place is so tiny that there is only enough counter space for one.

"No, thank you," Karen says. "Why don't you guys just sit there in the corner and tell me about your evening?"

Karen is a slight woman with wide hips and short brown hair. There is a kindness in her face that's difficult to describe. My mother's friends are all fit and trim and without a single line on their faces and yet they're not nearly as beautiful as Karen is when you really look at them.

She exudes warmth and softness. It's as

if the difficult life that she has led has not made an impact on her at all. It hasn't hardened her, nor has it made her callous and cynical.

I have never met anyone like her before and, frankly, I didn't even know they existed.

Karen throws a luxurious amount of chocolate chips on top of my pancake and covers Henry's with chopped up strawberries. I steal a strawberry off his plate but he refuses to have any of my chocolate. We devour the pancakes as quickly as she makes them, and this makes her incredibly happy. When the batter starts to run low, she finally puts a few on her own plate to enjoy.

"I'm glad that you like to eat, Aurora," she says. "That wasn't always the case with the girls that Henry brought home."

I glance at him and his cheeks get flushed.

Wow, so he is capable of being embarrassed, I say to myself.

I smile and give him a little wink. He shakes his head, looking straight down at his plate.

"Mom, please, can we not talk about that?"

"Why? What's the matter?" she asks innocently, as if she doesn't know exactly what she was saying. "So, Aurora, tell me about yourself."

"What would you like to know?"

"Well, what do you do with yourself?" My jaw tightens for a moment, but I take a deep breath to center myself and let it out slowly.

"I am actually pursuing my PhD in popular fiction."

"Oh, really?" she asks, raising her eyebrows. I nod.

"And what is that exactly?"

"Well, it's kind of like a PhD in English Literature except that instead of focusing on classic works, I analyze and try to find meaning in popular works. I'm particularly interested in genre fiction, like romance and thrillers.

"I think that the kind of books that people read says a lot about the culture that they live in. It influences the kind of shows that they watch and affects all aspects of culture, in general."

"Wow, that sounds fascinating. I actually love reading Danielle Steel and Nora Roberts. I know that Henry would make fun of me, but they can spin a wonderful yarn and that's all I really want at the end of a hard day."

"I totally agree with you," I say. "Their novels are fast-paced and easy to read and focus on relationships. There are many romantic elements but there are others as well, parents and children, sisters, brothers, and all sorts of other familiar relationships. We can learn a lot from the characters in the novels and the popularity of their books speaks to that."

"I'm not sure Henry would agree with you," Karen says, smiling out of the corner of her mouth.

In that moment, I see him in her face. They are different sexes and ages and yet it's as if he is a carbon copy of her.

"Do you not agree?" I ask him.

"No, I wouldn't say that," Henry says quickly. "Actually, to tell you the truth, I've never read a lot of popular fiction. I'm not sure why, maybe I'm a snob? But I have always been drawn to the short story genre and that's mainly what I read."

"Novels don't hold your attention?" I ask.

He shrugs and shakes his head.

"I think what I like most is the succinctness of the short story. All of the events are relayed immediately. Everything is resolved, or maybe not resolved. New characters are introduced and we only get a glimpse of who each of them are."

I smile. I have known many snobs, and a part of me suspects that he might be one of them. But I appreciate his polite comments for the time being.

8

HENRY

When I go to work the following morning, I'm not entirely sure if I have my old job on Aurora's boat. But at least, at the yacht club, Mr. Madsen has a bit less influence.

The day proceeds pretty much like all of the other ones this summer. The place gets busy around one, when the lunch crowd comes in from their morning on the water or at the golf club. This establishment has been around for at least fifty years, and very few things about it have changed.

The tables still have to be polished every day, and there are white tablecloths adorning each one. I have worked here for many summers, eventually ascending to the job of bartender. Bartenders make the most tips, followed by servers. We usually split a portion of them with the others but keep the majority to ourselves. Mr. Madsen comes in just as I am setting up all of the bottles and making sure that all of the glasses are extra clean for the lunch crowd.

I flinch, but only for a moment. Taking a deep breath, I brace myself for a possible firing. Much to my surprise, he doesn't appear to be as angry as he was earlier, when he was on the phone with Aurora. He's not working today, so he orders a scotch on the rocks. After talking about the weather and briefly discussing the game on TV above our heads, he asks, "What are you doing with her?"

"What do you mean?" I ask him.

"She's a Tate, don't you know that?"

"Of course I do," I say, polishing a glass that I've been working on for way too long.

"Don't get me wrong, Henry, I love that family and I appreciate everything they have ever done for me. However, her father is not anyone to mess with—"

"I know that he is a big-time CEO—" I interrupt him.

"You know nothing about Mr. Tate—" Mr. Madsen interrupts me, "and you don't want to know anymore than you already do."

"What are you talking about?" I ask.

He opens his mouth to say something but then closes it. He's choosing his words carefully. I wait for him to continue.

"Let's just say," he says after a moment. "Let's just say that what you know about Mr. Tate is only the Disney version of who he is and what he does for a living. He is a very dangerous man and he would not approve of you having any sort of relations with his only daughter."

A big gulp forms in the back of my throat. I swallow hard. I'm not sure what to say to this or how to react.

Mr. Madsen has never spoken to me in this manner before. He has always been stern but kind and fair. In fact, I know very little about his personal life and he knows very little about mine. He cultivated this distance, not just with me, but all of his employees, and over the years, I have grown to appreciate it.

So, for him to come out and suddenly warn me about dating Aurora is completely out of character.

"Tell me this," Mr. Madsen says, leaning over the bar top and getting as close to me as possible. "Is this just a one night thing or are you planning on seeing her again?"

I shake my head, not sure how to answer.

"I like her, Mr. Madsen. I like her a lot."

"Well, that's going to be a problem," he says and finishes his drink.

MR. MADSEN's words weigh heavily on my mind long after he leaves and way into the afternoon. I try to be friendly with all of the guests, but I'm just not here the way I normally am.

It's hard to joke around and talk about nothing in an interesting way when your heart is not in it. After I eat a brief and quick lunch in the kitchen, I go back to work. The afternoons are usually a quiet time, right before the big evening dinner rush, and I enjoy the solitude. Besides the hostess, I'm the only one here, manning the restaurant in case a big party comes in.

And right when I least want to see another person, let alone act friendly, four guys saunter into the place. They are all dressed in the yacht club's unofficial uniform, plaid, pastel colored shirts, dockers or khakis along with dark shoes with tassels. I would be surprised if any of their outfits cost less than five hundred dollars. They are not out of the norm for the clientele here, but what grates on me right now is that they're my age and total assholes.

The guys take seats around the bar, and quickly make themselves at home. They all order beers and make disparaging comments about the women on television.

"Hey," one of them says, "I'm telling you I can totally get three of those girls in bed with me."

"No, you can't." The others laugh.

"Yes, I can."

"What makes you so sure?"

"Look at them. Look at those faces and those hips. You know that no one really wants them. And they're just desperate for any sort of attention."

"You're such an asshole," the tall one with blond hair and pink pants says. "Yes, Connor, I know that already. That's my schtick, don't you know that?"

"And that works for you?" Connor asks. "Yes, you could say that."

I have seen them around before. The self-described asshole has a house not too far away and Connor owns a seventy foot Beneteau. They all work in the city, somewhere near, or right on, Wall Street. They have never been traders, that's kind of a low position, but rather investment bank associates and hedge fund analysts.

They probably make around one-hundred and twenty-thousand a year without bonuses, and they are just starting out. But all of them come from a lot more money than that, and they will be millionaires by the time they're thirty. On the other hand, I work as a teacher during the year in an underprivileged school district in Harlem and don't clear forty grand after taxes. I probably make another ten in the summer, and I give all of that to my mother to help with her bills.

Watching them, laughing and drinking with their friends, I suddenly wonder if I'm not the stupid one. I want to be a writer, yes, but working as an English teacher is not really getting me any closer to achieving that dream.

I am not a very good teacher. I will be the first one to admit that. I'm not very patient or very interested in teenagers. I find the job tedious and difficult, at best. It is absolutely awful, at worst.

I wish more than anything that I could be one of those inspiring teachers that they make movies about, the ones that change lives, but I just can't put 100% of me into that.

No, my passions lie elsewhere and the reason I got that job is that it was the only one I got offered after graduation. But now I wonder if I have made a mistake. Perhaps these assholes and my friend Taylor, an aspiring asshole, have figured something out about life that I haven't. Also, I wonder if Mr. Madsen would be having his little talk with me and warning me about dating Mr. Tate's daughter if I were one of *these* guys.

When the guys finish two rounds of beer and all of their fries and they are just about to leave, a group of girls comes in.

At first, I don't see her.

She's walking behind her friends, with her head hanging low. They grab a table not too far away from the bar and Ellis Holte, the tall one, waves me over. I hand them each a menu and take their drink orders.

When I try to make eye contact with Aurora, she looks away. I am not sure how much her friends know or don't know about what happened last night. A big part of me wants to tell all of them, but I know better and keep my mouth shut. If Aurora doesn't want anyone to know, that's fine by me.

The guys at the bar are quick to make their move. They grab seats nearby, pushing the tables together. When I come back with the drinks, Connor has his arm around

Aurora. Instead of shoving him away, she lets him rest there. Leaning in, his face is only a few inches away from hers. When he makes a joke, she laughs along with him and I clench my fists.

"Can I take your order?" I ask her, clearing my throat.

When she looks up at me, she pulls away from Connor, but only a little bit, as if she had not let him drape all over her.

I feel like a fool. An idiot! This is probably her boyfriend.

I can't believe that I let myself catch all of these feelings for her when, in reality, we just went out on one date and I know practically nothing about her real life.

Yes, we shared a few jokes and laughs, but so what?

Yes, she slept with me and had breakfast with my mother, but that doesn't have to mean anything, right?

Maybe she just wanted to slum it for a night. I thought they were assholes, but maybe it was me who is the asshole for thinking that I ever stood a chance.

When I take her order, I keep trying to

make eye contact, but it's all to no avail. She acts like she doesn't know me. Her demeanor is polite and professional but cold and distant.

We are strangers as far as she is concerned.

And this guy Connor? He is someone who is clearly significant in her life.

After putting in all of their orders, I take my position behind the bar and try to steel myself. I've had plenty of one-night stands and this one should be no different. She's just a girl. Just because you connected with her over some unheard of twentieth century short story writer, doesn't mean that she is actually interested in you.

Twenty minutes later, when the food is ready, I deliver it with a newfound coldness and professionalism.

I don't search her face to meet her eyes.

I'm no longer waiting for an inkling of affection.

And I am certainly not waiting for an introduction to her friends.

If she wants to pretend like she doesn't know me then that's perfectly fine. The truth is that I don't know her. A few personal nuggets does not make for a connection.

Connor covers the bill and pays the additional twenty percent in tip. They all take off together, leaving me alone in the dining room.

About an hour later, I receive the first text. It's from Aurora.

I am so, so sorry, she writes. *I had no idea that we were coming here until after Ellis suggested it and I couldn't get out of it.*

You coming here is not the fucking problem, I want to write back.

Connor, the guy that was all over me, is my ex-boyfriend and we have a very complicated relationship. I don't wanna go into it over text, I just want to apologize for being such a dick in there.

I shake my head and put my phone down. I don't have the energy to deal with this. Only a few moments ago, I was so ready to write her off, but now my certainty is wavering.

But her texts keep coming and coming. She apologizes over and over again and then asks where I am.

She says that she knows that I'm still at

work because she just called the front desk and asked and wonders why I'm not writing her back.

I guess I can assume that you're really mad at me, but please don't be. Please let me explain. I'm sorry.

I don't write back. This was all a terrible mistake. We live in worlds that are just too different and it's not worth trying to intermingle them.

She continues to blow up my phone.

I pick it up and run my fingers over the screen. I click on the text string. I stare at the blinker.

Please stop, I write.

9

AURORA

I don't know why I agreed to go to that stupid yacht club, but I regret it as soon as I see him. It wasn't that I was embarrassed that I had gone out with Henry; he is very cute and charming and attractive. But Connor was there and, when Connor is somewhere, everything is a lot more complicated.

Connor is my ex-boyfriend but it's more complicated than that. We were good friends at first. Then we started sleeping together casually then dating then we reversed back to something more casual eventually breaking up without actually breaking up.

Ostensibly, we are still good friends except that I can't stand the sight of him.

The reason I ignore Henry? I don't want to give Connor a target.

I text Henry as soon as Connor and his friends leave, but he doesn't get back to me. I know that he is angry. I text him some more. I apologize profusely, but I still hear crickets.

We only had one date.

Yes, it was magical and beautiful, but what the hell does he expect from me? He doesn't know how complicated my life can be.

He doesn't know anything about me, even though he thinks he does. The more time that passes with him not messaging me back, the angrier I get.

No one treats me like this. How dare he not respond?

I have already apologized, what more does he want?

The day fades into night and then becomes the next morning and the one after that. I send only one more text the following day and then I force myself to let it go. I deserve an answer and if he doesn't think that I do then he doesn't know the first thing about me. If he doesn't want to talk to me then he doesn't have to.

Later that week, Ellis invites me out with a guy she's been seeing. She says that she wants to introduce him to me, one of her best friends but, in reality, it's a blind date. She knows that I don't go out on blind dates but her boyfriend just happens to have a friend in town in need of entertainment on this particular night.

Ellis is almost a foot taller than I am with long lean legs that start somewhere near my shoulders. I'm exaggerating of course, but only a little bit. She spent many years dancing and as a result she knows her way around her body while I am still trying to get comfortable in mine.

She seems to be able to eat anything in the world without gaining a pound while I can barely look at a cheeseburger and gain ten. Still, we have been friends ever since we went to The Chasley School, the kind of elementary school for the elite in Manhattan that you have to get a spot in when you are still in utero.

I meet Ellis at a fancy but casual restaurant right on the water in West Hampton. Her boyfriend is nice enough, but I want to tell him not to get his hopes up since she is not the committing type.

Ellis's mother is a famous New York socialite, who has gone through numerous husbands, six to be exact, and even one wife. She's very forward-thinking in that way, especially for a seventy-year-old woman. She had Ellis when she was forty-five with her fourth husband, but he was never part of Ellis's life growing up. That's one of the reasons why Ellis carries Adele's maiden name of Holte, the same name that Adele kept all of these years.

Mitchell Bishop, Ellis's boyfriend, and Brock Kumparak, my date, joke around and reminisce about their days back at Princeton, even though that was only a few years ago. Now they both work on Wall Street, one in investment banking and the other in a hedge fund, but which one does what work I can't remember.

When the conversation runs a little dry, Ellis interjects and tells them about the new

painting that she is responsible for staging at
The Oliver Gallery. The Oliver Gallery is
one of the most prestigious places to work
for a rising art curator, and I am certain that
she would not have the internship without
her mother's wide connections. Still, art is
her passion and who can blame her for
taking advantage of every opportunity that
comes her way?

Of course, her internship doesn't pay
anything and requires almost eighty-hours a
week of work, but after having that on her
resume she will probably be able to work for
any gallery in New York, Paris, London, LA,
or Dubai unless she chooses to open
her own.

Over a course of fried avocados for
appetizers, Brock asks me about my work. I
tell him about my PhD and he barely feigns
interest. It's not fair, but I find myself
comparing him to Henry. He knows very
little about literature and has probably not
read a book since college. I don't want to
hold this against him, but I can't help myself.
I don't find anything else about him very
interesting so what choice do I have?

After a so-so dinner, the boys insist on showing us a good time by taking us out to a bar. I don't know why we need to go to another bar when there's a perfectly good bar here, but then again, I have never been much into the barhopping culture of New York City. Still, I do have to agree this place feels a little dead and it would be nice to see a few more fresh faces. We pile into Ellis's Maserati and drive the half a mile to the place that Brock suggests. It's more of a local place, not really rolling out the welcome mat to the summer people but it's not as much of a dive as the one that Henry took me to last week.

Walking in, Brock buzzes in my ear about some new financial instrument that his company has developed to make it easier for regular people to invest. It mostly goes over my head because I don't really care. I'm only going to stay for one drink, I say to myself, glancing over at Ellis and Mitchell with their hands all over each other.

And then, suddenly, I see them. Henry is sitting at the bar with a girl draped almost completely around him.

10

AURORA

I narrow my eyes to make sure that my eyes aren't deceiving me. I watch the girl run her hands up and down his leg. Henry shifts his weight from one side to another, trying to get comfortable.

So I guess this is it. He's over me, that is if he were ever really into me and everything that happened that day was not just an act to get a rich spoiled girl in the bed with him. Ellis sees me staring at him. She knows that I have spent the night with him and that I never do that. Of course, I've had a one-night stand or two, but I have never spent the night, and I definitely never had breakfast with the mother.

Perhaps, I shouldn't have told her, but I was on such a high when I came back that I wanted to share the good news with someone and she is my oldest friend.

"Forget about him," she says, nudging me with her leg.

"He doesn't deserve you."

"I know," I say quietly, looking around to make sure that our guys are still at the bar getting drinks.

"No, I don't think you do. Who does he think he is? I mean, he was cleaning the floors of your yacht and serving us our drinks, and he has the audacity to not call you back?"

"I should have never pretended like I didn't know him," I say, shaking my head. "That was really rude."

"But you apologized! I saw all of those pathetic texts you sent him. And he didn't even have the courtesy to text you back. Who does that?"

"You know that what I did had nothing to do with his job, right?" I ask Ellis.

She gives me a knowing smile.

I worry that she suspects that I am as

shallow as she is and is just waiting for me to stop pretending to be this way. But I am not.

"He's a teacher." I continue to explain myself. "It's not like he's *just* a bartender. No, that didn't come out right. Just forget it."

She smiles again.

"The only reason I ignored him is because of Connor. If Connor knew that I liked him…well, you know how he is."

"Whatever, they're both assholes," Ellis says, taking a sip of her martini and throwing her hand up in the air.

"But you know, that may be even worse. I mean, to be a teacher you need to have a college degree and you make less than most servers and bartenders in the city."

I shake my head and look down at the floor.

"Ellis, there is more to life than money," I say quietly.

She leans over to me and puts her lips right next to my ear. Then she whispers, "Honey, that's a lie that rich people tell everyone to keep them working so hard for so little."

Feeling completely disgusted by someone

I thought was my friend, I extricate myself from her and head to the bathroom. I want some privacy, but this isn't the place for it. There is a line of about ten women all waiting for the same dirty, dingy bathroom with used toilet paper all over the floor.

I step outside and head around the corner. I press my back against the wall and take three deep breaths.

"What the hell am I doing here?" I ask. "What the hell am I doing with any of these people?"

"What *are* you doing here?" His voice breaks my concentration and startles me a little bit.

Henry is standing less than a foot away from me, almost hovering over me. I want to step away to create more distance but there's nothing but a brick wall behind me.

"Are you following me?" he asks, crossing his arms and tilting his head to the side.

"No, I'm not."

"So, why are you here?"

"I had no idea we were coming here," I say quietly.

"That often seems to be the case."

"Ellis wanted me to meet her new boyfriend and he brought along a friend. So, I am currently on a blind date, not that I owe you any sort of explanation."

"No, you don't," he says sternly and takes a step away from me.

"I thought that I had explained myself enough," I say when he starts to walk away. The words just escape my lips before I can stop them.

"What are you talking about?" he asks.

"Didn't you get any of my texts?"

"Yes, I did."

"And you didn't think it would be polite to answer?"

"No, I didn't think that they required an answer. After all, you had already said everything you wanted to say with your actions."

I shake my head and cross my arms.

"That was an accident," I insist. He lets out a laugh, sarcastic, of course.

"So, you accidentally ignored me in front of your friends and your ex-boyfriend? You were accidentally embarrassed about being seen with me, a bartender?"

"No, it had nothing to do with that. It was about Connor. My ex-boyfriend. He has a temper and I didn't want him to get jealous and I didn't want him to make fun of you or be mean to you. I was, I thought I was, protecting you."

He doesn't say anything in response and I don't elaborate further. I had groveled and explained myself enough, much more than I ever have to anyone else. And if he's not interested or cannot find it in his heart to forgive me, there is nothing else I can do.

Without saying another word I head back inside. Somehow all of this time in the fresh air has made me feel even more claustrophobic than I ever felt in that busy, loud bar.

I find Ellis and Mitchell dancing near the front and grab Brock's hand to pull him onto the dance floor. He is clearly surprised but goes with the motions. He is actually a pretty good dancer, and we fall into a nice rhythm.

A few songs later, I see Henry out of the corner of my eye dancing with the girl he was talking to earlier. She rubs her body intensely against his as he presses himself against her. His hands make their way up and down her arms while her back presses against his groin.

As soon as our eyes meet, I do the same thing to my date. His body feels hard against mine. For a moment, I imagine it belongs to Henry but then Brock says something dissipating the illusion.

Glancing over at Henry again, I watch him watching me and I watch her and him together. My jealousy feels like it's going to boil over at any moment and make me explode. But nothing happens. The song comes to an end and we separate.

When Brock excuses himself to go to the bathroom and Henry's date runs into an old girlfriend of hers, Henry looks at me. The next song comes on and he takes a step forward.

The room is crowded and full of people yet it feels like we are the only souls in the place.

"Will you dance with me?" he asks and puts his arm out. I want to say no, but I can't.

Instead, I just put my hand in his and let him lead me.

"Where did you learn how to dance like this?" I ask.

"I used to take classes," he says quietly.

"Really?"

"Like what?

"Everything you can think of. I know how to do jazz, Latin, ballroom, some hip-hop. Actually, dancing was my mother's passion and she taught me a lot of what I know."

Suddenly, I feel quite embarrassed over my own lackluster dance skills. I've learned a few things from popular YouTube videos to not embarrass myself at a club, but I don't actually know anything about dancing. My go-to approach was to always try to mimic the girl next to me and hope no one notices.

"In that case, you should dance with Ellis, she's quite good," I joke.

"No, thank you," he says, staring deeply into my eyes. "I only want to dance with you."

The intensity of his voice and his eyes send shivers down my spine. He doesn't blink for a long time, watching me take it all in. Suddenly, I become a moth drawn to a flame.

"Hi," Brock says. "Do you mind if I cut in?"

11

AURORA

My heart drops when I see him. I had completely forgotten that I'm still on a date. I don't want to dance with Brock, but it doesn't feel like I have a choice. Luckily, the song comes to an end and I catch Ellis's eye and casually wave her over.

"Aurora, I'm not feeling that well. I think I'm gonna go home," she says.

"Oh, no," I say sympathetically. "I'll head back with you."

"You really don't have to," she says, but I insist.

I give Brock a small hug and wave

goodbye to Mitchell. I glance back only briefly to get one last glimpse of Henry.

"You really owe me for this," Ellis says. "That could've been a disaster."

"Yes. I know," I agree. "Thank you very much."

"What the hell were you doing dancing with that guy again?"

"I don't know," I say, shaking my head. "We were talking and then he just asked me to dance. He is such a good dancer."

"Yes," Ellis says begrudgingly, "I'll give him that."

Climbing into Ellis's Maserati, I can't help but look back at the bar one more time.

Maybe he'll be there.

Maybe he'll be waiting for me. But he's not there.

No, just forget about him, I tell myself. That was a good date and a good dance, but that doesn't mean that anything between us is any different.

"He's right over there, you idiot," Ellis says, shaking her head.

I follow her pointed index finger and see

him sitting on the front of an old car that looks like it was made in the 1990s.

"Do you really wanna get into that piece of shit?" Ellis asks.

"I'll talk to you later," I say, getting out of the car.

When I walk over to Henry, he hops off, opens the passenger door, and shuts it after I get in. After going around to the other side, Henry gets behind the wheel. The car starts out with a roar and we pull out of the parking lot with the tires screeching.

"Where do you want to go?" he asks. Our eyes meet. I swallow hard.

"I don't know," I say shyly.

"Somewhere private," he says more like an assertion than a question.

"The yacht club? To my boat?" I suggest.

There is so much to say and yet neither of us speaks. Instead, he puts his hand over mine, interlacing his fingers with mine.

He kisses me for the first time on the dock, just spins me around and presses his lips onto mine. When I kiss him back, we barely mange to get aboard before all of our clothes come off.

His mouth is strong but his kisses are soft. His tongue finds mine quickly and doesn't let it go. He walks backward with his arms around me as I lead him down to the main corridor and then into the master bedroom in the very back.

He pulls away from me for a second to take a closer look at the room, nodding slightly at the bathroom with a large sunken tub, but I shake my head no.

Tonight, I don't have the patience.

I just want him inside of me as quickly as possible.

Henry throws me onto the bed and climbs on top of me. He's no longer wearing a shirt and I run my fingers up and down his chiseled tan body with a protruding six pack. My own body is so much less perfect, and yet he adores it in every way that I adore his.

He kisses my breasts over my bra and then quickly removes it and throws it on the floor. He buries his head in between my breasts and inhales deeply. This is where I want to live, he mumbles. This is where I want to spend an eternity. I blush and bury my hands in his thick luscious hair.

He quickly moves his lips down my body. I feel my stomach rise and fall with each kiss. The spot in between my legs tenses and relaxes with each movement.

He pulls off my panties with his teeth and tosses them across the room. When he rises above me, all I see is abs. I help him unbuckle his pants and slide them down his legs. He stumbles a bit and knocks his head into mine.

We crack up laughing and then kiss again and again and again. In this moment, nothing else exists. There's only him and me.

He opens my legs slowly, kissing the inside of my thigh. But this time I take control. I flip him over on his back and climb on top of him. I take him into my mouth, but only briefly. He wants me to be on top of him as much as I want him to be inside of me.

When I take him inside of me, we move as one. We are dancing. There isn't one off-note or a misstep. It feels like our bodies have known each other for a great many years, but in a good way.

It's not boring, but there's also no awkwardness of those first few times. I've never experienced this with anyone else before. In fact, it felt more like I was going through the motions rather than letting myself enjoy the moment. But with Henry, he simply fills me up and takes over. When I get tired of being on top, he senses this and flips me over on my back.

Suddenly, an unfamiliar feeling starts to course through me. Tension starts to rise within me, escalating with each thrust.

Could this be it?

I have experienced this on my own, of course, but never with another person.

Perhaps I could never relax enough. With Connor, I had to fake so many orgasms, it was getting exhausting. He wasn't satisfied unless I made a lot of noise and a big production of the whole event. Ever since then, I'd decided that I would no longer lie to please the man in my life.

But with Henry, things are different. The moans come on their own. Just a little bit at first, barely audible. But as that feeling within me starts to rise, the sighs come faster and faster.

"Are you getting close?" Henry asks.

His question brings me out of a daze.

"This feels amazing," I say. "But I don't think I can go there right now."

"Oh, okay," he says into my ear. "Do you mind if I do? Because I'm not sure if I can hold on for much longer."

I give him a kiss and a nod.

"I promise I'll take care of you later tonight."

His words send shivers down my back. It's a promise as much as a declaration.

Henry's movements speed up as I dig my fingers into his shoulders. I feel him getting closer and closer as the intensity between us continues to build.

"Aurora," he whispers gently into my ear.

"Aurora!" Another voice interrupts us.

It takes me a moment to realize that the voice belongs to a female, and another few moments to realize that it actually belongs to my mother.

My heart jumps into my throat as I grab onto the comforter around me and pull it up to cover my naked body. Henry, a little disoriented, is not as quick, and stumbles a bit.

Someone standing behind my mother giggles. My eyes try to focus but the light from the hallway is too bright for me to actually make out their features.

"I think we need to give them a little privacy," he says. I immediately recognize my father's voice and wish for the ground to split open and swallow me whole.

The last thing I see before my mother closes the door is the disapproving look on her face.

I realize that I had been holding my breath this whole time and let it out quickly.

We start to get dressed in complete silence and my mind ping-pongs from one thought to another.

Shit.

Shit.

Shit.

Why the hell are they here?

"Those are my parents," I say, turning to Henry. "Just in case you were wondering."

"They sure did pick a good time to interrupt us," he says quietly.

"They are supposed to be in Albany on some work stuff, not in the Hamptons and definitely not on the boat."

"It's going to be fine," Henry says, taking me into his arms.

"No, it's not," I mumble and push him away from me. "You don't know my parents."

"We're all adults though, right? This is what adults do."

"Not in the master bedrooms of their father's beloved yachts, they don't," I correct him.

I buy as much time as I can getting ready and now it's time to go and face them. I don't really want to, but I also don't want my mother to come and check on us again.

I look at myself one last time in the mirror to make sure that I look as put-together as possible.

"Are you ready?" I ask, turning to him.

Henry shrugs his shoulders and gives me a wink. "Yeah, why not?" he asks casually.

He isn't at all intimidated or thrown off by what just happened but I am sure that my parents will change that attitude quickly.

I take a deep breath before opening the door. I have never been so embarrassed in my whole life except maybe the time that I got my period in the middle of seventh grade biology and got blood all over the nice upholstered white chairs that the teacher had just set up for us.

No, come to think of it, this is worse.

In the living room, I am greeted by my mother who introduces me and Henry to their guests.

I have never met the Hawthornes before, but my mother had mentioned them a few times. Apparently, she met Mrs. Hawthorne at the new Pilates studio that she has been attending and in addition to philanthropy they are also both very interested in the arts.

Many wealthy women are interested in those things, but Mrs. Hawthorne is into malaria and clean-water related causes, just like my mom, and she also likes the ballet. I think one of my mother's greatest regrets in life is that her daughter does not like the ballet as much as she does.

She put me in classes when I was a little girl and I attended them faithfully for four or five years, I can't exactly remember how long. What I do remember, however, is how much I detested it. When she finally let me quit, she thought that I would at least share her interest in *watching* ballet, but I proved to be a disappointment in that area as well.

Mom invites us to join them and the Hawthornes for drinks. I suspect that they all saw us when my mother was giving them a tour of the yacht but everyone is polite enough to not bring it up.

My parents are both true New Englanders in that they never discuss private matters when they have company. The Hawthornes may be their friends, but they would have to be the closest friends, if not their best friends, for them to talk about what they had just witnessed.

Knowing my parents, they do not have friends like that.

Close to the end of the hour, after my

parents have had two full drinks each, I see my opportunity to escape. We wish everyone a good evening, and head toward the door. Before we can make a clean getaway, my mother stops us.

"Aurora," she says. "I would like to invite you to dinner tomorrow night. Are you free?"

"I'm not sure," I say, "I think I have to check my schedule."

"Well, your father and I are very busy and tomorrow night is the only available time. So, please make sure to clear your schedule."

This is the kind of invitation that is impossible to say no to.

"Okay, I'll see what I can do," I say.

"And you, Henry? We would love to get to know you a little better," my mother says.

"Shit," I whisper to myself, just under my breath.

"Did you say something, honey?" she asks me with an innocent expression on her face.

"I'll be there, Mrs. Tate," Henry says. "It has been a pleasure to meet you both."

12

HENRY

The night at the yacht was magical up until the very end. That was not the ideal way to meet someone's parents, let alone a girl who I am falling in love with.

Did I really just think this?

Did this thought actually cross my mind? I look in my closet, for something decent to wear to tonight's dinner.

Aurora insisted that her parents are not going to bring up what happened last night, not because they are okay with it, but because it would be indecent of them to do so.

I'm not sure if I am supposed to take this as a good thing or a bad thing. For now, I'll just take it as it is.

So far, I have made a terrible first impression, and perhaps tonight's dinner is a way for me to make up for it. I enlist my mother's help in assisting me in choosing my outfit.

It's not much of a choice though. I only own two suits, both of which I wore to funerals. One is too big, because it was on sale and I couldn't afford the alteration fee, and the other is slightly too small.

My mother, who has never been very good with the needle, offers to help me alter the one that is too big. She goes through a few YouTube videos but quickly realizes that the job is too complicated for a novice like her.

"I guess I'll just wear it as it is," I say. "What else can I do?"

"You could wear something else underneath it," she suggests. "To help fill it out?"

"Yeah," I say, "I guess I could do that.

Though it is a little bit odd to wear a long sleeve shirt underneath a dress shirt. I think I'll just go with how it is and maybe take off the jacket if the evening calls for it."

"Don't be nervous, sweetie," my mom says. "I'm sure they're going to love you."

I give her a faint smile. I am certain that they will not, but I do not want to go into it right now.

Besides, it's not like I can tell her the embarrassing position in which they found both of us. We're very close, but she's still my mother.

"So, what do you think about Aurora?" I ask, taking a sip of a beer to calm my nerves.

"She seems like a very nice girl. But I do worry about the world that she lives in."

Even though my mom didn't recognize her at first, I have since filled her in on exactly what kind of family Aurora is from.

WHEN I GET TO DINNER, Aurora's mother opens the door and welcomes me inside. Mr.

Tate offers me a drink and I opt to have the same thing that he's having, scotch on the rocks.

The scotch is served out of a crystal decanter, so I don't know exactly what brand it is, but by the way it tastes, I can tell that it is very expensive.

The dark brown liquid is smooth to the taste, warming me from the inside out. I take another sip and feel a shot of liquid courage coursing through my veins.

Aurora comes into the room, dressed in a pristine black cocktail dress and high heels. Her hair is pulled up halfway and there are pearl earrings dangling off her ears.

She gives me a brief hug and a chaste peck on the cheek, the kind you give a cousin. Of course, I don't expect more. Her parents are here and I want to make a better impression than I had before.

A woman in her fifties with her hair in a bun and a thick Spanish accent walks up to us with a plate of hors d'oeuvres. She is dressed in a gray and white frock, clearly delineating her as one of the help.

When I extend my hand to introduce myself, she stares at me with big wide eyes without moving a muscle.

"Why don't you tell us about what you do for a living?" Mrs. Tate asks, taking an appetizer and leading me back to the sofa.

"I work in a high school in the Bronx, a charter school that focuses on underprivileged children," I explain.

"Isn't everyone there underprivileged?" Mr. Tate asks.

I'm not sure if he is trying to be funny or ironic and I don't know how to respond.

"Well, almost everyone is in comparison to you," I point out.

Mrs. Tate glares at me for a moment and then Aurora breaks out laughing.

I'm tempted to apologize, but I don't see why I have to. What I said is the truth. He's a billionaire and compared to him everyone has less privilege.

"Most of the students," I say, "do not grow up in an environment that is particularly conducive to learning. They often live in very cramped apartments, with multiple siblings, sharing one room among many of them. As a result, they do not have a quiet place to study. Also, their parents, if they do have both in the house, work too many hours to help them with homework or any projects. It's an uphill battle for teachers like us."

"So, is this something you plan on doing for a long time?" Mrs. Tate asks.

I swallow hard.

I should lie and nod and tell her that it is something that I want to do for the rest of my life. Partly because it's probably something I'm going to get stuck doing for the rest of my life. However, if this is the only time that I get to interact with Aurora's parents, I don't want that interaction to be false.

So, against my better judgment, I tell her the truth.

"Actually, no," I say, taking a sip of my drink.

She perks up a little bit and sits on the edge of her seat.

My eyes briefly meet with Aurora's who

furrows her eyebrows and looks at me with a confused look on her face.

"The truth is that I want to be a writer," I say slowly. "In fact, I already am. I have recently had a short story published in the New Yorker. I enjoy writing very much and it's a real calling of mine. Unfortunately, up until this point I have not been able to make a living at it so I took the only job that I got offered after college, teaching."

Mr. and Mrs. Tate seem to be taken aback by my honesty because they do not say anything in response for a few moments.

Afterward, Mr. Tate offers to refresh my drink and Mrs. Tate asks me more about my teaching position. Aurora mentions that her mom sits on the board of a few charter schools in Manhattan. We talk about that for a while but it does not go unnoticed that they do not ask me anymore about my writing.

Later that evening, after dinner is served, Mr. Tate asks me where I see myself in five years. This is a hard one to answer, and I simply shrug my shoulders and raise my hands in the air.

"You really don't know?" Mr. Tate asks. He wears his thick flowing hair just below his jawline, a little bit longer than you would expect.

He and Aurora's mom look so similar they could practically be related, and yet Aurora looks nothing like them. While they are both tall and broad shouldered, Aurora is short and a lot curvier than her mother.

While they have high cheekbones and thin aristocratic noses, Aurora's face is wider and a bit flatter. Nevertheless, she is one of the most beautiful women I have ever seen, but I cannot deny the fact that she looks nothing like her parents.

"No, I really don't have a plan. I mean, there are certain things I want to do like write a novel, but in terms of where I want my life to be, I am not so sure."

Mr. Tate stares at me, shaking his head.

"I know that you did not grow up with a father, son, but let me give you a little piece of advice," Mr. Tate says, after a moment. "You should always have a five-year plan, a three-year plan, and a one-year plan. Without goals you do not know where your life is going. Without goals, you will just drift along and one of these days you will find yourself at fifty wondering what the hell happened.

"If there are certain things that you want to achieve, you have to go after them. And you have to be willing to take out anyone who stands in your way."

"Is that what you did?" I ask.

"You can bet on it," he says sternly. "It's the only way that I would have gotten where I am. I don't know what Aurora has told you about us, but we both come from very humble beginnings."

"Yes, she mentioned that," I say.

"I was born on a dirt street and Gwen grew up with her grandparents, because her mother had her at fifteen. Some people would hide these facts, but we are proud of where we came from and how little we had. When we bought our first radio station, we spent our last cent on it and then went into debt for another hundred thousand. Our competitors thought that we were insane, but a year later we bought another one and another one. We knew back then that in order to protect ourselves, we had to spread our risk around. That way when one or two failed, which they almost always did, we would have others that didn't."

"That sounds like a sound plan," I agree.

"My daughter here, is a lot like you," Mr. Tate continues. "She doesn't have much of a plan for the future. She's getting her PhD in popular fiction, whatever the hell that is, and for whatever reason, I do not know. It feels a lot like she's just waiting around for something to happen."

"You know I'm right here, Daddy," Aurora says. "You don't have to talk about me as if I'm not."

"I know you're here, honey. I'm just not sure that you ever listen to me."

She resists the temptation to roll her eyes, finally succumbing but only a little bit.

"But Aurora is my daughter and as a result she has certain advantages that you did not," Mr. Tate says. "She will always have money and she will always have prospects, even if she chooses not to use them."

"Just because I am not interested in working for Tate Media at the moment," Aurora says, "doesn't mean that it is not something I might want to do in the future."

"Wake up, Aurora," Mr. Tate says. "The future is now. You are twenty-five years old. In five years, you will be thirty. Do you know where I was when I was thirty? Do you know where your mother was when she was thirty?"

"Things are different nowadays, Daddy," Aurora says.

"Yes, unfortunately, I have noticed a change. There used to be a time when you were an adult at eighteen. But now days, everyone seems to be a kid until they're forty."

"Anyway," Mr. Tate says, turning his attention back to me. "Whatever may be Aurora's shortcomings, she's my daughter and she will always be well taken care of. You, on the other hand, will have to learn how to stand on your own two feet."

I clench my fists to subdue the anger.

"Well, I do work for a living, fifty hours a week. During the school year, often more than that. I don't get paid much, but that's the reality of being a teacher. And in the summers, I work sixty, often seventy hours a week at the yacht club, bartending, and cleaning boats like yours, doing whatever it takes."

"Don't get me wrong, Henry. I am not saying that you are not a hard worker. I know that you actually work very hard, a lot harder than some people in this room." Mr. Tate winks at Aurora who doesn't find the joke particularly funny.

"All that I am saying is that to succeed in this world you have to be both a hard worker and a smart worker. You don't want to be one of those chumps out there working hard, doing backbreaking labor for twenty years, and then taking opiates to deal with the pain, and cutting your life short. No, you have to think for yourself. Whatever it is that you want, you have to go after it. No one else is going to do it for you. Do you understand?"

I take a deep breath and look deep into his eyes.

"Yes," I say. "I do understand."

As SOON AS we get outside, Aurora grabs my hand and apologizes profusely over and over again.

"I can't believe that my dad went on that tirade with you," she says. "I'm so, so sorry."

"No, that's okay, it was actually very interesting to talk to him."

"Oh, come on," she says, waving her hands and rolling her eyes. "You can't be serious?"

I shrug and tilt my head. "I've never talked to anyone about this before. But I think he's right. I mean, maybe I am wasting my time. Teaching is not something I want to do, so why the hell am I even there?"

"It's a good job and an honorable profession."

"Yes, that's true if you are passionate about it."

"You're just letting my dad get to you,"

Aurora says, tossing her hair. "You can't listen to him."

"No," I say, shaking my head, "he is right. I do need a five-year plan, or at least a one-year plan. I mean, looking forward, what are my goals for the year? What do I want to accomplish? Where do I wanna be this time next year? Maybe I need to ask myself these questions so I can finally get what I want."

13

AURORA

The following morning, my mother insists on meeting with me again for breakfast. They are going to Montana later today on their private jet for a few weeks, just to get away from everything. They do this every summer, and this is the third one that I have skipped.

I love it out there – the wilderness, the big blue skies, and the solitude - are amazing. But when my parents are in the state, all of the oxygen seems to be sucked out of it.

"So, what did you think of Henry?" I ask when the waiter brings us our croissants. I don't want to be here but she insists until I don't have a choice.

Mom is having a mimosa, but it is a little bit too early for a vodka for me.

"I think he's a very nice boy, Aurora. But he's not a very good fit for you."

I shake my head, averting my eyes.

"What made me think that she would ever give me a different answer?" I wonder.

"I just worry that you do not know your worth," my mom adds.

I shake my head again and cross my arms.

"Please don't look at me that way," she continues.

"Like what?"

"Like I am telling you something that you are actually surprised to hear. Is the only reason you are seeing him is to punish us for something?"

I stare at her. She really is the most self-centered person I've ever met.

"Are you serious?" I ask.

"Of course not."

"I am seeing him because I like him," I say.

"Well, nevertheless, he is not a good match for you."

"So, you don't like him?" I ask.

"Did I say that?"

"Not in so many words," I say with a shrug.

"Aurora, I don't have time for your games right now."

"Well, I don't have time for yours either. I don't understand what it is exactly that you don't like about him except for his lack of money. But, newsflash, Mom, no one has as much money as you do."

She shakes her head and stirs her coffee, making her diamond bracelet jingle.

"Maybe not everyone is as comfortable as your father and I, but there are plenty of wealthy eligible bachelors that would make for a great boyfriend for you."

"So are you telling me that I can't date anyone who makes less than, what exactly? Is there some sort of cutoff point? You didn't seem to have a problem with Connor, and he makes $150,000 a year."

"Exactly," Mom points out. "Connor was not rich by any standard, but he had a future in front of him. Henry, on the other hand, told us flat out that he has no idea what he wants to do in the next few years."

Your father was very disappointed with that fact.

"I don't see why," I say to myself.

"He wants the best for you, Aurora. As do I. We are just very discouraged by the fact that you don't seem to want that for yourself."

"You know what, Mom? There is more to life than money," I say. "I grew up with and around lots of it and I wouldn't say that it made me a particularly happy person. And yet there are people with a lot less who are perfectly content. Maybe they're onto something."

"You," my mom says, pointing her finger in my face, "you have no idea what you're talking about."

She narrows her eyes and stares deeply into mine, with a menace that I don't remember ever seeing before.

"We have given you everything, and perhaps that was a mistake. You have no idea what it's like to be poor, or how terrible it is. I grew up living in motels that charged by the hour with my grandmother because my mother disappeared. She had one abusive boyfriend after another, not counting her husband, my grandfather."

"Not everyone who is poor grows up like that," I say.

"Be that as it may," she says, "that was my experience. And I never wanted you to go through anything like that. Why do you think your father and I worked so hard to get where we are?"

"Are you serious?" I challenge her. "Are you seriously saying that you did it all for me? I hardly believe that."

"Well, we did."

"No, you didn't. You may have sent me to the best schools and gave me the best of everything but you did not do it for me. You two were going after conquering the world way before I came along. You bought your first radio station before you ever contemplated having me. And you and I both know that."

"Listen, I don't wanna fight with you, Aurora. I don't wanna fight with you about what we did or didn't do. All I want to do is to ask you to stop seeing Henry."

"I don't understand why you care so much. You never cared who I slept with before," I point out. "Connor didn't treat me very well, neither did some of my other ex-boyfriends. And yet you said nothing."

"Connor had prospects," my mom says, folding her hands in front of her and pursing her lips. "And as for those other ones, I knew that you would eventually figure your way out of those relationships."

"But don't you care that Henry treats me really well?" I ask.

"Yes, of course I do, but it's not enough. I can see you getting serious with him even after just a few dates. And trust me, he will always be a weight around your shoulders."

I shake my head.

"Right now, it feels like you can carry him because he feels light," Mom continues. "But after a little while, he's going to start to feel like an anchor, and you're going to feel like you're drowning."

14

AURORA

Despite my parents' protestations, we spend the rest of our summer together. Henry continues to work at the yacht club and on boats, and practically moves into my parents' home in the Hamptons with me.

It's a large five-bedroom villa situated on ten acres of prime oceanfront real estate.My parents' travels take them to Montana, then Paris, London, and Rome while we stay here by the water and spend every possible minute naked.

This becomes the most blissful summer of my life. We sleep in late, whenever we can, and Henry makes me pancakes and waffles from scratch. Sometimes, we run straight from bed to the pool. Other times, we put on our bathing suits and walk along the beach and bury our feet in the sand.

We do not argue.

We do not fight.

We just lose ourselves in each other's company.

We want to spend every waking minute together because we cannot get enough of each other. Each minute that we spend together is still not enough.

I crave him more and more, the more time that passes. While he's at work, I spend my days waiting and occasionally writing. My PhD work fills the need I have in the pit of my stomach to put together words on paper, but during the long days of summer, my mind starts to wander and I think what if I wrote something else?

Henry is so open with me about his writing, and yet I feel like I'm still in the closet about mine, not only with him, but also with me. Every day that I have free, I promise that I'm going to write in the afternoon, but when I sit down and stare at the blank screen and that blinking cursor, I lose my concentration.

One day, during the height of the heatwave, when the days are still very long and hot, we sit together by the pool watching the evening sun set over the horizon.

"This is the most beautiful place I have ever been," Henry says.

"Yes, it's pretty wonderful, isn't it?" I confirm, absentmindedly.

"But I'm not just talking about the house, or the Hamptons," he says.

When he turns his body toward mine, his bronzed skin sparkles and glistens.

"I love you, Aurora," he says, looking directly into my eyes.

"I love you, too," I whisper and look back out at the horizon.

I remember the first time that he told he loved me, I was sitting on his lap, checking my email.

When there was nothing in my inbox, I sighed and said, "Oh, no, no one loves me," to which he replied, "I do."

I thought that he was probably joking, but when I looked at him, I saw that he wasn't. In that moment, I realized that I loved him, too. We had only been together for three days and it was way too soon, but none of that mattered. He loved me and I loved him.

"I love you, too," I say, turning to face him. "You know that."

"This summer has been amazing, the best of my life."

"Same here," I whisper, giving him a nod.

"Will you move in with me?" Henry asks.

My chest tightens and my heart skips a few beats. I would love that, but I hesitate to say it out loud.

"How would that work exactly?" I ask. "Your apartment is all the way up in the Bronx and mine is on 116th Street."

I hope that he knows what I am thinking without me actually having to say it. It would be foolish of him to give up his place that is very close to work since affordable apartments are very hard to find.

"You don't think that it is too soon?" I ask.

He shrugs his shoulders and tilts his head so that his hair falls into his eyes.

"We have been living together this whole summer, haven't we?"

"Yes, I guess we have," I say with a smile.

My other hesitation has nothing to do with him; it's my parents. They don't know that he's staying with me here and they would definitely not be pleased if he were to officially move into my place near campus, which they are paying for.

"Do you really think it's not going to work out?" he asks.

"No, of course not. I'm just worried that you're going to get sick of the commute. Right now you are right across the street from your work, in the subsidized housing that they are providing for you. What about, just subletting your place out for the semester? That way you can test out the commute and see how everything goes."

He takes my hand into his and leans over closer. "You know, you are assuming that I was asking to move in with you, instead of *you* moving in with me."

I feel my mouth drop open. Of course,

that's exactly what I was thinking. He flicks my chin up to close my mouth.

"God, I know that my apartment is pretty shitty, but you could please do me a courtesy and pretend," he says, laughing.

WE OFFICIALLY MOVE IN TOGETHER two weeks later.

Well, I guess not officially, since my parents don't know that Henry is now living in the apartment that they are paying for, but he sublets his place for the semester and starts commuting to work from mine.

My semester begins and I enjoy being back in the flow of things. It's hard to explain why I like school so much, but I just do.

I like learning new things. I like challenging myself. I like to read and graduate school is nothing if it's not a lot of reading.

What's good about graduate school is that, unlike undergrad, I only take classes that I am interested in. Most of them require a lot of research and writing, and I like that, too.

This year, I will be mainly focusing on my thesis. I developed my PhD program from scratch, given that there was no PhD in popular fiction available at the department. But with a lot of hard work and cooperation from my professors, I was able to design and put together my own individualized research plan.

Romance and thrillers are the most popular genres and yet critics seem to pay very little attention to them. There is very little analysis and very little interpretation of what the popular genres say about our culture. This is what I am particularly interested in; how they influence culture and how they impact shifts in culture.

For example, the Me Too movement and talking about consent when it comes to sexual harassment and abuse has been a huge cultural shift in 2019. And immediately, these topics have started to appear in the books that have been independently published during the year by some very prolific and very popular self-published writers.

Most romances are written by women and consumed by women and because there are no barriers to what these authors put in their books, besides the market itself, many authors have been incorporating cultural shifts like the Me Too movement into their work. In fact, there are many instances where the Me Too movement is mentioned directly, something that has yet to happen in traditionally published books.

After starting school, I come home every day excited by all of the new things that I'm learning and that are making an impact on me as a researcher.

Henry, unfortunately, is not so lucky.

He is miserable in his job and all he wants to do is quit. Teaching is not his forte. He's not particularly patient and he isn't very interested in it at all.

"What do you want to do today?" I ask him while I make dinner on the stove.

Usually we order takeout, but this afternoon I was eager to make something from scratch. Of course, my enthusiasm wore off halfway through the meal, but at that point, I was already too invested.

Walking over to me, Henry flips me around and presses his body against mine. Running his hands up and down my hips, he looks at me with hunger in his eyes.

"No, no, no." I force myself to pull away. "I can't do this now, I'm cooking."

"Yes, I can see that," he says, moving my hair off my neck and kissing me.

"What if we just turn down the burner? You can leave it as is and join me in the bedroom for a little bit," he whispers.

When he runs his hand up my thigh, my legs open for him. I lose myself for a moment, quickly getting to that place where all I want is for him to be inside of me.

15

AURORA

"C'mon, we still have a few things to work out, don't we?" he asks, tugging on my hand and trying to pull me into the bedroom.

I shake my head, trying to resist him. But his kisses get more forceful and insistent and I can't bring myself to say no.

"I don't know what you're talking about," I whisper, giggling. It's a lie, of course.

"Oh, I think you do," he mumbles through his kisses. I don't want to admit it, but I know exactly what he's talking about.

I've told him that I can only orgasm on my own so he has made his mission this summer to change that. Every time, it doesn't work out, he doesn't give up and instead just tries harder.

AND WE ARE MAKING PROGRESS. A few days ago, I got there just with his fingers and now he wants to try with him inside of me.

"You know, it's very common," I say. "Not many women can orgasm while they are actually having sex. I've read about it online."

Henry pulls away from me for a second and looks at me.

"You know that I don't want you to feel bad about this in any way, right?"

I nod. He lifts up my chin and makes me look at him.

"I'm serious. I know that we're playing this game but I only want to go on as long as you're into it. If you don't want me to keep trying, that's fine. This is all about you. I just want to give you as much pleasure as possible."

I swallow hard.

I've always thought that I've had this

problem I would never be able to overcome. Yet there is a man who is standing before me who wants to help. I've never thought I would find someone who would try so hard and not get his feelings hurt when it didn't work.

I take his head in my hand and press my lips to his.

I kiss him softly at first, but then more forcefully and passionately. Our clothes come off quickly and he leads me into the bedroom. Just when we get there, I remember that the burner is still on, and run back to turn it off. When I get back to the bedroom, I find him sitting completely naked on the bed, his arms draped over the pillows.

Henry flexes his stomach and instead of six protruding muscles I count eight. Shifting his weight, he pulls me onto the bed.

"You are going to come for me today," he says.

"It sounds like a command, and I like it."

"I'll try," I say.

"No, you will."

He brings my hands up to the top of the bed and holds both of them with his.

"What are you doing?" I ask.

"I have a surprise for you," he says.

Pulling out a green tie with gold accents, he secures it over my wrists and then wraps it around the headboard.

Shivers run down my spine.

I have never done anything like this before, and I feel myself getting more excited with each passing moment.

"Do you want me to stop?" he asks.

I shake my head no.

He takes another tie, blue this time, and puts that one over my eyes.

With my eyes closed, my other senses come alive. With my hands tied up, the rest of me is exposed and overwhelmed with pleasure.

"Do you want me to stop?" he asks.

I shake my head no.

"Keep going," I whisper.

Henry runs his fingers down my neck and over my breasts. I arch my back when his hands make their way down my torso.

My legs seem to open on their own. But he closes them and says, "Not yet."

He starts kissing my toes then slowly makes his way up my legs.

This time, however, when my legs open to welcome him inside, he takes it a step further. His kisses which are soft at first, get more rushed and powerful with each moment.

He wants me as much as I want him. A warm sensation starts to build somewhere in the center of my core. I flex my toes to release some of the tension, but it doesn't go away.

When his fingers find their way in, I feel myself getting close. With my eyes closed, I am able to let myself go in a way that I could never let go before. It's as if I am suspended in animation. I don't focus on him, and I don't even focus on myself. Suddenly, I am just able to enjoy the moment.

His fingers start to move faster and faster, and I feel myself getting closer to that explosion. But then, he surprises me. Pulling away for a second, he opens my legs wider and pushes himself inside.

My body immediately welcomes him in. I wrap my legs around him and push him deeper inside of me. And then, just as our thrusts and movements become one, my body seems to yearn for his.

My heart rate speeds up and even skips a few beats. I feel myself getting closer. But it's not going to happen, right? It has never happened before. Why would it happen now?

And then, it does. The feeling takes over before I realize what is happening.

It overwhelms me and consumes me.

It catches me completely off-guard, and yet I somehow ride the wave all the way to the end.

"Henry!" I yell out.

His thrusts speed up and a moment later he joins me on that impossible high. When he finally collapses on top of me, he whispers my name over and over again, occasionally adding an *I love you*.

"I love you, too," I say, letting out a deep sigh of relief.

"What the hell is going on here?"

Her voice sends shivers down my spine.

It's not her, I say to myself. No, it can't be her. What the hell is she doing here?

"Aurora?" she asks in her disapproving and disappointed tone of voice.

I try to get up, but only then realize that my hands are tied up and that there's a blindfold over my eyes.

"Get these things off of me," I hiss to Henry.

Stunned, he doesn't move until I kick him. Then he jumps into action.

After my arms are free, I quickly pull down my blindfold.

Whatever mortification I feel doesn't make my face flush, but instead causes all of my blood to drain and pool in the bottom of my feet.

My breathing slows down, and I can barely feel my heartbeat.

My mother doesn't turn around to avert her eyes.

Instead, she glares at me and then at Henry then back at me. I tuck the blindfold and the tie from my wrists under the pillow, but it's too late. She has already seen them.

"So, I see that the two of you are still together," my mother announces, folding her hands across her chest.

I pull the sheet up around my body to cover myself up and briefly glance over to Henry who is already covered up from the waist down.

"We never talked about it much after you left for Montana," I inform her. "But, yes, Henry and I have been seeing each other since then."

"So, that little talk that we had?" she asks. "That just went straight in one ear and out of the other?"

"I wouldn't say that. I have taken it under consideration, but I feel like I have earned the right to spend time with whomever I choose."

I'm proud of myself for not causing a scene. I could have cried and yelled, but I remain steadfast.

Yes, she caught me in a terribly embarrassing position, but it's she who walked in on us.

"So, you don't even think you owe me and your father an apology?" my mom asks.

"An apology for what?"

"Well, we thought that we had reached an agreement with you, and we took you at your word."

"We did not reach any agreement," I insist. "You told me that you did not like Henry and I listened to you. But at no point did I promise you anything."

"And at no point, did you inform us that you would be moving in with him."

"And why would I?"

"Because we are paying for this apartment. We are paying for your monthly expenses."

"And that means, what exactly? That you own me?"

She purses her lips and raises her hand in the air to strike me. I shut my eyes and wait for impact. But nothing happens. When I open them again, she takes a deep breath and relaxes her shoulders.

"Don't be such a bitch, Aurora, it won't always look as good on you as it does now," she says.

.   .   .

"GET OUT!" I yell, trying to stay strong. "Get the hell out of here."

I bite my lower lip. My façade starts to break.

"I will. But you better start looking for another place to live," Mom says.

The first crack appeared when she walked in on us. And the longer we talked, the harder it was for me to pretend that I was okay. When the door slams shut behind her, my tears break free and spew out of me as if they are a geyser.

16

HENRY

When her mother leaves, Aurora lies back down on the bed and stares into space. I want to do something to help, but I don't know what.

"How could that happen?" she asks. "How could they catch us like that *twice*? And my hands were tied up. Why the hell did you put that blindfold on me?"

"I had no idea that your mother was going to be here today," I say defensively. "I thought that it would be something fun to try. And you seemed to like it."

She shakes her head. I kneel down before her and take her into my arms.

At first, she resists and then she gives in. Her shoulders move up and down as she sobs into my chest.

I hold her for a long time without saying a word.

Eventually, she pulls away, and wipes her tears off her face.

"I did like it," she says. "It allowed me to get out of my head and relax. How did you know that was gonna work?"

I look up at her.

"What do you mean *work*?"

"Well, you know…" Her voice trails off.

"Oh, you actually…?" She nods and gives me a wink. "And then she came in and ruined everything."

I shrug and find my pants in the hallway and my shirt in the living room. When I come back, Aurora hasn't moved. She's still hunched over cradling her legs and resting her head in her hands.

"Do you want to take a shower?" I ask. She shakes her head. I bring her clothes and lie down next to her.

"It's going to be okay," I say. "She'll get over it."

"No, she won't."

"What do you mean?" I ask.

Aurora takes a deep breath and exhales even slower. "I know my mother. She's going to make me pay for this."

"Okay…So, maybe she'll make you give up your apartment, so what? You can always move in with me."

"You know that they are paying for my school, right? And I'm also getting a monthly stipend to live on. I don't have a job. I don't have any way to pay for anything without them."

I take a step away from her, crossing my arms. "Well, you are twenty-five years old, maybe it's as good a time as any to learn to be an adult."

Slowly, she looks away from that spot in the distance that she has been focusing on and turns her gaze to me.

"This has nothing to do with me not wanting to get a job," she says coldly. "It's everything else. It's my whole life. My parents are assholes but they're still my parents. And I'm not ready to give up on them."

"I'm not asking you to," I say.

"It certainly sounds like you are." She shakes her head just as I shake mine.

I don't understand where she's coming from and I don't understand her.

I know that we need to talk about this more, but I just can't bring myself to do it right now. Besides, there's something else that is on my mind.

"I thought that your parents knew that we were living together," I say.

She doesn't respond.

"I mean, I knew that they weren't my biggest fans, but I also didn't realize that they hated me."

She looks down at the floor and doesn't respond.

"My mother had a talk with me about it after the boat incident," she says after a while. "I didn't wanna tell you because I thought that I could change her mind. I thought that we could meet up sometime in the city after they got back from Europe and have a do-over. I didn't expect her to come here today and just blow it all up."

17

AURORA

Two days later, in between my morning and afternoon classes, I meet with my mother at her favorite restaurant in Midtown, the one next door to the Ritz-Carlton Spa that she goes to religiously. It takes me forty-five minutes to get there, which she is well aware of. Yet, when she suggests it, I don't complain about the commute.

"How's your day going?" I ask, taking a seat across from her at the clothed table.

This is the kind of place where all of the waiters are old men who know way too much about wine and not enough about cocktails.

"I got my nails done this morning," my mother says after giving me two air kisses, careful not to mess up her makeup. "As you can see, they did not do a very good job."

I look down at her nails and don't see a single thing wrong with them.

"Right over here." She points to her index finger. "Look closer at the cuticle."

"Oh, yes." I nod demonstrably even though I have no idea what she's talking about.

After we place our drink orders, she intertwines her fingers, careful not to put her elbows on the table, and peers at me.

"Your father is not well," she says.

The statement hits me like a blow to the stomach.

"What are you talking about?" I ask. "Did something happen?"

"No, but he is not healthy. He's okay right now, but he has heart issues."

"I know that already," I say. "What happened?"

"Nothing happened." She shrugs. "I just want to create some context for you."

I take a sip of my martini and wait for a further explanation.

My mother has always been an enigma. I rarely understand where she's coming from or what she means. Ever since I was a little girl, I felt like we have existed on two separate plateaus, seeing each other, hearing each other but not really interacting with one another in any meaningful way.

"I don't know how to tell you this, Aurora, because we don't talk about things that really matter, do we?" Mom says, running her fingers through her perfectly coiffed hair.

"Can you just tell me what's going on?"

I don't know if she's trying to be tactful or just trying to build up anticipation on purpose, but I am running out of patience either way.

"Your father's business is not doing very well. He has been taking a number of shortcuts, the details of which I cannot go into at this point. But I just wanted to tell you that things are not as they seem and your relationship with Henry is not coming at a good time."

I stare at her, unsure as to how to react at first. But then anger starts to rise up.

"How dare you?" I ask her. "How dare you say that to me? My relationship with Henry does not exist on your timetable. I am sorry that there are problems in the business, problems you never bothered to tell me about before. But I don't understand what my relationship with Henry has to do with Tate Media. Or why you're even so concerned about it."

"Honey," my mother says.

And if you know anything about my mother, she does not mean it as a term of endearment.

"Honey, I worry about you. What do you really know about Henry?"

"What is there to know?" I ask her. "He's a teacher and a writer and that's it."

"But what if there's more?" she asks, tilting her head and narrowing her gaze.

"People are complicated, Aurora. You don't seem to know that. You have always buried your head in books where everything works out in the end, one way or another. The characters go through predictable ups and downs, they learn the lessons, or they figure out a crime, or whatever the heck happens but, in the end, everything is resolved. Right?"

"I'm sorry, Mother," I say. "Is this conversation about Daddy's health? Your business? My relationship with Henry? Or my poor choices when it comes to my studies? What are we talking about here exactly because you are going all over the place?"

"You are impossible," she says, taking a sip of her martini and tapping her long nails on the table.

Our food has arrived but neither of us have tried a bite.

"I wanted to meet with you because I wanted to talk to you about all of these things. They are all related because they all concern *you*," she says.

I sit back in my chair and wait for her to explain.

"Our business has taken a turn and there are certain issues that have to be resolved. I cannot go into it anymore than this here. I probably can't even tell you anymore than this at all because the less you know, the better."

"I am sorry to hear that," I say quietly.

"I have already told you my concerns about Henry and seeing what you two were doing did not alleviate them."

My blood runs cold as she mentions what had just happened.

Being the White Anglo-Saxon Protestant that she is, I did not expect for her to actually bring that up and her statement comes from left field.

I feel my cheeks get flushed and I force myself to take a few deep breaths.

"I know that it is not very tactful of me to bring it up, but I saw what I saw and I am concerned. I am your mother and when I was dating, we never took things that far."

I take a deep breath, struggling for air. At this rate I will need an oxygen mask to get enough air.

"Mother, if you wanna talk about my sex life, we should really make an appointment with a therapist. I'm going to need one."

She shakes her head dismissively.

"I don't want to talk about this anymore

than you do. I just had one question for you."

"Go ahead," I say cringingly.

"That was consensual, right?"

"Of course it was! What the hell do you think is going on?"

"I don't know anymore," she says, shaking her head. "All of these women on television talking having been sexually assaulted or made to feel uncomfortable by things that men have done for centuries. And now suddenly it's wrong?"

This is the first time I have ever heard my mother talk like this. My mouth nearly drops open.

"That's the whole problem," I say when I finally regain the ability to speak. "That's the whole *fucking* problem. They have been doing the same thing for years. And finally someone is calling them on it. Grabbing women's asses when they are just walking past them. Telling a complete stranger to smile so that she will look prettier for him, as if she owes him something. Women have been putting up with these unwanted sexual advances for as long as there have been women in existence, and we are sick of it."

"If that's the case, then what the hell was going on in that apartment that I walked into?" she asks.

My mother doesn't curse, and the fact that she uses the word hell instead of heck chills me. But she is genuinely confused and as much as it pains me to talk about my sex life with her, I decide that I don't have any other choice.

"That was consensual," I say. "It was just something we were doing for fun. He thought that the blindfold and the restraints would take me out of my head and relax me a bit, and he was right."

She shakes her head, finishes her martini, and asks for another round. I don't know what I was expecting. Perhaps some understanding or compassion, but she lives in an entirely different world, one that I could never access, no matter how much I try.

"Okay, I think we have gotten off track here," she announces.

"Yes, I agree," I say, letting out a sigh of

relief.

"But we do we understand each other?" she asks. I look up at her and into her wide green eyes.

"About what?"

"About Henry."

"Well, I know that you don't like him, you've made that perfectly clear."

"So, you will not be seeing him again?" she asks.

I furrow my brows and shake my head. "No, absolutely not."

"So, I guess we have not reached an understanding."

"No, we haven't," I say.

"Okay then, let's put it this way. If you want to keep seeing Henry then you can do so on your own. But your father and I do not want him living in the apartment that we are paying for."

Blood drains away from my face and I look down at the table, picking at a little crumb left by the French baguette.

This is what I have been afraid of, a definitive no.

She has showed her disapproval before,

but she has not come out and actually said that I would have to move out.

"I don't understand why," I say. "What do you think Henry is doing? Do you think that he is lying about who he is?"

"No, I don't think that. I think he's telling me the absolute truth and that's what scares me the most."

I shake my head.

She puts her hand over mine, startling me.

The tone of her voice suddenly becomes softer and quieter.

"I know that you have feelings for him, Aurora. And he may be a good person."

"He is," I insist. "He's a good man."

"That doesn't matter," my mother says. "I am very sorry. Perhaps I should have prepared you for this sooner and that's my fault. But you are a Tate, and though your personal life can be your personal life, that does not mean that you can make any sort of significant commitment like moving in with someone, let alone marrying someone, without our permission."

"And why is that?" I whisper, pressing

my fingernails into my palms as hard as I can.

"You are a Tate. You're not just an Aurora Penelope whomever. And you have certain responsibilities that come with that."

"Don't you want me to be happy? I mean, how much money do we need to have so that I'm not forced into a marriage of convenience?" I ask.

"I'm not forcing you into anything. Do you see me introducing you to eligible bachelors? No, this has nothing to do with that. All I'm saying is that Henry Asher is not a good match for you and your father and I will not support you living with him."

"You know, you two came from nothing. I thought you would be a little bit more sympathetic to people who are struggling," I say, trying to hold back the tears that are building up at the back of my eyes.

"We are sympathetic, but he is not going after anything. He is perfectly content just being a teacher, and his greatest dream in life is to write short stories. How is he going to support you on that? Or is he going to depend on us forever?"

"Is that what you're really concerned about?" I ask. "You have more money than anyone could ever spend in ten lifetimes and you're worried about spending a little bit of that to make sure that your daughter has a comfortable life with the man of her dreams?"

"No, that's not what concerns us. We are worried about you not following the rules. We are worried about you doing whatever the hell you want."

18

HENRY

When Aurora shows up that evening after she had lunch with her mother, I took her into my arms and promised her that everything would be okay. I don't renew my weekly sublet and we move back into my apartment. She thought that it would be horrible to live above 120th Street in a fourth floor studio walk-up, but our life is total bliss for the next two months.

My work is right across the street so I never get in late even when I have overtime. Now, it's her turn to do the long commute to Columbia and, at first, I worry about her, not sure how she will handle it.

The whole trip with the bus change and the subway ride and the walking takes almost an hour, but after the first few trips, she stops complaining.

In fact, she even tells me how much she enjoys having that time to think and process everything that has happened. She has never ridden the subway much before, or the bus, and she enjoys the people watching.

Frankly, I thought she would have a much more difficult time adjusting to life as I know it, but she surprises me. She stops using credit cards that her parents pay for, and even gets a job at the Humanities Library to bring in some extra money.

Of course, there are a lot more better paying positions in the city like being a server or waitress, but she seems happy at the library so I keep my thoughts to myself. For now, I'm just happy that she is contributing anything at all and we're not relying on her parents' money to make ends meet.

The kids in my class relax a bit as the semester wears on and I start to enjoy my job more and more. I don't have time or space to write, but I'm okay with that, too. We are getting our life figured out and starting our life together.

And then, right after Thanksgiving, before the last two weeks of the semester, everything falls apart.

"How was work?" she asks, rifling through the boxes near the closet.

I don't say anything and instead head straight to the mini-fridge.

We live in a small studio apartment with an almost nonexistent closet.

Some of her clothes are laid out on the floor, the others are on the bed and there are more in the boxes.

"How do I look?" she asks, spinning around in her high-heeled shoes to look at me.

"Beautiful. Where are you going?"

"I haven't seen Ellis in a long time and she texted me to catch up."

I shrink and bury my head in the fridge, grabbing a beer and looking for something edible.

"Why don't we ever have any food?" I ask.

"Because you never go and get any," she snaps back.

"Oh, is that how it is now? It's my job to do all the grocery shopping?"

"Do you think it's my job?" she asks.

She slips on a different dress, shimmery and green with a tight, high waist and looks at herself in the full-length mirror that she brought over from her old apartment.

The mirror is enormous, reaching all the way to the ceiling. Of course at her old place, it had fit nicely, but here it makes it look like we live in a matchbox.

"I'm the one who is commuting for two hours a day, you work right around the corner. The least you can do is pick up some food."

"Don't you remember what we talked about?" I ask.

She flips her hair and turns to look at me. She has never looked more beautiful.

Her face flushes red with anger, making a little crinkling spot in between her eyebrows. I can see the fire in her eyes and it's all I can do to stop myself from throwing her onto the bed.

"No, I don't remember," she says with her hands on her hips.

"There are no good grocery stores anywhere near here," I say. "None that have any fruits or vegetables anyway. Remember, they even did an NPR story about how this area is a food desert."

She rolls her eyes.

"So, just because I happen to go to school in a place with a grocery store, that means that I have to lug all of that stuff back up here, on my commute?"

"I don't see any other way," I say, sitting down on the sofa.

There is barely any room for it, but she had insisted that we get it so that we would have somewhere else to sit beside the bed.

"I don't wanna argue about this," I say after moment. "That's not at all what I wanted to talk about."

"What do you want to talk about?" she asks.

"They fired me," I say quietly.

"What? What are you talking about? I thought you had a contract for this year."

"I did, but they are breaking it.

Apparently, the school is losing money and they're cutting back on some teachers."

"But who is going to teach your classes?" she asks.

"I don't know. I guess they'll be combining some classes and sending some of the students to another school. I don't really know what's going on, but they are laying off about five other teachers. There are rumors that the owner has been funneling money to some of his other businesses and the state's attorney might be investigating him. But in the meantime, I'm out of a job."

"I'm so sorry," she says, walking over and wrapping her arms around me.

I breathe her in. Her hair smells like flowers, and I want to stay in this moment forever. But when I exhale, she pulls away.

"So what's going to happen now?" Aurora asks.

"I have no idea," I say.

I know what she's thinking. What's going to happen to this apartment, which was subsidized by my job?

How are we going to afford another place in a city that's so expensive?

I take a deep breath and drop another bomb.

"We have to be out of here by the end of December," I say quietly.

She stares at me in disbelief.

"No, they can't do that," she says, shaking her head. "We have rights."

I shrug and finish my beer, going to the refrigerator to get another one.

"Yes, we do. But they want us out of here. I don't know what's going on, but it looks like the school is shutting down."

"Well, no, we're *not* moving."

I plop down on the bed and stare at the ceiling. "Of course, we don't necessarily have to move right now, right before Christmas. We can probably stay here for a month or two, maybe three, before they will be able to actually evict us. But that will ruin my credit and what then? I doubt I'll be able to get a job by then, a good paying one anyway."

She looks at the time on her phone and

quickly finishes applying her lipstick and some final touches around her eyes.

"You look… magnificent," I say without a hint of irony in my voice.

"Thank you, I hope it's enough."

"What do you mean?" I ask.

"Well, I am meeting up with Ellis and I haven't seen her since I've moved up here."

"You know, some people would say that friends are there to support you in your time of need," I suggest.

"You just don't understand. We have been friends since we were kids and this is what it's like to have friends from back in the day," she says with a shrug.

"Yes," I say, "I am familiar with the concept of a long-term friendship. But you and Ellis don't seem to be very close. I mean, why else would you go through all of this trouble to impress her instead of just telling her what you're going through?"

"Okay," she says quickly, waving goodbye. "I don't have time to get into another argument with you. I've got to go."

After the door slams shut, I whisper, "I love you."

19

HENRY

Two months later, we get the dreaded eviction notice. We have been expecting it, but it still comes as a surprise.

Aurora's job at the library pays five cents over minimum-wage and she can only do twenty hours a week. Even those hours take her away from her studies, and I can tell that she is falling behind on writing her thesis.

She comes home exhausted both from the commute and the classes as well as the hours at work. The time that she should be writing, she instead spends procrastinating, watching television or scrolling through her phone.

I want to do something to help, but I can't. I fill out application after application after application for every teaching job available, along with about one-hundred other jobs that I'm not particularly qualified for, but no one is hiring.

All teaching jobs in the city are taken until the fall except for some prestigious tutoring centers, that only have a few hours available a week and are located in lower Manhattan.

I get one offer and I brave the long commute for measly pay and teach basic concepts to spoiled rich kids who could not care less about anything that I have to say. When I come home and vent about them to Aurora, she gets defensive.

"You know what," she says one evening. "I'm really tired of you talking like that. Is that what you think my childhood was like? Is that who you think I was?"

"No, not at all," I say even though that's a lie.

I know that that's exactly how her parents were when she was little and that's probably how they told her to treat her tutors as well, as if they were there to serve her.

"I'm just very tired right now," I say, trying to steer the conversation to something else. "How was your day?"

"I didn't go to class today," she says.

"Really? How come?"

"I don't know," she says, staring absentmindedly at her phone. "I didn't have work and I just didn't feel like going all the way down there."

"Things are going to get better," I say, trying to stay optimistic.

She turns to face me and gives me a blank stare. "How is that exactly? I mean, what's going to happen to make it better?"

I don't have an answer to that. "I think we just need to stay positive and not let this tear us apart."

"Do you want to know what I think?" she asks. I nod.

"I think that we need to ask for help. I think it's about time that I go to my father and ask him to pay for our apartment."

"No, absolutely not."

"Why not?

"Because they made it very clear that they want nothing to do with us."

"No, they did not. They did not want me to see you. But that doesn't mean that they don't want to have a relationship with *me*."

"So, what are you saying exactly?"

"I don't know what I'm saying. I'm very confused. All I know is that we need help and they are the only ones in a position to help. I mean, why are we doing this to ourselves? They love me and they would be freaking out if they knew the financial position that we are living in. They would have a heart attack if they saw this apartment. It's as small as my mom's shoe closet!"

"But what about what they said about me?" I ask quietly.

"I think that they're going to change their mind," Aurora insists. "I have been absent long enough from their life and I think they're going to be happy just to hear from you again."

I shake my head no.

"Why do you have to be so stubborn? Why can't you just give them a chance?"

"They never gave me a chance," I insist.

She gets off of the sofa and goes to the tea kettle. She runs some water in it from the sink and then stands there and watches as it comes to a boil.

"I wasn't going to tell you this," she says, pouring the hot water into her favorite blue cup, "but my mom has been giving me money for the last four months."

"What?" I gasp.

"I should've told you earlier, but I just didn't want to make things more difficult. My mom has been helping us with money for a long time because the truth is… I haven't been working at the library."

"How could you lie to me about that?" I whisper.

"Henry, they pay minimum-wage. I'm in my last year of the PhD program and I can't spend twenty hours a week working for so little so we can afford this ridiculously shitty apartment. I'm already commuting two hours each day and…"

The voice trails off.

I don't say anything for a while.

"Are you mad?" she asks.

"No, I'm not. I thought I would be, but I am actually disappointed," I admit.

"Don't you understand that I have to finish my PhD? I've been working on it for years."

"Yes, I do understand. But I also understand that after all of these years, you have grown accustomed to a certain lifestyle, one that I will never be able to afford. It just makes me a little sad."

"What are you talking about?" she asks.

"What I'm talking about is that I don't think that we are ever going to be on the same page. You're never going to think that I make enough money. And whatever it is that I do make, you will never be happy with it."

She shakes her head vigorously and promises that it's not true.

Unfortunately, we both know that it is.

I can't compete with the world in which she was raised in. It's not like her parents were doctors or lawyers. She has had more in this life than most people can ever dream up or even imagine.

How stupid was I to assume that she

would be willing to give all of that up for me?

"My mother has invited us to dinner," she says coldly. "I think they want to give it another chance to get to know you better. It's tomorrow night. Please say that you'll go."

20

AURORA

We arrive at my parents' apartment on Park Avenue, and their doorman lets us in. Edward has been working there ever since I can remember, and I think of him as a friend rather than an acquaintance or an employee.

I ask about his wife who has been battling cancer, which is now in remission, and his children, who my father has employed at Tate Media. They both attended state schools and submitted their resumes through the normal hiring process, but after my mother found out, she streamlined their hiring process.

"So, they're happy in their jobs?" I ask.

"Yes. Very happy. We are both so grateful to your parents."

"Good, I'm glad to hear that," I say, giving him another brief hug.

I haven't seen him for a while and I actually just realized how much I have missed him.

"So, this is the infamous Henry Asher?" Edward says. "It is a pleasure to meet you."

"Yes, you, too," Henry says, shaking his hand.

"Well, I think we better be going, they're waiting for us," I say, waving goodbye. As we ride up in the elevator, I wonder why my father was perfectly fine with giving Edward's children positions at the company and has not extended the same courtesy to Henry.

I'm not familiar with the woman who answers the door as my mother goes through servants often. Very few make it longer than six months and a number of them barely survive a month. My father and I used to joke that my mother isn't actually interested in having a servant at home, but only has one because it is something that is expected of her.

"Thank you both for coming," my mother says, giving me a brief hug and shaking Henry's hand.

She shows us through the sitting room into the living room, where my father is standing next to the built-in bar, putting together a drink menu.

After a brief hello, he asks Henry what he wants to drink and makes two scotches on the rocks. My mother and I opt for glasses of white wine. When I find a seat next to their roaring fireplace, I wonder if this is going to be strong enough.

I come into the dinner not knowing exactly what to expect. They have already expressed concerns about Henry and our relationship, but over these last few months my mother has softened her approach.

I got the sense that she regretted saying what she said the last time we were at lunch together. I haven't seen her again, but we have texted and occasionally spoken on the phone and even video chatted one time.

The few times that I have asked her to

send me money, she has been more than generous. I regretted lying to Henry about my library job, but after the interview, they offered me the position and told me about the pay and I couldn't go through with it.

Twenty hours a week for a job that paid minimum-wage was just not something that I could afford to do in my last year. I knew that he wouldn't understand and that's why I kept it from him for as long as I did.

My mother, however, understood very well. Even though she is not entirely on board with my PhD, she is very big on finishing projects that you start. And since I was already enrolled, she did not want me postponing graduation just so I could work hours I couldn't afford to get the $800 in rent that we needed.

When I talked to her on the phone, I only asked for that month's rent. When I hung up, I saw a text that she had deposited $10,000 into my bank account. I thanked her politely and considered returning a portion of it, but then decided against it.

I might need it in the future and I didn't want to have to ask again. In the meantime,

I promised myself that I would spend the money wisely and not buy anything extravagant that we didn't need.

Over dinner, we focus mainly on general topics of conversation. We talk about my little brother who is going into seventh grade and who is currently at his fencing lesson. He is heavily involved in musical theater, which my mother loves and my father hates, so I asked her about that along with about a million other things that have nothing to do with Tate Media, my PhD program, or Henry's job. The dinner goes nicely enough and I think that it's actually going to be a success.

But then just as the dessert is served, my father asks Henry about his work.

"Well, as you probably know, the school is shutting down and they have laid off almost all of the teachers."

"No, I didn't hear that part," my father says, tilting his head in a concerned manner.

"Yes, the state's attorney is currently investigating the entire board of trustees. It's an unfortunate situation and a lot of the kids are really suffering," Henry says.

"And the teachers as well, I'm sure," my father says.

"Yes, the teachers are as well," Henry agrees.

I wonder if Henry thinks that my father is being cold and distant. He doesn't know him, but he's actually acting as compassionately as I have ever seen him. I hope that he doesn't make him regret that.

"Henry is looking for a new job," I cut in, "but as you can imagine there are not a lot of teachers being hired in the middle of winter."

"No, I imagine not," Daddy says.

"I am working part-time as a tutor for a few kids in lower Manhattan," Henry says rather defensively.

"And, are you interested in any other opportunities?" my mother asks.

"Yes, of course. I have sent out my resume to a number of research and writing related positions, but I haven't heard anything back yet."

"Well, that's one of the reasons I wanted to talk to you today," my father says. "We are actually starting a new division at Tate

Media that's going to be focusing on crime. We will have a television division, and online magazine division as well as podcasts and even programming on various social media networks. We are doing a big hiring spree and I would love for you to send your resume to our HR people for consideration."

"Oh, wow," Henry says slowly, completely surprised. "Yes, of course. That would just be wonderful."

"Good," Daddy says, nodding his head and giving me a wink. "I'm glad to hear that. Send me a resume tomorrow and I'll pass it along to my people. I can't make any promises, of course."

"No, I completely understand. I appreciate the opportunity."

In the cab back, Henry is on cloud nine. Smiling from ear to ear, he gets home and immediately opens his laptop and starts working on his cover letter.

"Are you going to do it right now?" I ask.

"Yes, of course. Your dad wants to see it tomorrow so I want it to show up in his inbox first thing."

"You know, you can take your time," I say.

"No, actually I can't. This is the first time that your father has shown any interest in me and not just that, he actually made me an offer. I don't take that lightly."

Henry works late into the night. He must have rewritten that cover letter and resume a hundred times before finally sending it off. I ask to see it, but he refuses to show it to me. Afterward, he paces around the place, cracking his knuckles. I don't remember him ever being this nervous before.

"I had no idea that you were so interested in the job," I say when he crawls into bed, completely exhausted.

"Actually, I am. I was thinking of all the articles that I could write and this is an amazing opportunity. He's putting together a new network and networks need writers. If I can only get this job…"

"What did you think of the dinner?" I ask.

"I think it went really well, don't you?"

"I do. Shockingly well," I add.

He laughs. "Maybe they're just coming around? Just accepting the inevitable?"

"Which is, what exactly?" I ask.

"That I love you and you love me and we're going to be together forever."

I smile and run my fingers up and down his chest. He flexes, pushing my hand up, and making me laugh.

"I love you very much," I say.

"I love you, too."

"I hate fighting with you," I say.

"Me, too," he says, leaning over and giving me a wet kiss.

"Let's not fight anymore," I whisper into his ear.

"I won't if you won't," he says, pressing his lips softly to my neck and moving closer and closer to my collarbone.

With one swift motion, he pushes me down onto the bed and I lose myself in his body.

21

AURORA

M y mother calls me the following morning.

At first, I don't really want to answer, but then I think that it might have something to do with Henry's resume, so I do.

"Glad I was able to catch you," she says in a particularly chipper voice. "How's your day going?"

"Fine," I mumble.

"Your classes?"

"Actually I don't have any classes today. I'm going to focus on writing my thesis."

"Good, good," she says.

I can hear that she's distracted, or

perhaps just waiting for the right opportunity to bring up whatever is on her mind.

"What's going on, Mom?"

"Well, since you asked," she says slowly. "I am calling about a particular issue."

"Okay… does this have something to do with Henry?"

"Oh, sort of, I guess so. Well, no, not really."

I don't say anything.

"Okay, why don't you just come out and say it? I'm all ears," I say.

"Well, I need to ask you a favor."

I wait for her to explain.

"I would like you to accompany one of your father's friends to the Callum Theater Gala this weekend."

"What? Why?"

"Well, I use that term *friend* loosely, as you know. Your father knows him and he's an acquaintance, and associate, but he's too young to be a close friend. He's closer in age to you actually."

"Okay," I say slowly, "but what does this

have to do with me? Why can't he get his own date?"

My mother exhales with exasperation. "I don't know why you have to be so difficult."

"Franklin Parks is going to be taking over the new crime division at Tate Media, the one that Henry has submitted his resume to, if you remember? Anyway, not to be so blunt, but Franklin will be making all final decisions regarding new hires."

"Is that why you want me to be his date?"

"No, not at all. The thing is that we think that you should start taking a more active role in representing Tate Media at public functions.

"I know that you are not interested in working at the company at this point, but your father and I are both unable to attend this gala and our presence is greatly needed there. We have supported that theater for many years and they do a lot of good work there.

"Anyway, Franklin is going and we would also like you to get to know him a little better, so that you can give us input about the type of person who will be in charge of this new direction in the company."

I swallow hard. I want to say no, but she has me between a rock and a hard place. "Okay…" I say slowly. "When is it?"

I GO to this gala partly as a favor to my mother and partly as a favor to Henry. The guy that is supposed to be my date will be the one who will be interviewing and hopefully hiring Henry. This is definitely not an official date, but we are sitting next to each other at the same table.

I am nervous to tell Henry my plans, thinking that he will for certain want to come with me, but he actually has plans with some of his teacher friends. I don't mention the fact that I will be meeting with his possible future boss. I only tell him that this is a favor for my parents.

At the gala, guests wear ten thousand dollar dresses with shoes and purses to match. Luckily, I don't stand out in a bad way because my mother had couriered over one of my old dresses from home.

After getting a drink, I find my assigned table and take a seat. After a few minutes of small talk with the rest of the round table, I see a man walking slightly unevenly and talking a little bit too loudly.

I don't know how many drinks he has had, but he is clearly intoxicated.

Please don't be him, I say to myself over and over again until he takes the seat right next to mine.

"Well, hello there," he says, extending his hand to me. I take his hand reluctantly and he quickly pulls it up to his lips and gives me a big kiss.

"You must be the elusive Aurora Penelope Tate!"

"It's nice to meet you," I say, "Franklin Parks, I presume?"

"Your presumption is 100% correct."

He enunciates each word in that way that drunk people do when they are trying to appear sober. A waiter in a white tuxedo comes around and asks if he can get us another round of drinks.

"No, thank you," I say quickly. "I'm still working on mine."

Franklin motions for the waiter to pour him another glass.

"Well, well, well," he says, sitting back in his chair and propping his hands around his head. "It is a pleasure to meet you. Your father has told me a lot about you."

"I wish I could say the same thing about you," I say and he bursts out laughing.

"Now, I have heard a lot about your sense of humor, and the fact that it does not take any prisoners."

"Well, I say you have to consider the source. The men who have told you that are probably not used to dealing with strong women."

I take a sip of my drink, and look around the room, for someone else to talk to. Anyone else.

It's not that Franklin isn't easy on the eyes, it's just that he rubs me the wrong way. He's arrogant and self-absorbed, very self-absorbed.

A few people come up to me to talk about this and that but as soon as Franklin interjects, they leave as quickly as they came.

After dinner is served and I am a little bit drunk and completely bored by the conversation about golf and media station acquisitions, I turn to Franklin and ask him, "So, why exactly am I here? You don't seem like the type who can't get his own date."

"You're right, I guess my reputation precedes me."

I toss my head back and laugh.

"What's so funny? Let's just say, I haven't heard a thing about you until a few days ago when my mom asked me to come here but I got the sense of exactly who you are when you showed up."

He leans a little bit closer to me and then raises his finger, points in my face, and starts to laugh.

"Ha, ha," he says, "you think you know everything about me, don't you?"

I shrug and adjust my strapless dress.

"Well, you don't know the first thing."

"So, you haven't dated every eligible bachelorette in the city?" I challenge him.

"Well, I wouldn't say that…"

"Have you ever even been in a serious relationship?" I ask.

"Now, why do women go around asking that? It's like some sort of litmus test with you all. Do you want to be the first woman to plant your flag in me, so to speak?"

"No, absolutely not." I smile.

He sighs demonstratively and slides down into his chair.

"That's what I'm starting to understand," he says, shaking his head. "And why is that exactly?"

"Well, you're what thirty-seven?" I ask, being extremely generous.

"I'm forty," he says.

I doubt that, but I don't challenge him.

"Here's the thing, we expect that a man who has reached the ripe age of forty, is it? We expect, for you to have experience in at least one serious, monogamous, and preferably quite extensive relationship. Otherwise, we get a little bit suspicious."

"Why? Why do you get suspicious?"

"Well, to tell you the truth," I say, putting my elbow on the tip of my knee and getting as close to him as possible, without actually touching him. "It's like a warranty. It means that you are reliable. You can be trusted. If another woman has trusted you and things just didn't work out, well, that happens. But, if you have never been in a marriage before, or, God forbid, a serious relationship, well, red flags are going off all over the place."

"But what if there isn't anything menacing about it?" he asks. "What if it just means that I didn't find the right woman?"

A smile starts to form at the corner of my lips and quickly grows into a grin and then a full out laugh.

"What?" he asks innocently. "What's so funny?"

"There is something missing. You have been dating since you were what, fifteen? And you weren't able to find a single woman who could put up with you? Or even worse, you couldn't find a single woman who *you* could put up with? No, no, no… Danger ahead," I say, shaking my head.

"So, tell me about you, then."

"There's nothing to tell," I say with a

shrug. "I have dated a few guys, and finally found someone that I really care about."

"Oh, really? What's he like?"

Suddenly, my throat closes up. Do I tell him the truth? Do I tell him that he's the guy that he will be interviewing tomorrow morning? Or do I just let that little piece of information slide?

"What's the matter?" Franklin asks. "Cat got your tongue?"

"I met him in the Hamptons," I say. "We spent a glorious summer together and now we're living together."

"And what is it that he does?"

"He's sort of between things right now," I say as casually as possible. "He's a very talented writer, but he has been working as a teacher for a few years."

He doesn't ask me anything more, and I don't volunteer. Tomorrow morning, he will probably make the connection between teacher and writer, but I don't want to sway him one way or another about Henry's position.

The truth is that I'm not really sure if I have any influence.

Yes, I am his employer's daughter, but my father would never make it clear to Franklin that he absolutely has to hire Henry. We would have to be married for at least a decade for that to happen.

I excuse myself and head to the bathroom, angry that the heels that I have chosen for the occasion have given me blisters on the back of my heels.

I don't know how some women can stand to wear heels every single day, but I really hate them. I think that they were invented by some terrible man who hates women and wants to make them suffer. But in truth, it's the women who subject themselves to this punishment just to look tall and hot.

I glance at myself in the tall leaning mirror in the center of the enormous bathroom. It's no longer the holiday season, but the mirror is still decorated in winter-style garland celebrating the season.

I don't want to admit it, but the heels do make me look magnificent. I'm not very tall, only five foot four, but with these heels, my legs look long and flamingo like. They accentuate my hips and minimize my waist and even, somehow, prop up my breasts. If only Henry could see me like this, I say to myself, immediately regretting that it is not him who is my date for tonight.

I hate lying to him. I don't want to, and it always makes me feel like a total shit, and yet I find myself doing it more and more. I lied to him about working at the library. I lied to him about taking money from my mom. And now I'm lying to him about attending this gala.

The truth is that these are all things that I could explain to him, but they aren't things he would understand.

A part of him knows that the only reason why he has an interview with Franklin Parks tomorrow about the research writing position at Tate Media is that my father owns the company.

He knows that, but if he knew that in return for that favor, I am on a date with Franklin himself, as a favor to my mother, steam would come out of his ears.

And I don't want him to feel like he isn't good enough.

He is.

The problem is that the game is fixed. My father and mother took a lot of shortcuts as opportunities presented themselves to them, and that's why they are where they are.

That's just how the world works. You have to take whatever advantage is presented to you, because it's an uphill battle no matter what.

But for some reason, Henry doesn't understand that. He thinks that there is a noble way to get what he wants. I'm not saying that you have to lie and cheat and be a terrible person and that the only way you can become successful is to be a vile human being, because that's not true. But you do have to grab every opportunity.

This meeting with Franklin Parks is not a date, even though it seems like it is. It's a meet and greet.

It's an opportunity for me to talk to a few people that my parents are friends with and to show up here as the face of Tate Media. Given that Franklin will be heading a large new division within the company, my mother wants me here to get to know him better, in a more casual environment.

What will I report back? Nothing particularly encouraging. I don't know how he is as an employee and a boss, but so far, he has not made the best first impression.

But that's good to know. It's good to be informed.

I'm saying all these things because I'm trying to think of a possible explanation of what I'm doing here, something that I will have to explain to Henry later on tonight.

I'm tired of lying to him, but that doesn't mean that I'm willing to allow him to get less than what he deserves just because of his pride. Henry is a very good writer and since that is what he wants to do for a living, I will do everything in my power to help him reach his goals.

"Well, hello there." Franklin comes up to me at the dessert table.

We are at the back of a banquet hall, and this isn't the usual gathering place. It's dark and quiet here and there are a lot of beautiful pastries and cakes to look at, so that's where I had escaped after using the bathroom.

"I thought that maybe I would find you here," he says, winking at me. He leans against the wall but only slightly and looks me up and down in that way that men do when they are assessing you.

It was sexy when Henry did it, but with Franklin, it's creepy. I take a step away from him.

"No, honey, don't be scared, I didn't mean to frighten you."

"You didn't," I lie, trying to appear to be strong.

"So, what are you doing all the way over here, hiding in the shadows?"

"I guess you answered your own question," I say, crossing my arms.

"You know, you're not very nice, has anyone ever told you that?"

I stare at him but say nothing.

I hate how he expects me to be nice just because he is paying attention to me.

I was polite enough, but when he is pressing me and pressuring me, I don't have to be polite.

Still, I say nothing.

"So, how's your evening going so far?" Franklin asks, taking a step closer to me.

I take a step back, and then hit the wall with my back.

"Fine, I guess." "You know, you never answered my question."

"Which was?"

"How come you are here with me instead of a real date?" I ask.

"Well, your parents have asked me to do them a favor."

What is he talking about?

He takes another step closer to me. I can feel his breath on me and it makes me wanna squirm.

"Do you mind?" I ask, sliding along the wall to try to get away from him.

He grabs my arm and pulls me closer to him. Then he presses his lips onto mine, hard.

"What are you doing?" I ask, pushing him away from me. "I told you that I wasn't interested."

"Oh, you were serious?"

"Yes, of course I was serious."

"Ha," he says in disbelief. "I thought that you were just joking."

I shake my head, not believing what is actually happening.

"I told you about my boyfriend," I say.

"Oh, boyfriends come and go, you know how it is."

"No, I don't. I have a serious boyfriend and I have no interest in anything happening with you."

"You know, you would be a lot more fun if you weren't such a bitch," he says, pointing his finger in my face.

He takes a step to the side and trips.

"And you would be a lot more fun if you weren't such a drunk," I say, walking away from him.

I'm relieved by the fact that I never told him who my boyfriend really is, and I hope that he doesn't remember any of the details when he interviews Henry tomorrow morning.

I walk out of the gala completely disgusted.

I'm angry with my mother for asking me

to go there. I'm even more angry with her for setting this whole thing up.

Why did she think that he would be such a great date? Why does a man like that even have a job at Tate Media?

Haven't they been paying attention? The world is changing.

Men like that are going down for doing exactly what he has done to me; made me feel uncomfortable and humiliated at the same time.

And I'm not even someone who works for him. Hiring him, and giving him a position of power, is asking for a lawsuit. Don't they know that?

Sitting in the back of the cab on the way to my apartment, I wonder if my parents just don't see the tide rising. They are so ingrained into the minutiae and the rhythm of everyday life at the company, they are not seeing the big picture. Men like him should not only *not* be put in charge of new departments, they should be fired from their jobs.

I grab my phone and dial my mom's number. She picks up on the second ring.

"How is everything going?" she asks in an upbeat tone.

"Not very good," I say. I tell her what happened and how rude Franklin was to me. She listens intently and I feel like I'm getting through to her, but then at the end she throws a curve ball.

"That's just how men like him are, Aurora. Don't you know that by now?"

"Of course, I do. But that doesn't mean that they have to work at Tate Media."

"Well, that's a much more complicated situation than you know it to be."

"What are you talking about?" I ask. "What's so complicated about that? He threw himself at me and even kissed me without my consent and that's not good enough for you to get rid of him? Do you want him to be another Harvey Weinstein or Matt Lauer? How much more do you want him to do before you think it's reasonable to get rid of him?"

"Aurora, please don't blow all of this out of proportion. He asked you out, you were probably flirting with him, I'm sure that you looked beautiful. Just take it as a compliment."

I shake my head, at the same time shocked and completely surprised by the words that are coming out of her mouth. It's not that she doesn't believe what I just said, it's more that she thinks that it's okay.

"The thing that you just have to understand, Aurora, is that boys will be boys. It has been this way for centuries if not since the beginning of time, and it's not gonna change anytime soon."

"It will if women in positions of power and women everywhere say that it's unacceptable."

"Well," she says, "that's not gonna happen anytime soon, is it?"

I shake my head and stare at the phone.

"You know that you have the opportunity to change this. He came on to me and when I pushed him away, he came on to me again. I'm your daughter. He works for you, my parents. What could be more simple than that?"

"Aurora, what you don't know about our business could fill volumes," Mom says. "It's very complicated and, no, we cannot just fire him over something like this. And if you are smart, you won't tell Henry about this either."

I bite my tongue. I want to tell him, of course I do, but if Franklin will still be his boss tomorrow morning, I don't think I can.

"I have to go," I say and hang up.

Taking a deep breath, I look out of the window trying to decide what to do.

22

HENRY

She comes home late at night in a strange mood. I can tell that there's something on her mind, but instead of talking about it, she just wraps her arms around me and kisses me as hard as she can.

Once my lips drift down her neck and further down her body, we no longer talk. Instead, I take her to the bedroom and show her how I feel about her. It has taken a long time, but she finally relaxes enough to actually reach that point where she lets go.

When we first met, I didn't think that I would be able to get her there, but as long as she was okay with me trying, I kept at it. It doesn't sound very romantic, because in romantic stories, things like this are supposed to happen spontaneously. But that's not real life.

Our attraction for each other is innate and comes from some deeper place. But something like this, taking her out of her head, required some work, work that I am completely willing to do.

Tonight, our bodies move as one. She lets me into the most private part of her being and I appreciate the invitation. Again, I tie up her hands and again she lets me blindfold her.

This time, however, I make sure that the front door is dead bolted so that we do not have any interruptions. I spread her legs to each side carefully, taking my time as I kiss the inside of her thighs. She tastes like heaven.

If it were up to me, I would live in this place between her legs. But as my fingers speed up, her body tenses and I feel her getting close. This time, however, despite how much I want to thrust myself inside of her, I do not.

Patience is a virtue for a reason.

Anticipation takes time to build up, but it is worth it in the end. It's Christmas morning again and I have been watching the presents piling up under the tree for two weeks straight. I have touched them and rattled them, trying to figure out what is inside and finally it is time for me to rip into that beautiful wrapping paper and tear it apart as quickly as possible.

As soon as she reaches climax and yells my name at the top of her lungs I push myself inside of her. She moans again and again but I keep my movements slow and deliberate to take her there again. I'm not sure if it will work, but I give it my best shot. I feel her body relaxing again. I know that this is the first step.

I have learned to appreciate and love her body, not just for how beautiful it is but for everything that it can do. I press my hands over her breasts and pinch her nipples in between my fingers.She arches her back and raises her chin into the air.

Another breath and she presses her back into the sheets.

"Come for me," I whisper through my

moans. "Come with me."

With the blindfold still on her face, she moves her head up off the pillow as if she were opening her eyes and giving me a wink. I can feel what she is feeling. Her body is tensing up again, building up steam.

My movements become even stronger and more deliberate. With each thrust I go deeper and deeper inside of her, and she takes me further and further into herself. And then, when my heart rate speeds up, so does the movement of her hips. We grind against one another until I finally feel gravity pull away from me.

"Aurora!" I yell.

"Henry!" she screams back.

WE STAYED up way too late the night before, and I feel it this morning. When the alarm clock goes off, my head throbs.

I haven't gotten up this early since I was a teacher, but this is one meeting that I cannot miss. Aurora is still in bed when I leave at eight o'clock sharp.

Luckily, I had ironed and prepared my outfit the day before, I even ironed my tie. The suit had cost me a fortune, but it is not very expensive.

My only hope is that it doesn't look cheap. I know that I'm not applying for a position at an investment bank or some customer facing job that requires me to look like a million bucks.

It's a writing job and writers should have a certain sense of realness to them, right? Kind of like a man of the people?

Walking through the marble tiled lobby and taking the elevator to the 16th floor of a glass office that looks over Manhattan, I'm not so sure.

After a brief wait, a man by the name of Franklin Parks invites me into his office. He is tall and broad shouldered with good looking features but has an effect to him that makes me feel off.

His eyes are bloodshot with dark circles, indicating that he either stayed up all night working or partying. I'm not entirely sure which.

He looks at my resume as if it is the first time he has ever seen it.

"So, it looks as if you have spent quite a little bit of time teaching," he says. "What was that like?"

"It was very rewarding," I say. This is my standard explanation.

"And why is it that you are applying at a job here?"

"Well, to be honest, teaching has never been a big passion of mine. I mean, I enjoy spending time with children, but I have always wanted to be a writer. Teaching just happened to be the job that I got right after college and something that I just kept doing."

"So, what's different now?" he asks.

"Well, I heard about this new division starting up and I saw that there were a lot of research writing positions, which I think I will be perfect for."

"Have you ever done anything like that before?"

"No, I haven't, but I have a lot of experience writing research papers and conducting research in college. I did my thesis on—."

"What sort of writing have you had published?" Mr. Parks asks me, appearing completely uninterested in my exaggerated research experience.

"I have attached a few short stories there. One of them was published by the New Yorker."

"Wow, The New Yorker. Isn't that like the Holy Grail for a short story writer?"

"Yes, actually it is."

"Given all of your experience, you think you'll be okay with writing *just* true crime?"

"Yes, of course," I say, nodding my head. "Those are important stories to tell, especially the unsolved ones. The public has a lot of interest in them as well so I see it as a win-win."

Franklin skims my resume again and then gets up from behind the table and walks over to the elegant wooden sideboard with glass cut outs. Glass bottles of liquor crowd the top shelf and he pours himself a tumbler of vodka.

"Would you like anything?" he asks.

I don't want to remind him of the fact that it's not even ten o'clock in the morning, but I politely decline.

"Suit yourself," he says with a shrug. "But you would be joining me if you had the kind of night that I had last night."

"Oh, yeah?" I ask. "Do I dare ask?"

"Well, I went out with this girl."

"Did it go well?"

"Not exactly," he says, tossing his head back and laughing. "I've had an eye on her for quite some time. She's one of those girls who happened to say no to me and as you probably know, those are the ones that stick in your mind the most."

I give him a slight knowing nod.

"The thing that's really fucked up is that I have a somewhat complicated relationship with her parents. Let's just say that her father owes me a favor, a big favor. Things are not looking so well for him and it looks like everything that he has worked for will be going up in flames really soon."

"That's too bad."

"I really shouldn't be talking about this," Franklin says, waving his hand.

"I'm all ears," I say, sitting back in the chair, trying to make him feel comfortable.

"You know, of course, that this is the booze talking, right?"

He's asking me this because he's trying to look for a way out. He has already said too much and he's full of regret. Act as if none of that really matters.

I don't particularly want to hear anymore, but it's the only way that I think I'm going to land this job.

"Anyway," Franklin says, "Cutting this very long story short, let me just say that I wanted to go out with her for a very long time and last night I finally got my wish."

"Was it everything that you had wished for?"

"No, and yes."

"What do you mean?" I ask.

"Well, it's hard to explain exactly. She shot me down and it was quite a sight to see, but it just made me want her even more. This may sound like I'm bragging, but I haven't had many experiences with women saying no to me. And I found it utterly irresistible."

"Really? I've had a few women turn me down and I found it to be mostly embarrassing and humiliating."

He looks at me, and then laughs from the pit of his stomach. "You know what? You're funny," he says.

"Hey, I'm only telling it like it is."

"Hmm, maybe that's what I was experiencing all along," Franklin pauses. "What did you call it, a little bit of humiliation and a lot of embarrassment? Is that what it is? When they say no to you and it's all you can do to try to convince them that they're wrong?"

"The thing is that sometimes they're just not interested," I say, feeling our conversation drifting.

"No," Franklin says, definitively. "That's where you're wrong. They may not want you right *now*, but that doesn't mean that they won't change their mind. Besides, you know how it is in the movies. The guy that they have the most tension with, the one that they claim to hate, that's the one that they always end up with."

I clench my jaw and look away.

"That's just what happens in the movies," I say. "That's not really what they want."

Franklin finishes his drink and puts it down on the table, making a loud clicking sound.

"I am very glad that you came here to see me, Henry Asher. I wasn't sure what you could bring to the table really, but now I know that we have been brought together for a reason."

"Really?" I asked.

"Really. The thing is that you have a lot to learn from me. A lot."

My hands form into fists, but I don't say anything in response.

"The thing is that in this life, Henry, you have to go after whatever it is that you want. Be it a job or a woman. You can't take no for an answer. Otherwise you'll never get what you want."

THE NEXT DAY, I find out that I got the job. I'm glad, of course, but a part of me is concerned. He is the last person that I'm interested in working for and yet he's the only one who is giving me a chance to do what I want.

I decide not to tell Aurora about what really happened at the interview and simply celebrate the fact that I have a job that pays over forty grand a year with benefits.

"I knew that you would get this job, I just knew it." Aurora gushes over dinner at a swanky midtown restaurant that we avoided like the plague before tonight.

"Well, I wasn't so sure. It was really helpful that you had gone over some of those popular true crime stories that all the podcasts are covering," I reassure her. "He really liked the pitch that I put forth."

This part is true, even though the rest of what I told her is not. When our wine arrives, I promise myself that this is going to be the last time that I'm going to lie to her about anything. From this point forward, I'm only going to tell her the truth. Little did I know how difficult keeping that promise would turn out to be.

23

AURORA

Henry got the job. It's hard to believe. In fact, I'm still in shock over it. Why would Franklin hire *my* boyfriend to work for him? The only possible explanation is that he doesn't actually know that I am Henry's girlfriend.

I search my mind for everything that I told him and then for anything that my mother could have. No, I'm certain that if Franklin knew that Henry is my boyfriend, he would not have hired him. But then again…

What if he did?

I ask Henry for details of what happened in the interview and he becomes evasive.

There is something that he's not telling me, but I have no choice but to let it go.

I'm happy for him. And after all, it's not just Franklin who made the decision to hire him. I'm certain that my father has had some amount of influence. Maybe, that's why. Maybe despite what Franklin wanted, my father had insisted that they give Henry the position to help *me*.

Despite the fact that I am happy that Henry's now doing what he loves, and he really does love it, I miss our days off doing nothing. Well, not completely nothing. I'm still going to classes and working on my thesis, but I miss having him at home to hang out with.

After we were evicted from his apartment, my parents let us move into my old one, which they of course have not rented out like they said they would. They sent their assistant over to help us get settled, and the moving guys lugged all of our stuff from one place to another.

"I can't believe that you don't actually move when you move," Henry said with a wide grin on his face.

I rolled my eyes. Honestly, the perks of being upper class have still not gotten old.

When we first make the move, everything is great. Henry works long hours, but we're trying to carve out whatever time we can in our schedules.

I miss him and he misses me and we make up for it with intense love-making sessions in the shower and in the kitchen and everywhere else, just like we did when we first moved in together.

But then, as the weeks turn into months, something changes. His hours get longer and longer as he works on one deadline after another. He starts to travel. At first, it's someplace local like Long Island or Albany or Rhode Island. But then his travels take him to Chicago and Iowa and even Nevada, and I don't see him for weeks on end.

When he does return, things are different. We spend time together, but we are out of sync. There are things that I do around the house that are in complete contrast to what he thinks I should be doing, and there are things that he does that annoy the hell out of me.

I keep telling him that we should reconnect and we promise to try.

We go on dates. At first, we go to the movies, dinner, and after a while, when we get really tired, we just Netflix and chill. The only problem is that after all this time apart the chill part is no longer a metaphor for sex. We curl up on the couch, each taking a separate side, and fall sleep, like old friends, or even worse, distant roommates.

Still, we stay together. We are going through what I assume is just a dry spell. It's bound to get better. People have been through a lot worse and have made it to the other side. But the more weeks that pass, the harder it becomes. With each trip, he gets further and further away from me until one day, I've had enough.

"I don't think that we should live together anymore," I say when he gets home from his trip to Nebraska.

"What are you talking about?" he asks.

"I don't know, but I don't feel like we're a couple anymore. Do you?"

"Listen, I'm really tired," he says, shaking his head. "I just took the red-eye home and I can't talk to you about this right now."

I know that this is the wrong time to bring it up, but I've been thinking about this ever since he's been gone and I didn't want to talk about it over FaceTime.

"Can we get back to this tomorrow?" he asks.

I give him a slight nod and open my computer back up. I have so much work to do on my thesis, and yet I can't seem to focus. I haven't written a word in two weeks.

The following morning, he sleeps in late, and I go to class. When I get back, he's no longer there. Franklin has asked him to cover a breaking story.

"THAT's the gist of the text message that I got," I tell Ellis over dinner.

I've called three other friends, but no one was available to talk. Ellis who had just broken up with her boyfriend was more than happy to go out on a girls' night and have a few drinks and rag on some guys.

"He's an asshole," she says quickly.

I shrug. "He's just working too hard and this job is taking over his life."

Ellis shakes her head. "All the guys in this city are the same," she insists. "I used to date a hedge fund manager, and he only came over to fuck. Actually, come to think of it, it was probably one of my most honest relationships."

I laugh nervously, too embarrassed to tell her that it has been months since Henry and I have done it. At first, it was just the one thing that kept us together and gave our relationship some spice and then it was the thing that drove us apart.

I had so many resentments toward him for being away, the last thing I wanted to do was to have sex with him when he got back.

"I'm sure it will get better," Ellis says, not very convincingly. "Either that, or maybe you should just dump him and find someone without a high-powered job."

"That's the whole problem," I say. "I'm glad that he is pursuing his dreams, but I just wish that he had a little bit more time for me in the process."

"What can I say?" Ellis asks. "You know how I feel about guys, what one man can do another can as well."

It's a cynical way of thinking about relationships but then again, Ellis doesn't get hurt easily, so maybe she's on to something.

Still, I don't want to give up. Not this easily and not without a fight. My phone vibrates and I look down at the screen.

"I need to talk to you," Henry texts and I pay my bar tab.

When I get home, I brace myself for another fight disguised as a disagreement, but he surprises me. He takes me into his arms and kisses me and tells me that he's going to be better and that he will make it all good again. I take him back and our bodies fall into that familiar dance.

He runs his fingers up and down my sides and makes me feel alive. I try to protest, but my legs open up for him on their own.

This time, we don't make it to the bedroom. Our clothes come off only halfway and he presses me against the kitchen counter, bending me in half.

Still wearing the stilettos I wore to dinner I am the perfect height for him to come at me from behind. His hands search hungrily for my breasts and his lips kiss mine in that sloppy way that only two people completely overwhelmed by their senses can.

This time I don't need the blindfold or the tie around my wrists.

This time I just let myself go and I take off immediately.

I want him so much that I can't even stop if I had wanted to.

He moans my name soon after I scream his. Afterward we lie in each other's arms on the hard tile for a few minutes, catching our breath. When he reaches over, he kisses me and we go again.

24

AURORA

I had hoped that night would have changed things, but two days later he is sent on a story to Kentucky and the distance engulfs me like a tsunami.

We text and FaceTime, but only occasionally, when he has a few minutes here and there. I know that couples in previous decades have endured longer separations with less technological connections, but this relationship is too new and I need more reassurance.

In addition to writing articles, Henry is now hosting a True Crime podcast that he researches and records himself, having only nominal producing help. This is a great opportunity for him. His following is growing and he is really making a name for himself in the space, but that doesn't change the fact that we continue to drift further and further apart.

Finishing my thesis is an uphill battle. I waste time on Instagram and real brick and mortar bookstores reading books for pleasure rather than for analysis. Eventually, during the last two months of the semester, I really force myself to focus and finish it.

My presentation is scheduled for May fifth at two in the afternoon. I have to summarize all the research and the findings that I have done and take questions from the public. Technically, anyone can attend a PhD defense, including students, teaching assistants, professors, and even deans at the university.

I am not big on public speaking, meaning that I actually despise it, so I hope that my time slot does not prove to be particularly enticing for the university community.

When I show up to the empty lecture hall, I let out a brief sigh of relief, only to be unpleasantly surprised to discover that I'm in the wrong room. When it's almost time for me to present, and there's still no one here, I double check the room number, and realize that mine is across the hall.

Shit.

Shit.

Shit.

Peering through the little window in the door, I see that the room is packed.

I take a deep breath and try to block out every negative thought that creeps into my subconscious.

They are not going to laugh at me.

They are not going to make fun of me.

Everything is going to be fine.

I'm not going to embarrass myself.

When I open my mouth and start to talk, slowly but surely, my anxiety begins to dissipate.

I have practiced my presentation about a hundred times, and after a shaky start, the words flow out of me. When I lose myself and what I'm saying, all of those other people stop mattering as much. I don't care what they say because I know that the work that I have done is important and meaningful.

A professor who focuses on pop-culture asks about what impact I think that a book like Fifty Shades of Grey had on the modern female experience and a crotchety old English literature professor wonders why the focus should be so much on sexuality versus other things.

My responses are thoughtful prompting more discussion, this time from students and other faculty in the auditorium. After a little while, I lose control of the room as the focus shifts away from me, and I couldn't be happier.

THAT FRIDAY, I wear a cap and gown and walk across the stage to get my diploma. Henry is supposed to be there, but he's not. He didn't make it to my defense either. There are major developments in the case that he's working on and he's even doing interviews with NBC News and Dateline. Plus, Franklin had scheduled him for an impromptu live recording of his podcast at the Louisville Theater that sold out within twenty-four hours.

It's not that I am not happy for Henry and all of his success, it's just that I feel like we're not on the same page. Even though we still have the occasional moments when we are in-sync, there are more and more where it feels like there is an ocean separating us.

I don't know exactly how to deal with it or what I can do to change it. I'm here for him and I wait for him, but there's only so much I can take. Of course, now that I'm done with my PhD, I can theoretically join him on his travels, but I'm not sure if there's a place for me there.

He works twelve hours a day and what would I do in Kentucky? Just sit in the hotel room and wait for him? I can do the same thing here in New York.

These are the thoughts that spin around in my head as I walk out with the rest of my class. My parents wait for me out on the lawn, along with hundreds of other graduates' parents and grandparents and children.

This is a happy day in my life. I have worked really hard to get to this point and I'm not going to let thinking about Henry ruin it for me.

My parents give me a warm hug, practically at the same time. They have brought a few of their friends and after a few customary congratulations, they go back to the work on their phones.

Thomas is here as well, probably on my mother's insistence. He is twelve years old and not particularly interested in attending family functions, but when I give him a brief hug, he hugs me back.

Later that night, after dinner and after Thomas goes back home, my parents tell me that they have something to discuss with me. I've had a few drinks, and I'm still feeling a little bit in a celebratory mood, so I ask if it can wait until tomorrow.

"No," Mom says. "This is very important. We have to talk about this now."

They are guests in my apartment and I can't quite make them leave so I figure the best thing to do is to just hear them out.

"I know that this is your big night,

honey," my dad says. "And I want you to know that we are very proud of you."

"Thank you very much," I say, nodding my head.

"The thing is that...The justice department is investigating Tate Media."

I hear what he has just said but the words don't make any sense.

"What are you talking about?" I ask.

"I can't go into it here," he says, looking around the room.

I furrow my brow.

"What are you talking about?" I ask him again.

"Without saying too much," Mom interjects. "We are fighting against a case that the people in the justice department are building against your father."

I still don't understand. My mother motions for me to follow them outside.

25

AURORA

The cold fresh air feels nice against my warm skin. I tighten the collar of my coat and walk in between them. My parents are not the type to take walks at nine o'clock at night, but tonight is an exception.

"Your father doesn't want to tell you this," my mother says. "But he is in a lot of trouble. It's very serious."

My mouth drops open.

Despite whatever issues I've ever had with either of them, they have been these God-like creatures in my life, untouchable by anyone or anything.

Looking at them now, I find it hard to

believe that things have changed. My hands tremble a bit, but I force myself to focus and to remain calm. I can't freak out before I know what is really going on and I can't let them see how worried I really am.

I have to stay strong.

We walk down one block, and then another. I wait for them to start talking, but they don't. Finally, when we reach the bodega three blocks away, I turn to face my father and ask him flat out, "What is really going on?"

My father looks down at the ground but says nothing.

"The company has been losing money for a long time," Mom steps in. "We have gotten involved in a lot of investments that did not go as well as we thought they would. A number of the companies went bankrupt, and there were a few financial irregularities with some of the other ones that we had invested in."

I nod, nudging her to continue.

"We have been trying our best to figure out what to do, and so far, we have not been particularly successful. The best thing to do would be to find a buyer, but it is important to make sure that we can get a good price. And as you know, we can't get a good price if people don't think that Tate Media is worth very much."

I give her another slight nod just to show her that I'm paying attention.

"We have had a few buyers fall through," Dad interjects. "We thought that they were going to go for it, but at the very last minute they pulled out."

"Why didn't you tell me about any of this?" I ask.

"We didn't really wanna bother you with everything that has been going on," he says.

I shake my head and walk in place to stay warm.

Everything within me tells me to run back to my apartment and just climb under the covers, but I can't. This is very serious and I have to face it head on.

"Here's the thing, Aurora," my mother says, putting her arm on my shoulder.

"We did find one buyer, and he's very interested."

"Good," I say with a forced smile. "So what's wrong?"

"The only way that he will go along with the sale, given how poorly the company has been doing, is if… *you* are part of it."

"What are you talking about?" I ask.

"Well, you have apparently made quite an impression and he wants you to…" Her voice trails off.

My gaze goes back-and-forth between her and my father.

My father is looking down at the ground, and she is looking somewhere past me.

"What is going on here?" I ask both of them.

"The thing is…" Mom starts to say, but then her voice trails off.

"Just tell me," I insist.

"Okay," she says, taking a deep breath.

Mom starts again, but again she is unable to come out with it.

"He wants you to marry him," my father says, cutting her off. "He wants you to be his wife."

"What? No," I say, shaking my head. "Absolutely not."

"See," Dad says, turning to my mom. "What did I tell you? There's no way she'll do it."

"Why would he want to marry me? Who is he?" I ask, tugging at his overcoat to get him to turn around. "Tell me everything."

"It's Franklin Parks," my mother says softly.

I stare at her.

"What do you mean?" I ask.

"Franklin is the buyer."

"No, no," I say, shaking my head. "He works for you."

"It's more complicated than that," my father says, taking a step away from me.

His eyes won't meet mine.

I have never seen him so defeated looking.

I shake my head and tap my foot on the ground.

"What is going on?" I ask both of them over and over again.

"Franklin is running the crime division because he wanted to get some experience and learn a little bit more about the culture of the company and how we do things here," Dad says. "He also wanted to be involved in the hiring process of all new employees. It's a test case for him. But in reality, he's a very wealthy man who is ready to buy Tate Media, for the right price."

"So, why doesn't he just buy it?" I ask.

My mother raises her chin a little bit into the air, focusing her eyes directly on mine.

"He has heard a lot about you," she says after a long pause. "Saw pictures of you, watched you on social media."

"And he's very interested in what he has seen," my father adds.

My skin starts to crawl.

I hate the way that they talk about me as if I'm some sort of commodity.

"Wait a second," I say, shaking my head. "Is that why you asked me to go to that gala with him?"

"Yes, of course," she says. "He wanted to get to know you a little better and, apparently, he liked what he saw."

"How could he?" I ask. "I rejected him. I told him to go fuck himself, in so many words."

"I don't know," Mom says.

"Why is he even interested? He told me that he didn't care about dating anyone in particular, let alone marrying someone. Why the hell does he want to *marry me*?"

"I don't know," my mother says. "We don't know. He has his reasons, I'm sure. The one thing that we know is that the only way that he will purchase the company and make this justice department investigation go away is if you agree to marry him."

We can't talk inside in case the place is bugged so I talk to my parents for a long time standing on that street corner.

I keep asking them why, why, why, but they keep repeating the same thing over and over again without giving me anymore information.

Eventually, I give up and go home. I tell them that I'm going to consider it but, in reality, I have no interest in doing anything like that.

There must be another way for them to sell the company, if that's even what they want to do.

I still don't know if that's the right decision.

They have spent their whole lives building it from scratch, so why sell it now?

All of the things that I don't know about this deal could fill the contents of the New York Library.

When I ask them to explain more about what's going on with the company itself, they decline. They argue that it's for my own safety because the less that I know, the less that the justice department can accuse me of knowing.

But where does that leave me?

When I get home and curl up in bed, for the first time in a long time I'm actually happy that Henry's not here. I was angry at him for missing my graduation, but given this bomb that my parents have thrown into my lap, I'm glad that I don't have to pretend that everything is all right.

The following morning I wake up with a throbbing headache and it only gets worse with every passing hour. I drink lots of water, and a few cups of coffee, but nothing makes it go away. Perhaps the coffee makes it even worse? Last night was difficult to handle.

I keep trying to process what has happened, and it's all to no avail. Did they really ask me to do what I think they did?

Did they really ask me to consider marrying Franklin Parks?

Do they even know who he is?

Besides, what century are we living in that this is a realistic proposition?

Still, I know my parents well enough to know that they did not do this with an easy heart. They love me and care about me, even if it's not as much as I would want them to.

Deep in my heart, I know that they would never ask me to do this if they thought that they had another choice.

But why? Thoughts keep spinning around in my mind until I feel dizzy.

I had asked that question over and over again last night, but they couldn't give me an answer that was any better than that which they had already given me.

No, I need to go to the source.

I need to talk to Franklin.

My phone rings and it's Henry. I consider ignoring it and telling him that I'm busy, but another part of me can't bring myself to lie to him about one more thing.

No, it's better to talk to him now because he will probably be busy later.

"Hi," I say, putting him on speaker phone. "How are you?"

He tells me about his day and about the investigation that he's working on.

I only half listen, waiting for my turn to speak.

"So, can you believe that that happened?" he asks excitedly.

"Wait, what?" I ask absentmindedly.

I had apparently spaced out for a little too long.

"Are you even listening to me?" Henry asks.

The irritation in his voice is difficult to ignore.

"Yes, of course," I say. "It's just that, well, you know that I graduated yesterday?"

It comes out more like a question than a statement.

"Oh my God, yes, of course! I'm so sorry. I can't believe that I forgot. I mean, I didn't forget but—"

"You didn't even text me last night," I point out, bitterly.

"I'm really sorry," he says.

"It's okay. I know that you're busy."

"Still, it's no excuse. I'm such an asshole," he admits.

Yes, you are, I say silently to myself.

"Anyway, I went out to dinner with my

parents and Taylor and it was nice enough," I say with a shrug.

"Listen," he says, cutting me short. "I'm sorry, but I really can't talk right now."

"Weren't you the one that called me?" I ask.

"Yes, but I'm sorry. There's someone on the other end and I really have to take this call."

I shake my head in disbelief.

I wasn't going to tell him about Franklin, but I at least wanted to talk to him, have a real conversation for once.

"I'm tired of this," I say quietly.

"Okay, give me a second," he says and puts me on hold. When he comes back, he asks, "What do you mean you're tired of this?"

"I just don't understand what we're doing here," I admit. "We are so great together when we are actually together, but things have felt off for a long time. Do you agree?"

"Yeah, I guess so," Henry says distractedly.

"It's like we're not on the same page and

we haven't been for a long time. What are we gonna do about it?"

"I don't know, Aurora. I just can't talk about this right now. I have a lot of things going on."

"That's the problem!" I say loudly. "That's the whole fucking problem."

I hang up the phone and throw it on the bed. This was not what I wanted to happen today and yet suddenly my life seems to be filled with things that I don't want.

A few moments later, Henry calls me back via FaceTime.

I glance at myself briefly in the mirror. I'm not wearing any makeup. My face is puffy and my hair is out of control.

I don't want to, but I answer anyway.

"What do you want?" I ask, fully expecting him to apologize.

"I think we need to talk," he says.

"I thought that you didn't have time to talk," I say.

"I don't, but I'll make time."

I don't know what to say so I just wait.

He looks down at the floor and then slowly back at me. He takes a deep breath.

"I agree with you," he says quietly. "We have been drifting apart, for a while now."

"I know," I say.

"I keep thinking that it is going to get better but it's not happening. I was hoping that you would be interested in coming out here after graduation. I was going to ask you today, before we got into this ridiculously stupid fight."

I take a deep breath and exhale slowly.

"And what am I gonna do there?" I ask. "Just sit around in the hotel room and wait for you like I do here?"

He shakes his head, uncertain as to how to answer.

I'm lost as well. I feel like we have reached an impasse. I want to spend more time with him but all of his time is consumed by his job, which I'm not even sure that he will have for much longer.

I want to tell him this and everything else that has happened, just like I used to when we were first together.

But something is holding me back. I don't know what's going on with my parents and I'm afraid of telling him too much.

I don't know what's going on with the justice department or the investigation or why they are so certain that Franklin is the only way that they can save their company. I'm afraid to tell Henry about any of it in case I can't protect them or him if it all goes to shit, even more than it has already.

Henry and I talk for a long time, going in circles for most of it. He keeps insisting that it's just one more project, but that's the same thing I've heard for the last few months.

A big part of me feels ridiculous asking him to take time off work just to be with me, but another part of me thinks that I deserve a boyfriend who wants to spend time with me.

When I feel our conversation coming to an end, we are no closer to resolving what we have been talking about.

"So, what do you think?" he asks. "Will you come live with me here?"

"In Kentucky?" I ask.

"Yes, of course. Just for the time being. I mean, it's not like you're working right now."

"Yeah, no, I can't," I say.

"Why not?"

Because I have to figure out what is going on with my parents' business and why they're asking me to marry your boss, I want to say. But of course, I don't.

"The thing is that Tate Media is having a few issues," I say slowly.

"Okay. But what does that have to do with you? I thought that you had no interest in running it?"

"That doesn't mean that it doesn't concern me. And it doesn't mean that I don't want to help my parents."

"It's something that we're all going through," I say. "I thought that you would understand that."

"No, I do understand that. I understand that I have waited for you to finish your PhD so that you could have some time off and actually spend it with me. But instead, you're going to stay in New York and do who knows what."

"Why are you getting so angry?" I ask.

"Because I don't understand what's going on with us," Henry snaps. "I love you and you don't seem to care at all."

"Of course," I say. "Of course I care. I love you, too. But they have reached out to me and told me that they're having a lot of problems and they have never said that to me before. And I can't just ignore it."

"Whatever," Henry says, shaking his head.

He puts the phone down so that all that I can see is the ceiling.

"Henry! Henry? Please, come back to me."

"What?" he asks after a little bit. "What do you want?"

"I want to talk to you."

"No, you don't," he says, picking up the phone and staring straight at me. "I want to spend time with you and I want you to be here with me. What do you want?"

I want to be there with you, too, I say silently to myself.

"I need you to give me some time," I say out loud. "I just found out that they're having problems. Last night, in fact."

"It's just their way of manipulating you, Aurora. Can't you see that? They don't want you to be with me and they gave me this job to drive us apart. I'm thankful for it, but I know exactly what they're doing. They're just pretending to be okay with us and hoping that the distance will break us."

"Well, don't let it!"

"I'm trying not to, but you're not trying hard enough," he says.

This makes me angry. My cheeks get flushed and my hands form into fists.

"You have no idea what you're talking about," I say, furrowing my brows. "You don't know the first thing about what's going on here."

"So why don't you tell me?" he asks.

"I can't. I don't even know what's going on here. But if you want to know, I suggest that you come back here and stand by my side."

"No," he says, shaking his head. "I'm done."

My blood runs cold.

"What are you talking about?" I ask.

He looks dead into my eyes and doesn't blink.

"I'm done," he says coldly.

"No…" I whisper.

"I can't handle this anymore," he says. "I'm just so tired of fighting and arguing and everything else that we have been doing besides just enjoying one another. Relationships are not supposed to be this hard."

"Sometimes," I say with my voice breaking. "Sometimes, you have to fight for them. You have to go through the hard bits to get to the good parts."

"Well, I've been doing that enough and I don't have the energy anymore, Aurora."

27

AURORA

A t first, I don't hear back from Henry for the whole day. It's as the longest day of my life and time feels like it's completely standing still. I keep waiting for him to call me, to apologize for what he said, but he doesn't. The following day, I give up on waiting and call him instead. He doesn't answer and again I wait. I wait until the third day, when I can't wait any longer and I pick up the phone again and text him. Once, twice, and a third time. It's stupid and pathetic and ridiculous and I feel dumb doing it, and yet I can't stop myself. I need to hear from him. I need to know where we stand. I need to know if this is a real breakup. But the more time that passes, the more I realize that of course it is. He broke up with me and now he doesn't wanna hear from me. And I am just a stupid little girl who doesn't understand when I don't get my way.

By Friday, I give up. I know that he doesn't want me contacting him anymore so I don't. I promise myself that I will never contact him again. When Ellis calls and invites me to go out for a drink, I don't want to, but I force myself to do it. I need the distraction. I need to get out of my head and do something productive. Drinking is not productive, but at least it's cathartic.

"I can't believe that you did that," Ellis says, shaking her head when I tell her how pathetic I have been. "You deserve so much more than him. You deserve someone who at least fucking answers the phone."

" I know," I say nothing. "I'm so stupid."

"Yes, you are," she says. "You should not

have ever gone out with him in the first place. You should have listened to me right from the beginning, but of course you haven't. Of course you had to go out and make your own mistakes."

"Okay," I say, waving my hand. "I've had enough with the lecture. Can we just move on to the parting portion of the evening?"

She laughs, tossing her head back as she takes another shot and follows it up with yet another one. I follow along with her, knowing that I'm going to regret drinking all of this tomorrow and not giving a shit one bit.

She congratulates me on my PhD and then asks me what I intend to do with such a useless degree.

"Aren't all PhDs useless?" I ask. "Well, no, not really. There are those who get them in chemistry or biology or math even."

I was joking, of course. I was just

referring to the fact that research doesn't pay much in comparison to industry and so by their nature all PhDs seem a little bit out of touch, let's put it that way.

"WELL," she says, "you'll have to admit that yours is particularly useless."

I SHRUG and look down into my glass as the liquid rolls over the ice. "I like reading and I like reading popular fiction and I like studying, so it was a good combination of the three. A lot better than going out there and trying to figure out what the hell is going on with Tate Media." I look up at her to gauge her reaction and see her bite her lower lip.

"Oh shit," I say. "What do you know?"

"WELL, I didn't wanna bring it up…"

"Come on, you have to tell me. God knows, my parents don't tell me much."

. . .

"WHAT ARE YOU TALKING ABOUT?" she asks.

"Well," I sigh deeply. "They told me that the company is in trouble, but they are refusing to elaborate on it to any degree whatsoever. So I'm just left here worrying without the ability to find any solutions."

"As you probably know," Ellis says, "it's all over the news. All the analysts on CNBC and other places are predicting that the company isn't worth as much as your parents say it is." I roll my eyes.

"THE ANALYSTS ARE ALWAYS full of shit," I say.

"BE THAT AS IT MAY," she says, "that doesn't change the fact that Tate Media is important as much as your parents say, is it?"

"I don't know," I say. "That's the whole problem. They keep me in the dark and then just cherry-pick what they tell me."

. . .

"WELL, you don't officially work there," Ellis points out. "Maybe they just don't want you to worry."

"THAT'S THE WHOLE PROBLEM," I say, shrugging my shoulders. "That's the whole fucking problem! They don't want me to worry? I'm worried now.

"On the day of my graduation, they throw this bomb at me saying that they're trying to sell the company, a fact that I had no idea about, and then they tell me not to worry. Well, I am worried. And I don't work there now, but maybe I should. Maybe then this sort of thing wouldn't be happening."

"Yeah, maybe," Ellis says.

We talk about this for a long time until last call. Sometimes Ellis isn't a very good friend, but tonight she is. And I really appreciate that. The only problem is that I wish I could tell her more. I wish I could tell her what my parents told me about Franklin and I wish I could tell her that tomorrow I have a meeting with him to talk about whatever the hell all of this is. I wish I could tell her the truth because someone should know. Someone besides me.

28

AURORA

I arrive at his penthouse at seven the following evening. He has invited me here, I said no, and then my mother called me and begged me to hear him out. Somehow, she has persuaded me that by taking this meeting I could convince him to simply purchase Tate Media and not include me in the process. Not knowing what else to do and wanting to help my parents, I reluctantly agree.

Franklin's home is beautiful and extravagant and modern. But mostly, it looks like it belongs to a bachelor.

It doesn't matter that it is a five-thousand square-foot apartment in one of the most prestigious areas of the town, all I see is the pool table in the middle of the dining room and the obnoxious black rug underneath.

His tailored suits and the location of this place made me think that he may have some style and fashion sense, but this atrocity reveals the truth; he's just an overgrown fraternity brother.

Still, I'm pleasantly surprised when he meets me at the door and is not intoxicated.

After inviting me inside, Franklin offers me a drink. I decline and he pours each of us a glass of water, showing me to the sitting room.

The view from up here is magnificent. There are floor-to-ceiling windows lining the entire south facing wall of his apartment, looking out at the twinkling lights outside.

"You have quite a beautiful apartment," I say, looking around.

"I'm glad you like it," he says, leaning back against the couch.

The statement is a bit off-putting.

I watch him run his fingers through his thick hair and take a sip of his water.

"Are you not drinking today?" I ask him.

"Actually, I'm doing a cleanse. If you can believe that."

"I can believe many things," I say.

"Well, you don't know me very well. Actually, that reminds me. I wanted to apologize for what happened at the gala. I acted like a total asshole and… I'm sorry about that."

I sit up a little in my seat and tilt my head.

"Thank you," I say after a moment.

"I appreciate you saying that." He gives me a knowing nod and finishes his water.

"Can I get you another one?" he asks, heading back to the bar.

"No." I point to the nearly full glass in my hand. "I'm good."

"I wanted to congratulate you on finishing your PhD program. That's quite an achievement," Franklin says, taking the seat next to me this time.

Our knees are almost touching, but he's careful to avoid actual contact.

"Thank you," I say with a slight smile. "It was a lot of work and it has been very rewarding."

"What are your plans now?"

"I'm not entirely sure, but I'm considering my options at Tate Media," I say. I've had enough of the small talk and want to wind this conversation toward what I'm here for.

"And what kind of options are you considering?" Franklin asks, leaning back against the couch.

"I'm not really sure right now. But my father has informed me that you are actually interested in purchasing the company. Is that correct?"

"Yes, it is."

"So, if that is the case, I guess I don't really have a future there, right?"

"That depends on you," Franklin says.

Our conversation is going in circles and I'm getting tired of it.

"Okay, let me put it this way," I say, placing the glass carefully on his coffee table. "My parents have informed me that in order to complete the sale of the company, you are interested in marrying me. Is that correct?"

I wait for him to apologize and make amends or at least explain himself. But instead, he just says, "Yes, I am interested in marrying you."

"Why?"

"Why am I interested in marrying you?"

"Yes, of course. We hardly even know each other. Besides, you told me that you are not interested in marriage at all, not to anyone."

"Well, let's just say that you have changed my mind."

"You don't know me," I insist. "You would hate me."

"Why don't you just leave that to me?" he asks.

"Because it's not gonna happen," I say, shrugging my shoulders.

I get up and walk away quickly. Before reaching the door, I spin around on my heels and find him only a few steps away from me.

"I'm not going to marry you," I say, staring straight into his eyes. "You can't ask for me as part of some business deal. I'm not for sale."

He laughs, tossing his head back.

"Everybody is for sale."

"No, they're not," I say. "And definitely not me."

He doesn't say anything in response and I'm about to spin back around and head toward the door when something else hits me.

"Is that why you gave him the job?" I ask.

"Who?"

"Henry Asher, my boyfriend."

"Oh, yes." He laughs. "I heard the unfortunate news. I'm really sorry to hear that you two have broken up. Henry mentioned something alluding to that."

"No, you're not," I correct him.

"No, I'm not." He laughs.

"So, is that why you offered him the position? And is that why you have been keeping him in Kentucky and West Virginia and God knows where else all of his time?"

"Of course," Franklin admits. "What's the easiest way to break up two people who are very wrong for each other? Add a little pressure and a little distance and poof, the relationship evaporates."

"Why don't you just go to hell?" I say and walk away from him.

"I will, don't worry!" he yells after me. "But you're going to be right there with me."

At the door, I turn around one last time and say, "And just in case you are wondering, no, I won't marry you. I will never marry you."

———

THE FOLLOWING MORNING, my doorbell rings and I am greeted by my mother, who is completely distraught and in tears.

I haven't seen her like this in... I have never seen her like this.

"What's wrong?" I ask, pulling her close to me.

She sobs and cries and mumbles something that I can't make out.

I ask her to calm down and to tell me what's going on.

"They have arrested your father," she finally manages to say. "They showed up this morning at six and pointed a gun in his face.

And when they were taking him out to the car, he had a heart attack."

"Oh my God," I whisper, putting my hand over my mouth. "No, no!"

"I told you," she snaps, pointing her finger in my face. "I warned you about this. I told you that he is not well and that the justice department was closing in."

"I'm really sorry," I mumble.

She buries her head in her hands and cries. When I put my arm around her shoulders, she lifts her eyes up and glares at me.

"This is all *your* fault!" she hisses.

"What? Why?"

"You were the one that went over there and told him that you would never marry him."

"Franklin?"

"Yes, Franklin," Mom barks. "He's the most powerful man that you've never heard of. This is all happening because of *him*. This is all happening because *you* said no."

THANK you for reading Dangerous Engagement. Henry and Aurora's story continues in the second book of this epic trilogy. **One-click Lethal Wedding Now!**

To save my father's life and our family's legacy, I have to marry a cruel man who wants me only as a trophy.

I THOUGHT Franklin Parks was a bad man before, but now I know he's a monster.

TO SURVIVE, I will have to beat him at his own game. But then Henry Asher, my one and only love, comes back into my life and things get a lot more complicated.

FRANKLIN IS NOT ONLY my fiancé but also Henry's boss, and he will stop at nothing to get ***everything*** he wants…

HENRY ASHER

I WAS a fool to let her go. Now, I'll have to do everything to get her back…

AURORA NEVER THOUGHT I could be a rich dirtbag who would do anything to get what he wants but I am proving her wrong.

TO HELP HER, I had to teach myself a few things.

. . .

To PROTECT HER, I had to become my worst enemy.

To SAVE HER, I will have to do the unthinkable.

THE PROBLEM IS that she doesn't want saving. She has her own plans. But the wedding is approaching and time is running out…

One-click Lethal Wedding Now!

———

SIGN up for my **newsletter** to find out when I have new books!

You can also join my Facebook group, **Charlotte Byrd's Reader Club**, for exclusive giveaways and sneak peaks of future books.

I appreciate you sharing my books and telling your friends about them. Reviews help readers find my books! Please leave a review on your favorite site.

CONNECT WITH CHARLOTTE BYRD

Sign up for my **newsletter** to find out when I have new books!

You can also join my Facebook group, **Charlotte Byrd's Reader Club**, for exclusive giveaways and sneak peaks of future books.

I appreciate you sharing my books and telling your friends about them. Reviews help readers find my books! Please leave a review on your favorite site.

Sign up for my newsletter: https://www.
subscribepage.com/byrdVIPList

Join my Facebook Group: https://www.
facebook.com/groups/276340079439433/

Bonus Points: Follow me on BookBub and
Goodreads!

ALSO BY CHARLOTTE BYRD

All books are available at ALL major retailers! If you can't find it, please email me at charlotte@charlotte-byrd.com

Wedlocked Trilogy
Dangerous Engagement
Lethal Wedding
Fatal Wedding

Tell me Series
Tell Me to Stop
Tell Me to Go
Tell Me to Stay

Tell Me to Run
Tell Me to Fight
Tell Me to Lie

Tangled Series

Tangled up in Ice
Tangled up in Pain
Tangled up in Lace
Tangled up in Hate
Tangled up in Love

Black Series

Black Edge
Black Rules
Black Bounds
Black Contract
Black Limit

Lavish Trilogy

Lavish Lies
Lavish Betrayal
Lavish Obsession

Standalone Novels

Debt

Offer
Unknown
Dressing Mr. Dalton

ABOUT CHARLOTTE BYRD

Charlotte Byrd is the bestselling author of romantic suspense novels. She has sold over 600,000 books and has been translated into five languages.

She lives near Palm Springs, California with her husband, son, and a toy Australian Shepherd. Charlotte is addicted to books and Netflix and she loves hot weather and crystal blue water.

Write her here:
charlotte@charlotte-byrd.com
Check out her books here:
www.charlotte-byrd.com
Connect with her here:
www.facebook.com/charlottebyrdbooks
www.instagram.com/charlottebyrdbooks
www.twitter.com/byrdauthor

Sign up for my newsletter: https://www.
subscribepage.com/byrdVIPList

Join my Facebook Group: https://www.
facebook.com/groups/276340079439433/

Bonus Points: Follow me on BookBub and
Goodreads!

facebook.com/charlottebyrdbooks

twitter.com/byrdauthor

instagram.com/charlottebyrdbooks

bookbub.com/profile/charlotte-byrd

Printed in Great Britain
by Amazon

37684321R00184

MOTHER HOOD

A MANIFESTO

Also by Eliane Glaser

Elitism: A Progressive Defence

*Anti-Politics: On the Demonization of Ideology,
Authority and the State*

*Get Real: How to See Through the Hype,
Spin and Lies of Modern Life*

MOTHER HOOD

A MANIFESTO

ELIANE GLASER

4th ESTATE • *London*

4th Estate
An imprint of HarperCollins*Publishers*
1 London Bridge Street
London SE1 9GF

www.4thEstate.co.uk

HarperCollins*Publishers*
1st Floor, Watermarque Building, Ringsend Road
Dublin 4, Ireland

First published in Great Britain in 2021 by 4th Estate

1

Copyright © Eliane Glaser 2021

Eliane Glaser asserts the moral right to be
identified as the author of this work in accordance
with the Copyright, Designs and Patents Act 1988

A catalogue record for this book is available from the British Library

ISBN 978-0-00-831188-9 (hardback)

Typeset in Minion by Palimpsest Book Production Ltd, Falkirk, Stirlingshire

Printed and bound in Great Britain by CPI Group (UK) Ltd, Croydon CR0 4YY

MIX
Paper from
responsible sources
FSC
www.fsc.org   FSC™ C007454

This book is produced from independently certified FSC™ paper
to ensure responsible forest management.

For more information visit: www.harpercollins.co.uk/green

CONTENTS

For Ezra and Anna

INTRODUCTION

It was a cold morning in February. My children were aged three and one. I was still in my dressing gown when my husband left for work. It took two hours to get out the door. We went to a toddler sing-along at the community centre. I spoke to nobody. The other mums seemed to know each other, and the words to the songs. I mouthed along like an MP weathering the second verse of God Save the Queen. We went to the park, and my baby daughter nodded off in her pram, making me yawn. My son asked to be pushed on the swing. I complied until my arms ached, and then sat down on a bench while he explored the properties of damp sand. It started to rain. A woman in her sixties on grandma duty sat down next to me. She asked me my children's ages. 'The most important job in the world,' she said. 'Enjoy it while it lasts.'

She meant well, of course. But an irritated little critique started forming in my exhausted head. Being told I was doing the most important job in the world by a stranger in a deserted park didn't seem to count for very much. Her words felt like compensation for actual status, or a warning against seeking it in the first place. Perhaps she sensed that I entertained a suspect wish to be doing something else. You have nothing to complain about, she seemed to be saying. But if motherhood is the most important job in the world, where is the public recognition? And why isn't it paid?

There was an undertone of warning, too. Be careful, she implied. You are responsible for these supremely precious beings. Don't mess it up. Don't put a foot wrong. And as well as the subtle injunction to do my best, I was also meant to be finding it fun. There is something coercive and undermining about that seemingly innocuous phrase 'Enjoy it while it lasts' – it reminds me of white van men shouting 'Smile! It might never happen' at me in my twenties. I was clearly not looking like I was enjoying it enough. She was right in a way, of course: now that my children are eight and eleven, I see that those early years pass by in a flash. But back then, a morning could feel endless.

I have a strong urge at this point to stress that this is not a motherhood misery memoir: the pressure to be sunny is that intense. But the sunniness is real, too: their narrow, brave chests when they're getting changed into their pyjamas, their forays out in the morning with their schoolbags on their backs – these are not in question. Their spirit-lifting joy at small things, their unfiltered questions and their emerging, autonomous sense of humour – none of this is in doubt. Nobody needs to ask for proof that my face lights up when they come out of school. I don't need to describe how, when they fall over and graze a knee, empathetic pain shoots down through my legs.

You don't need to know it. Maybe you tried to have a baby and it didn't work out. Maybe you have one and couldn't have any more. Maybe you are a mother who is finding it hard, or you feel that – although you are doing your best – motherhood isn't quite for you. Maybe motherhood is your uncomplicated, cherished vocation. It's mine too, much of the time. But what does it benefit mothers – or others – to read about the good bits? The reason I have written this book is that even now, after decades of social progress and feminist campaigning, motherhood is still much harder than it needs to be. In some ways it has become even harder. I believe it's high time for that to change.

In her classic study *Of Woman Born*, Adrienne Rich distinguished between motherhood as an experience and motherhood as an institution: what it's like, intrinsically, to be a mother, and how motherhood is managed in society.

Let's take motherhood as an experience first of all. It is a state that is idealised everywhere in our culture and media. Even if you manage to find an article about one of the darker aspects, it will invariably be accompanied by a shot of the mum laughing with her brood. Try it as an experiment. As a culture, we just can't help it. Shortly after the birth of her first baby, Serena Williams gave an interview to *Vogue*. She revealed that she'd had an emergency caesarean and then nasty complications which left her bedridden for six weeks. And that was just the start. 'Sometimes I get really down and feel like, Man, I can't do this,' she said. 'No one talks about the low moments – the pressure you feel, the incredible letdown every time you hear the baby cry. I've broken down I don't know how many times. Or I'll get angry about the crying, then sad about being angry, and then guilty, like, Why do I feel so sad when I have a beautiful baby? The emotions are insane.' Yet there she was on the front cover, a glowing image of happiness and fulfilment.

Though motherhood can be a delight, at times it is frustrating and infuriating. Being with children pushes you to the limits of what you can handle. It presses your buttons and stress-tests your temper. For me it is the best of times, the worst of times, and – at least in the early years – sometimes just quite dull.

But – and here we turn to motherhood as an institution – society does not like to acknowledge this mixed, ambivalent reality. And that makes the whole business even more difficult, because mothers are made to feel that they alone are struggling, that they should be finding it easy and instinctual and are therefore failing, and that there is little rationale for support.

The way motherhood is organised today is an outrage that would be clearly visible if we didn't think it was the job of individual mothers to hold it all together. Motherhood as an institution currently involves women being frightened into settling down with the wrong man because they're worried they will soon be infertile and 'left on the shelf'; once pregnant, being policed into renouncing pleasures that keep them sane; and in childbirth, suffering traumatic and life-changing injuries. After birth, they are left to cope alone and slide towards depression; childcare is a headache that can last fifteen years; the gender pay gap is actually a motherhood pay gap; and they eventually give up the prospect of either achieving life goals or attaining equality with men – either work colleagues or partners. I'm not talking about all mothers, of course; but quite a number of these experiences will be familiar to a disgracefully high proportion.

Yet the dominant mood of many mothers is not indignation but guilt. I felt guilty when I ate a Brie sandwich while pregnant. I felt guilty when I had an epidural for my first baby, and an elective caesarean for my second. I felt guilty when I had my six-week-old baby looked after for six hours a week while I wrote a book. I feel guilty when I sneak off for a quick scroll through Twitter when my children are at home, or peek at the paper while they're trying to tell me something detailed about Lego cards. And, most of all, I feel guilty when I lose my temper.

The problem is not the children. The children are great. They can't help being too young to control their emotions, trade opinions on the day's news, or do the washing-up. The problem is the context. Too often, the discontent that mothers feel is not directed at society, but at themselves. Modern mothers feel they must be not just good enough, but perfect, and that any misstep will lead to dire consequences for their child. Yet this is a misperception that leads to real harm.

* * *

Feminism has enjoyed something of a 'moment' in the past few years. #MeToo has achieved public prominence, if not substantial real-world change. Yet there is something awry in the way the media tends to gravitate towards varieties of feminism that concern sex. Where is the #MeToo for mothers? Millennial women are moving into their thirties and starting families of their own, yet attitudes have regressed, without large-scale social media pushback. Expectations have been ramped up, while communal networks and state support have fallen away. #MeToo exposed what it was really like to be harassed as a woman; surely it's time for similar honesty about the realities of being a mother.

What is the barrier, the great exception to the general feminist forward-moving trend? I believe it is threefold. First of all, motherhood is such a common experience that its problems go unnoticed. As a friend put it: 'It just happens to you.'

Second, as I'll argue in the course of this book, so-called woman-centred healthcare policy has become attached to a certain approach to motherhood – the 'natural' style. Debates about parenting, sometimes called 'the mummy wars' – midwife-led birth unit versus labour ward, breast versus bottle, feeding on demand or on a schedule, full-time work or stay at home, attachment parenting versus leaving babies to 'cry it out' – are portrayed as even-handed. Those shelves of advice books appear to offer a bewildering *variety* of advice. Yet this is an illusion. There is not a real debate. There is not real variety. Because only one side – the 'natural' side – is considered valid. Natural childbirth and motherhood is presented as the counter-cultural 'minority' option fighting for recognition in the face of the prevailing orthodoxy. The reality is the opposite.

The false impression of different schools of thought competing on a level playing field is accompanied by another myth: that of women's choice. Choice is presented – in our fake-feminist, consumerist era – as being a matter of individual freedom. But choices are determined not only by necessity and expediency but by social norms. If only one option is considered 'natural', and if there is only one way to be considered a good mother, there is no real 'choice' to be made. And because they are apparently free to choose, mothers must carry the burden of individual responsibility. Any failure is their fault.

As I will argue, natural motherhood is deployed as a covertly misogynistic weapon aimed at successful 'career women', encouraging them to act more like animals (sometimes explicitly) and put their ambitions aside, replacing those with time-consuming, intensive parenting techniques. But it rebounds not only on so-called 'career women' but on all women, and especially those short of cash: natural parenting may seem like it is free, but it actually involves a hidden cost. Breastfeeding for a year or even two, weaning babies on home-cooked purées, and using washable nappies: the way work is currently set up, these practices are not very compatible with earning.

Science was once the business of mastering nature and correcting its deficiencies; now, where motherhood is concerned, science is invoked in order to supposedly reveal nature's truths – or rather to project a partisan, culturally specific version of nature that serves to oppress women. As a society, we are happy to take advantage of technological innovation in every other area of modern life, from video-conferencing to self-driving cars, but motherhood must remain pristine. This nature-worship functions, perhaps, as a reassuring cultural response to accelerating technology: the maternal bosom acting as a compensatory haven. So the evaluation of every action and decision, the micromanagement of every minuscule detail (forwards- or backwards-facing buggies?) is combined with base atavism and the conviction that motherhood should not need to be second-guessed. Parenting advice is highly prescriptive, yet if maternal instinct exists, mothers surely shouldn't need advice at all.

To be clear, I am not judging some parenting styles as better than others. I respect parents' autonomy and freedom to bring up their children according to whatever philosophy they hold. What I am criticising is the underhand validation of a particular parenting style and the dubious uses to which it is put. The rhetoric of natural motherhood is implicitly child-centred. I am for the child, but I am for the mother, too. I believe their interests have been set up in an opposing zero-sum game, where a gain to the mother is assumed to be a loss to her child. But mother and child are not rivals: it is in each of their interests that the other is well and content.

This is the third reason, I believe, why motherhood presents such a barrier to women's equality. Because unlike the other liberation movements and waves of identity politics that have swept our culture in recent decades, this is not just about the empowerment of a neglected group. In this case, there is another person in the room, a vulnerable person. Misogynists are not attacking *women* if they suggest that maybe they shouldn't have that glass of wine while pregnant, if they bottle-feed, or come back to work full time; no: they are just thinking of the child.

In the UK, unborn children do not have separate legal recognition from their mothers. When they are pregnant and when they give birth, women are free to make choices against medical advice, including when this is said to protect the baby. Yet this simple fact may come as a surprise to all those women who read scare stories in the media about caffeine in pregnancy, or are dissuaded from having an elective caesarean, or told they can't have a home birth. As recently as 2020, the National Institute for Health and Care Excellence (NICE) proposed recording pregnant mothers' alcohol consumption on their child's medical records: proponents argued that the risk of foetal alcohol spectrum disorder (FASD) to an unborn child meant the mother's right to privacy should be 'secondary'. As a society, issues of consent and autonomy are well known in relation to abortion, but we are barely out of the starting blocks when it comes to pregnancy and childbirth.

What about after birth? While the interests of mothers and children are from then on held in balance, I believe the scales have tipped heavily to one side. Since the late twentieth century, the laudable promotion of children's safety and welfare has been accompanied by the aggressive delegitimising of mothers' needs and wants. And this is having perverse consequences, I argue, for both mothers and children.

I partly blame the media for its judgemental attitudes, but the problem is also there in the science: the vast majority of research commissioned in this area sets out to assess the impact of maternal behaviour on infant outcomes. When I spoke to Clare Murphy, the chief executive of the British Pregnancy Advisory Service (BPAS), she told me: 'You can count on one hand the number of studies that focus on maternal outcomes, because no one's particularly interested in anal sphincter tears, or postnatal depression. The narrative is invariably "mother does something to baby".' There is a dearth of research into the questions that actually matter to mothers: the safety of medicines in pregnancy, say, or managing stress before and after birth. In this book, I argue that it is time we looked after mothers, too.

* * *

Escaping the confines of my own four walls and taking my babies out into the city, I regularly ran the gauntlet not of danger, but of social mortification. I remember the mix of fury and humiliation at being told off by a man on the bus because my son was asleep in a sling with his head lolling slightly to the side. How dare he, I fumed, before discreetly edging him more upright, while trying desperately not to wake him up. I'm sure that chagrin at the entitlement of complete strangers to censure a knackered and conscientious mother in public also drove me to acts of rebellious stupidity. I find it almost incomprehensible now, but once, when I was feeling especially frumpy and fat, I took my son in his pushchair down into the bowels of a tacky clothes shop, determinedly stepping onto an escalator with a 'no pram' sign. The buggy got terrifyingly stuck at the bottom, and women started rapidly backing up behind me, not disguising their annoyance and blame. He wouldn't stop crying as I pushed him around the racks of horrible teenage-wear, and I eventually hid on a bench outside a changing room to breastfeed, defiant yet defeated.

The severe risk aversion of parenting advice is frequently unscientific. There's often a confusion, for example, between relative and absolute risk: a news report might state that the risk to a baby of taking a certain action is 'doubled' or 'tripled', but if the risk is 0.1 per cent in the first place, the higher risk is still only 0.2 or 0.3 per cent. Instances of harm coming to children are unconscionable, but very rare. And if something does happen to your child, it is most likely not the result of anything you have done.

Parents today are more anxious than ever. Yet as David Spiegelhalter, Professor of the Public Understanding of Risk at Cambridge University told me, not only is childhood (age seven to be precise) the safest age to be alive in the UK, today's children are safer than they've been at any point in history. Across the world, over the last two millennia, around a quarter of infants died before their first birthday, and around a half died before adulthood. Child mortality rates have decreased dramatically during our lifetimes (although in the UK they are relatively high compared to other Western European countries). Here, the infant and child mortality rate stands at about four per 1,000 live births. Most deaths in childhood occur in the first month of life, as the result of premature birth or congenital anomalies.

As the doctor and statistician Hans Rosling has observed, risk is often associated with what is frightening rather than what is actually dangerous. Nothing is more terrifying to me than the idea of my children being harmed. But there is also no such thing as absolute safety, just the rational weighing up of risks – which in the case of children are extremely slight.

Perception of risk also increases with disapproval. A 2016 study by researchers at the University of California, Irvine, found that certain parenting behaviours are judged to be dangerous if they are socially unacceptable. For example, in the US there have been recent cases of concerned citizens seeing children playing alone in a park or walking home on their own and calling 911: in some instances those children have even been taken into care. Yet driving kids around in a car is statistically more dangerous than letting them roam freely.

While children's needs are approached with an iron precautionary principle, those of the mother are considered to be below consideration: even referring to them is regarded as culpably selfish. The perfectionism of modern motherhood is both impossible to maintain – which is where the guilt comes in – and counterproductive.

Motherhood is feminism's unfinished business.

* * *

You'll have noticed that a certain somebody is absent from the equation. If we accept that the presence of a small helpless being compromises a person's ability to throw off the chains of subjection and stride off into a satisfying career, why can't that responsibility be shared by the father? But the reasonable assumption that by now women would have equality with men in the home has turned out to be false. Journalists have become so bored of the oppressed woman narrative that they've penned feature after feature on the rise of the hands-on dad, and that has lulled us into a false sense that the dial has shifted significantly.

Yet observe a school gate at pick-up, or a PTA coffee morning, and it's clear that fathers' participation has flat-lined. When my husband attended a curriculum meeting for our child's year group recently, twenty women turned up; he was the only man. This is quite normal. Men are entitled to take parental leave, but only a shocking 2 per cent take it up. Just 1 per cent of dads arc full-time parents. In homes up and down the country, modern mothers are crouching under the high-chair or dinner table three times a day with dustpan and brush as if half a century of progress never happened. The housework gap between men and women is narrowing, but slowly: in North America and many European countries, the pace of progress peaked in the 1980s. The real picture may be even worse than it seems, as men consistently overestimate their domestic labour in surveys.

Inequality in parenting plays out in a million tiny details: on a country walk, it's generally the men striding out in front having an interesting conversation while the women at the back take up the stragglers with the leaking wellies. On a joint family holiday, it's the men opening the second bottle of wine while the women mentally strategise for kids' tea and impending meltdowns. These divisions of labour are played out over such apparently trivial minutiae that they often evolve unformulated, registering in mothers' minds as a background hum of vigilance, distraction and concern rather than a clear recognition of imbalance.

There is a pattern to very many modern partnerships that dares not speak its name. Right from the start, when the mother spends the first long night with her baby in the hospital ward alone, an expertise gap opens up between herself and her partner. This is cemented into resentment during the solitary months of maternity leave. Like a part-time worker, many fathers – even if they are liberal and enlightened, and class themselves as feminists – fail to acquire the finely tuned skills of everyday, hands-on parenting. Many also, it has to be said, resist acquiring these boring competences, just as some male employees somehow never learn how to unjam the printer. Mothers start to treat their partner as another child, scolding them for forgetting the snacks or grabbing the non-waterproof coat. This is sometimes called the maternal gatekeeper syndrome, but 'gatekeeper' implies that the mother has power. In reality, dominion over the domestic sphere is thin gruel. The dad's refuge is outside in the public world, where he spends more and more of his time.

* * *

Is the experience of motherhood – with its ups and downs – beginning finally to be properly recognised? A slew of powerful motherhood memoirs have appeared in the last few years: on the decision to have them or not to have them, on the experience of being a young mother, on the impact of infertility, on having a large brood. Yet despite the fact that more open and frank discussion appears to be coming to light, there is still a tendency to focus on individual experience. It's as if broad-brush analysis or political demands put you at risk of questioning other mothers' choices. Yet although experiences vary greatly according to whether you take the natural or the medical approach, work outside or inside the home, are rich or poor, black or white, gay or straight, in a partnership or single, I believe it is still possible – and essential – to critique the way that society makes life unnecessarily difficult for all mothers.

What about the new world of online support and solidarity, the ability to trade intel and reassurance via internet forums, or the new meet-up apps for lonely mums in parks? While many find these a rich source of information and camaraderie, they also propagate competitiveness, insecurity, and inaccurate information. Collective demands get lost in the multiplicity of perspectives, and collated, digested advice dissipates in lengthy, subjective threads. Alongside the sisterhood is quite a lot of judgement, whose expression ranges from a rhetorical or emoji-raised eyebrow to explicit condemnation. Public hostility and disapproval towards mothers is incorporated into the experience of motherhood and perpetuated, peer to peer. It's in the acronyms: as well as HTH (hope this helps) and IKWYM (I know what you mean), there's AIBU (am I being unreasonable) and YABOS (you are being over sensitive). This is the language of apprehension and exclusion. It is also telling that 'controlled crying', 'elective caesarean', 'exclusively breastfeeding' and 'rearward-facing' (as in car seat) are used frequently enough to have their own acronyms, as well as – of course – 'stay-at-home mum'.

We might like to think that in these self-expressive times no topic is out of bounds. But where motherhood is concerned, there are still multiple taboos shrouding the most ordinary feelings and experiences, particularly around the consequences of being driven mad through lack of sleep, a partner not home till seven in the evening, toddlers playing up – or a mixture of all three. Online forums can be a haven, but they also reveal the strong resistance towards picking up the phone to a friend: perhaps, given the stigma of imperfect motherhood, it's easier to open up to anonymous strangers.

Because we don't like to admit the downsides, they leak out

between the cracks: in these threads, in the hushed warning to outspoken mothers not to reveal what it's really like for fear it will put younger women off, and in the popular trope of the 'relatable bad mum'. In some ways, this more realistic figure – a few years ago known as the 'slummy mummy' – is what we've been waiting for. She is irreverent, tells it like it is, cuts corners, and suits herself. There's ready-mixed G&T in the coffee mug and bath-time is at wine o'clock. Books and blogs like *Why Mummy Drinks*, *The Scummy Mummies*, or *The Rise and Fall of a Slummy Mummy* appear to give mothers licence to behave badly, and they're often cathartically accurate. Yet the humour functions as a kind of safety valve, and it's often at the mother's expense.

The frantic, harried protagonist of BBC2's *Motherland* is often hilariously well observed, yet likewise – perhaps as an inevitable consequence of the fact that the show reflects the world we still live in – she is not liberated. The series documents the challenges of keeping on top of sports days, parents' evenings and birthday parties, while also holding down a semi-high-powered day job, but by exhibiting on screen a woman trying and failing, even now, to 'have it all', these portrayals have a curiously confirmatory effect, reinforcing the status quo.

We exist in a kind of zombie, post-progress era. In a way, it's worse that feminism has been around for such a long time: nothing's really changed, and everyone wants to move on. Affordable childcare or flexible working? Forgive me if I stifle a yawn! The energy and enthusiasm of politicians and society has been exhausted before any real change has occurred. The figure of the funny bad mummy embodies this surreal, stalled era. Invariably middle class, these women are not *really* bad mothers, because they spend their lives driving the little rotters to piano lessons, and resentfully steaming tenderstem broccoli: that's why they have to drink so much wine. These vilified posh women are in a sense the flipside of our culture's perfectionism and high expectations. They symbolise our failure to improve the experience of motherhood; the only suggestion we can offer is to just drink through it. Mothers have for some time ricocheted between two archetypes: the impossible ideal and the despised stereotype; this trope somehow manages to combine both. These books, blogs and TV shows critique the problem with a sharp eye, but they register a curious pessimism about our collective ability to solve it.

* * *

Simone de Beauvoir wrote that 'the mystery of incarnation is repeated' in every birth – it's an individual miracle each time – but those who write about motherhood are always vulnerable to the implied question: 'So you think you're the first person ever to have a baby?' There is a kind of generalising corrective here: think of all the millions of other women who have given birth before you. It's pointing to the universal in the least helpful way: without the mass solidarity. Women around the world do this every day, mothers are told, but try to team up and share the burden, and you'll soon find out you're on your own. Unlike you, these other women are not making a fuss. The ideal, ordinary mother is – in that supremely silencing phrase – just 'getting on with it'.

Perhaps the reason for the ubiquity of the clownish mum-who-drinks stereotype is the fact that the self-satire pre-empts the social censure of any mother who questions her lot. What do you have to complain about? There is a close connection between motherhood and privilege in the intolerant public mind. High-status mothers are hate figures in our culture, because they are assumed to be putting their own interests before those of their child. Thus we have the hoary old stereotype of the career woman, still used in the reactionary press, and that dreaded phrase 'too posh to push'. The *Daily Mail* may be the best known haranguer of 'career women', but it's not alone: the term is a mainstay of the broadsheet as well as the tabloid press. Even *Guardian* articles bemoaning the difficulty of high flyers getting back to work after a long maternity leave – 'I used to phone up Leonardo DiCaprio and now I'm in rubber gloves in other people's toilets' – have this reinforcing effect. When I address the plight of high-status women in this book, it's not through some kind of unthinking default. I argue that ambitious, successful women are targeted for a specific reason: whether deliberately or unconsciously, the patriarchy has in its sights those who have the best current chance of achieving equality with men.

Recently, the 'career woman' put-down has segued into a new guise: motherhood memoirs by white, middle-class women are dismissed as out-of-touch, elitist, and even oppressive in themselves: this attitude fuelled the vicious reaction to the anthropological study of Upper East Side stay-at-home moms, *Primates of Park Avenue*. It is true that non-white and non-privileged experience is underrepresented in the media, culture, and literature. Yet to imply that a certain demographic of mothers should not talk about their experiences is to unwittingly echo patriarchal demands for silent acceptance. There is also an uncomfortable generational aspect to this, too: young women suggesting that privileged older women have had enough air time. Young women – and BAME women of any age – face particular disadvantages. However, this suppression of complaint results in a race to the bottom where aspirational women are slapped down by old-fashioned patriarchy and the new identity politics alike. Privilege – or the suspicion of privilege – too often leads to reticence about expressing disappointment, frustration and injustice: the learned impulse is just to keep calm and carry on. Women are damned either way: if they say how great motherhood is, they are insensitively trumpeting their advantage; if they complain, well, they don't know how lucky they are.

Although the British media tends to dislike pushy, posh mums, it is intimately preoccupied with their habits nonetheless. 'You have encouraged them to eat their greens, battled to get them into the best school and sweated with them over their homework – all to give them the best start in life.' Yes, it's the *Daily Mail*. 'But your children's prospects may have been determined long before all the hard work. A growing body of research suggests the first 1,000 days of a child's life – the nine months in the womb and the first two years out of it – are vital to their long-term health. If conditions are not perfect at each step, problems can occur later.' Such is the high-stakes hair-splitting pressure that the media routinely imposes upon mothers, particularly those imagined to possess the sharpest elbows – perhaps in an effort to boost sales and clicks.

Meanwhile, of course, there is a whole other population of women who live in poor housing and on low incomes, or in countries with inadequate nutrition and sanitation and high levels of maternal and infant mortality. They may not find themselves targeted in the media on account of their worldly ambitions, but they are often vilified (single mothers especially) or overlooked. It is important that critiques of modern motherhood don't ignore them, too.

* * *

As I'll show in this book, much of the science that prompts those media articles and underpins the socially approved version of motherhood is ambiguous, contested, or even non-existent. Take the gold standard of research: the randomised controlled trial (RCT). The way this works is that the researcher assembles a group of people to take part in a trial. They then randomly assign some of them to do one thing, and the rest to do another, and then they can see what difference it makes. These experiments are 'blind': if the subjects knew what group they were in, that would consciously or unconsciously influence their behaviour, skewing the results (they are in fact double blind: the researchers don't know who's in which group either, lest that influence them).

But where mothers and babies are concerned, there is a relative absence of good evidence from randomised trials to draw on. Why is this? In the course of researching this book, I kept reading that in this area it is considered unethical to randomise trials. Yet, as I'll show, the blanket ban is bunk: it conceals a reluctance to prioritise the investigation of 'women's problems'. For issues that attract such intense media debate – such as the safety of epidurals, for example – it is extraordinary, and maddening, that there is so little properly funded probing of the facts. The conclusion must be that, on some level, society is content to let women worry.

The authorities have responded to these evidential gaps by erring on the side of caution, but this undermines mothers' autonomy and imposes unrealistic demands. A single example is the WHO's advice to mothers to breastfeed exclusively for six months: in the UK, just 12 per cent are still doing that at four months; a tiny 1 per cent at six months. It seems an absurd state of affairs that the prescription diverges so far from prac- tice, and so many feel bad as a result. The science behind this advice is actually subject to debate, but this is tactfully concealed from mothers. They are treated like children, at precisely the moment they are also being told to assume scrupulous respon- sibility. I believe that parents can handle the ambiguity and act sensibly if the science is clearly explained.

Public health authorities understandably have their sights set on improving outcomes for the population as a whole, even by 1 or 2 percentage points. But this has an underappreciated impact on individual women. If a medical procedure carries a 1 per cent risk of harm, say, a mother might reasonably decide that it's pretty safe to go ahead (of course, if the procedure does go wrong, the impact will loom large). There is also an ethical consideration here, to do with paternalism and the social contract. By overemphasising risks, the guidelines are effectively lying to women.

Because of the disinclination to conduct RCTs, the vast majority of the research on what women eat and drink during pregnancy, what childbirth technique they use, and how they rear their children, follows a different model: the observational study. These either follow two cohorts following different courses of action and see what happens, or examine an existing set of data about a group or population – surveys for example – and look at what happened to the people who said they did one thing as compared with those who said they did another.

The problem with observational studies is that they don't reliably measure cause and effect. For example, women who give birth at home, say, or breastfeed their babies, have deliberately chosen to do so, and the very factors that influence those decisions may be responsible for how those babies turn out, rather than the fact of home birth or breastfeeding itself. The most important determinant of a child's life chances, in fact, is not whether you have a natural birth or an elective caesarean, stop breastfeeding at six weeks or six months, or work two or four days per week. It's your income and education. Much of the scientific evidence is not effectively controlled for socio-economic status. And when it is, the benefits of particular parenting practices tend to disappear.

In fact, discussions about parenting often take place in a social and cultural vacuum. Western mothers are warned off bottle-feeding on the basis of advice given to parents in countries with little access to clean running water. Working mothers are admonished on the basis of evidence taken from the brain scans of children raised in squalid Romanian orphanages in the 1980s. As I will show, liberatingly diverse parenting styles from different communities around the world and from the historical past are not common currency among mothers here and now, who are led to believe there is a single, correct way; while contexts and behaviours that are not relevant to Western women are held up as punitive exemplars.

Motherhood is an intensely bodily business – I'm recalling the panoply of pregnancy symptoms, labour pains and breast-feeding hormones. But it is not a uniform process that every woman must repeat alone. The new regressive emphasis on the natural and physical – on genes, hormones and brain development that I will discuss in this book – is part of a wholesale denial of sociology and anthropology: of human control. What we need is not Mother Nature with an ironic makeover, but mother nurture: an appreciation of the effects of economics and social context, and an investment in policies that improve modern motherhood. On both a political and a personal level, it's time we nurtured mothers.

* * *

If there was a single, true, time-honoured method of having children and bringing them up, derived from ancient nature and confirmed by modern science, then why has parenting differed so much through time? In the UK in 1900, more than 95 per cent of babies were born at home, but by 1940, more than half of all births were in hospital; this figure had risen to 99 per cent by 1969. From the 1970s onwards, with the rise of the natural childbirth movement, middle-class women in particular started choosing to give birth at home once again. Eighty per cent of mothers breastfed their babies before 1920; by the 1950s only 20 per cent were doing it; but in the 1980s the rate was up to 60 per cent. It is true that some of these shifts were in the right direction, some in the wrong; but their dramatic nature tells us something about the power of social norms.

As with history, so with geography: in Japan, the epidural rate is around 5 per cent; in France it's over 80 per cent. More than half of all babies in Brazil are delivered by caesarean section; in Finland, the rate is less than 7 per cent. A full third of Dutch women give birth at home, and only 10 per cent have pain relief (but a maternity nurse provides home care for a week after the birth, doing everything from changing nappies to cooking and cleaning). These variations have the potential to free parents from the straitjacket of rigid contemporary expectations.

If practices alter over time and across space, so has the advice. As I'll illustrate in this book, an entire library of advice has been produced in Britain, Europe and America, starting with the morality manuals of the medieval age, moving on through Puritan 'conduct literature' and on into the primitivist ideali-sation of motherhood by Jean-Jacques Rousseau and his followers. This latter strain was reinforced by the rise of the bourgeois nuclear family in the eighteenth and nineteenth centuries: the more sentimental prescriptions of the Victorians gave way to the rise of medical and scientific expert advice in the twentieth century.

It is tempting to read these books as accurate descriptions of common practice at the time, but they also functioned as entreaties to recalcitrant mothers to change their ways. What looked like an 'is' was often a persuasive or disapproving 'ought'. As Sarah Moss writes in *Night Waking*: 'It seems that the rela-tionship between the theory and practice of parenthood may be inverse.' These books laid the ground for restrictive modern advice, instructing women to sacrifice their social and intellec-tual ambitions for the putative wellbeing of their children. The fact that those expectations – and therefore our own – emerged out of specific, patriarchal and distinctly unenlightened histor-ical circumstances should enable us to take them with a large pinch of salt.

Although it may seem surprising, mothers in the past were often more liberated than they are today, in both attitudes and practices. Puritan theologians may have thundered from the pulpits, and enlightenment philosophes waxed lyrical about buxom milkmaids, but despite the weight of historical conduct literature, maternal anxiety and guilt appear to be largely modern inventions.

Could it be that society has simply learned how to raise healthier, happier children? Certainly it is right to be vigilant about child illness, abuse and neglect. Science and medicine have made great strides: the reduction of infant mortality, vaccination, myriad innovative treatments; the list is long. Universal education, the banning of underage labour, and the provision – if patchy – of professionalised childcare have improved children's lives immeasurably. Yet the common assumption of automatic progress conceals missteps and back-slidings. It is not clear that today's teenagers – often anxious, depressed, and screen-addicted – necessarily have optimal levels of wellbeing.

For mothers, too, things have in many ways improved: there is a welfare state – struggling, but still intact. In some areas, however, the clock has run backwards. In the early years of the twentieth century, women may not have had the vote, but after giving birth they would stay in hospital for up to two weeks' 'lying in' – a mixed blessing in some institutions, but at least an acknowledgement of the need for postnatal help. Those women lacked access to modern medicines, but there was an active campaign for pain relief in labour. Remarkably, mothers spent less time looking after their children in the 1950s than they do today.

Well into the twenty-first century, we've ended up with a set of poorly reconciled desires and demands. As both white-collar and blue-collar industries shrink, women who work are climbing an ever-greasier pole, or managing zero-hours contracts in the precarious gig economy. Fertility treatments have advanced, yet women who have children older for reasons they cannot control are still finding it desperately difficult to have a longed-for child, and the social expectation that all women must become mothers is barely dented. As couples are having fewer children, each one is more freighted with concern. Work and family is still a tug-of-war. In a high-stakes, social-media-scrutinised, global-competitive world, every aspect of children's life chances must be optimised. Motherhood has become airbrushed, privatised and atomised.

These problems are just as common among millennials: in fact, in some ways they work harder at it all. They feel compelled to use apps to track their baby's development, wade through endless WhatsApp chat, and gaze at other families' progress on Instagram. Whereas in their own day their grandmothers may have briskly ignored the complaints of fussy eaters and thought nothing of serving a low-stakes shepherds' pie to friends round to tea, mums now find themselves cooking three separate meals of an evening and wearily 'liking' their frenemy's latest sourdough loaf as they scan Facebook for a break on the loo. Drowning in unfinished digital admin and organic vegetables rotting at the back of the fridge, today's millennials are labouring under expectations higher than they've ever been. 'I am constantly frustrated and frazzled,' attested EJ Dickson, a millennial mother and writer; 'and – to be honest – angry that having children and a career is still such a heroic feat.'

Looking back through history also reveals a surprising abundance of collective demands by mothers for better support, provision and treatment – demands that are rather thin on the ground now. It is true that some Sixties and Seventies feminists found the whole topic of motherhood both dull and demeaning. But the notion that the second wave ignored motherhood is a myth. In this book, I will recall some of their many forgotten campaigns and argue that we would do well now to update them.

This book is a manifesto for change, but the conditions of contemporary motherhood are so retrograde that big improvements are well within reach: proper care before, during and after birth; infrastructure to combat endemic isolation; a rethink of work for both women and men; and the transformation of society's incessant chastising of mothers into due value and respect.

There is a further neglected perspective I emphasise in this book. Accompanying the new natural fundamentalism there has been a devaluation of psychoanalysis as a useful tool. Yet the insights of analysts such as Donald Winnicott and Rozsika Parker offer generous and illuminating ways to understand motherhood, diagnose its problematic aspects, and provide the key to unlocking some solutions.

Psychoanalysis helps us understand why society is so hard on mothers. Perhaps we resent our own mothers' cruelties, withholdings, or ordinary imperfections. Perhaps it's about ambivalent attitudes towards authority: while fathers play the symbolic part in our culture of the risk-taker, the good-time buccaneer, rarely there so always desired, mothers carry the can: like social workers who get more public blame than abusers themselves, mothers are meant to take care of everything.

The psychoanalytic writer and academic Jacqueline Rose extends that idea: prior to the eighteenth century, she argues, children were regarded as naturally naughty and had to be trained to be good. But now, they are regarded as innocent perfection. When we have babies, we fantasise – as individuals, and as a society – that finally here is an opportunity to recover an imaginary blank slate, untainted by the problems of the world and the reality of being human. We project onto our offspring the fantasy of starting again, of the renewal of our tainted, partly defeated adult selves. Mothers, she writes, are meant to 'trample over the past and lift us out of historical time . . . to secure a new dawn'. Since they are doomed to fail, mothers become scapegoats for our personal and political disappointments. Rather than make motherhood a proxy for politics, we should use politics to improve motherhood.

When mothers are made to carry the burden of these expectations, when they are demonised and made to feel anxious and guilty, it is not only bad for mothers and the cause of gender equality, but for men, too: they are not happy when their partners enact private revenge for society's sexism by portraying them as useless dads. And it is bad for children, too, if they grow up with mothers who are bitter and dissatisfied. By understanding and normalising maternal ambivalence – the anger a mother inevitably feels at times about being a mother and towards her child – psychoanalysis destigmatises it. It helps mothers forgive themselves, and relax into their relationship with their child.

It is only by recognising these profound yet subtle dynamics that mothers can feel justified in seeking change. We must not only feel indignant, but entitled to our indignation – and not silenced by either the projected requirements of children, or accusations of supposed privilege. It's time to push back.

1

MOTHER NATURE

I got out of bed one Sunday morning, and my waters splashed onto the floor. I was about to have my first baby. At the hospital the midwife told me to come back when labour was 'established'. Throughout the day, my contractions gently ramped up; exciting but inexorable. It was November. It got dark early. My husband and I tried to distract ourselves with television, but the pain of the contractions started to cut through. It got to ten o'clock. We went to the hospital again. We saw a different midwife. I said I wanted to stay. I held a green paper towel between my legs and showed her I was bleeding. She told me that this was normal, that I wasn't yet in proper labour, and that I should go back home. She laughed lightly as she walked off down the corridor.

Weeks later, that blood would come up in an investigation as a key warning sign of placental abruption, a rare but dangerous condition in which the placenta becomes detached from the wall of the uterus, starving the baby of food and – more urgently – oxygen.

When we got home, it was nearly midnight. My husband lay next to me on the bed while I kneeled over the headboard. The pain was more than I could bear. I felt each contraction approach as if from afar, and each time I didn't know how I would cope when it broke over me. Time passed, impossibly. The midwife had advised me to have a bath. It seemed an insanely banal suggestion, but I dutifully crouched in the water as dark wisps floated around me. At two in the morning, I was in wild agony. We drove back to the hospital. I writhed in the passenger seat. I had to stop in the brightly lit hallway as another wave of contractions took hold. People say you forget the pain of labour, but even now, over a decade later, I still remember very clearly what it felt like to have to endure the seemingly unendurable.

A different midwife saw me doubled over the reception desk and offered me an epidural. As soon as I was hooked up to the monitor, we heard the baby's heartbeat slow right down, like a tape machine running out of batteries. The doctor arrived and told me I was going to have a caesarean, right now. My baby was not getting the oxygen he needed to stay alive. I was rushed down a corridor, strip-lights flashing over my head. My husband was told to wait outside the operating theatre. There was no time to top up my epidural; I was given a general anaesthetic. I was scared to lose consciousness. The anaesthetist was probably inserting a cannula, but I imagined he was holding my hand.

When I woke up, it was morning. There was a baby on my chest.

My son was fine: they had got him out just in time. But it was five years before I was able to tell that story without my voice cracking. Even now I have to concentrate on getting to the end.

TELLING THE TRUTH

My experience was shocking, but it did not come as a surprise. The Birth Trauma Association estimates that each year, around 30,000 women in the UK develop Post Traumatic Stress Disorder (PTSD) after having a baby, and as many as 200,000 may feel traumatised by childbirth in some way – nearly a third of all women who give birth. Instead of a joyful experience, these women find childbirth frightening, are left with injuries, or feel they weren't properly looked after. A 2020 survey by the association of 798 of its members who had been left with PTSD found that nine out of ten said poor communication from staff was a contributing factor, and one in three cited unkindness. The Care Quality Commission's 2017 survey of 18,426 women's experiences of maternity care found that of those who raised a concern during labour or birth, 19 per cent felt that it was not taken seriously. Nearly a quarter said that during labour they were left worried and alone.

Years after my son's birth, I came across a Twitter thread by a woman in the US who had given birth in a hospital designated as 'baby friendly'. American women are generally more likely to give birth on a labour ward and be offered an epidural, but the trend towards natural birth is on the rise there too. In 'baby friendly' hospitals, the woman protested, there is no nursery for the baby: the idea is that the mother should stay with her baby all the time. Nursery, I thought? Nursery? I had an emergency C-section under general anaesthetic at four in the morning; I lost a litre and a half of blood and had to have a transfusion; every time I shifted in bed my hasty stitches pulled alarmingly; I could barely walk. Yet I was expected to look after my baby alone through the first night, when I didn't really know how to breastfeed or change a nappy. I remember being told off by one of the postnatal nurses because I'd fallen asleep with my baby lying over my stomach. I knew this was not good for him, so the fact that I let it happen was a sign of how exhausted I was. When he cried and I couldn't manoeuvre myself to lift him out of his crib I had to summon a nurse with a button, and although some were caring, others acted like I was on a plane calling the air steward in the middle of the night for a G&T.

It is customary for stories of gothic gore and touch-and-go

risk, of forceps and tearings and cuttings without anaesthesia to end with a statement to the effect that well, it was worth it though; or, he or she is fine, and that's the important thing. Some acquaintances said similar things to me after I told them my own birth story: at least you and the baby are fine. I have always felt a spike of irritation at this, and also guilt at what I fear is my own narcissism for presuming to believe there are other important things. These people mean well; but why should women go through something so violent, terrifying and life-threatening, and yet feel they should not dwell on how it was for them?

When I was pregnant with child number one, I looked forward to having him out in the world, but there was an unimaginable hurdle to get over first. I found myself reaching for metaphors – camels and eyes of needles, trains speeding inexorably towards wreckage, the film *Alien* . . . Given the available methods of exit, fear of childbirth seems an entirely rational response, yet in research terms it is only recognised in the form of an extreme syndrome called tocophobia. Researchers have estimated that around 14 per cent suffer from it worldwide, although this is an average: higher estimates of prevalence reach 43 per cent.

The expectation that mothers should maintain a dignified silence about what they went through has produced a curious vacuum. A media storm blew up in 2018 when Catriona Jones, a senior midwifery lecturer at the University of Hull, claimed social media is partly to blame for the widespread unease. 'You just have to Google childbirth and you're met with a tsunami of horror stories,' she said. 'If you go on to any of the Mumsnet forums, there are women telling their stories of childbirth – oh, it was terrible, it was a bloodbath, this and that happened.' Is the idea that we are exaggerating, or that we should just keep the truth to ourselves? Justine Roberts, Mumsnet's chief executive, countered Jones's comments: 'One of the most common complaints we see on this topic is "Why on Earth didn't anyone tell me the truth about how bad it could be?'" Women are looking for that truth: a 2016 study by researchers from Bournemouth University found that 79 per cent of pregnant women in the UK read blogs, watch YouTube, or join social media forums to 'fill voids in their knowledge about the realities of childbirth'.

Not knowing the reality also makes it harder to deal with when it comes. The National Childbirth Trust is supposed to prepare women for childbirth, but I've lost count of the women who have told me that their birth experience came as a shock after what they'd been taught in their NCT classes. My group was no exception: nearly all wanted a natural birth, but most ended up having an emergency caesarean, or were induced without anaesthesia – a barbaric combination. Whereas we'd all been giggling and optimistic in the classes, after the event my fellow mothers were wan and disillusioned, with thousand-yard stares. We felt not only traumatised, but tricked.

Before the birth, I was particularly curious about the pain. I searched dozens of message-board threads. On Yahoo, women were asking questions such as: 'Be honest, how painful is giving birth on a scale of 1-10?' Google listed popular searches for: 'How painful is childbirth without an epidural', 'How painful is childbirth naturally', 'How painful is childbirth scientifically' and 'How painful is childbirth compared to a kick in the balls' – evidence of male curiosity perhaps.

The definitive answers I was looking for online turned out to be – unhelpfully – starkly divided. Some, like Marlon Brando in *Apocalypse Now*, gestured at an ordeal only imaginable by those who'd been through it: 'the horror!' But others insisted it was the most incredible experience of their life. I couldn't tell if those women found it so because the pain didn't seem so bad, or because it did, and they survived it. Those who 'succeed' are not consciously lording it over the rest of us, but giving birth without pain relief has become – even against women's better judgement – a competitive test.

I will never know how painful childbirth really can be. During labour, your cervix dilates ten centimetres: I had an epidural at six centimetres, and minutes later was rushed into theatre. I was later told that my son was 'back to back', the wrong way around, which is apparently especially painful, so perhaps that bumps me up a couple of notches on the scale of endurance and achievement. What I do know is that at six centimetres I was already in more pain than I felt I could take. I often think about those other four centimetres: about the notorious 'transition stage'; about pushing, and crowning, and tearing. I feel like I got six out of ten.

BE NATURAL!

Because I was sent home, I didn't receive the care I wanted, including pain relief. And I started to see the same pattern everywhere. Friends had told me that their requests for an epidural had been discreetly ignored; that they'd been advised to 'see how you get along', only to be told later, as they screamed for one, that, sorry, it was now too late. They had told me that the pain was so bad, they wanted to die. One friend was induced and then left alone at night on a labour ward where her screams were ignored, and when a midwife found her on all fours about to push, she said: 'We all thought you were making a fuss.'

In 2011, a Mumsnet post, 'Anyone else tricked out of an epidural?', attracted over a thousand replies in less than two weeks. 'Why is there such a stigma around having an epidural?' asked one poster in 2019. 'I've been watching a lot of videos on YouTube & people seem to be celebrating the fact they didn't have an epidural. A close relative has even told me to "never have an epidural no matter what".' She continues: 'Not looking for a row before anyone starts just genuinely interested in why.'

A respondent is careful to stress: 'I didn't have one,' although she adds: 'but zero judgement towards anyone who has. Everyone has different pain thresholds . . .'

Ah, the apparent generosity of the 'pain thresholds' licence. Mine were clearly lamentably low. Another Mumsnet poster added: 'I know someone who had epidurals with their births and developed fibromyalgia after the first and it gradually got worse with the next two. Not saying they're linked but who knows . . .,' illustrating the way that rumours of unproven risks can be fomented online. Too often the underlying message – although muted and disavowed in the cheery agora of social media – is that those who rely on drugs are either feeble or selfish. That judgement is also implied in the praise for those who do it without: the approving comment 'she did ever so well'. Even among my friends, though we all reject the social judgement, it was the big question: did you have one? We always had to know.

Friends had also told me about their NCT classes: how they'd been gently encouraged to prepare to give birth naturally without 'interventions' such as anaesthesia or a caesarean, and how they felt like a failure if they'd ended up needing them. I also found that the NCT – while purporting to be neutral and non-prescriptive – did indeed subtly promote natural birth. We were told stories about African tribeswomen and an Irish farmer's wife who spent her days milking cows and scrubbing floors, and who wouldn't dream of using pain relief to aid her birth: she slipped her baby out like the proverbial bar of soap.

The promotion of natural childbirth is often accompanied by such humbling references. One American natural childbirth website notes that 'the ease with which childbirth was accomplished in indigenous tribes stands in stark contrast to the phenomenal rate of birth interventions and caesarean births in the Western world'. There is a large subgenre of 'natural' or 'normal' birth videos on YouTube, often filmed in non-Western settings; perhaps that Mumsnet poster was watching one of them. 'Tribal Woman Gives Birth In Forest' is a real, and representative, title. Another such offering, of a Utah doula giving birth to her fourth child in a stream in an Australian rainforest, has been watched nearly a hundred million times. 'My parents had been missionaries in Papua New Guinea,' she explained to the *New York Post* in 2016. 'I remember mom often telling us when a local lady had her baby [she simply] found a nice spot, pushed out the baby, breastfed it, and wrapped it in a carrier cloth, tied the child to her back and went about her business.'

The idealisation of natural childbirth is ubiquitous in antenatal education, in the advice literature, on social media and in the press: '11 hours' labour and all natural! How serene Kate sailed through a textbook delivery as she goes through the perfect birth she was hoping for', ran a *Daily Mail* headline after the birth of 'gorgeous George'. And underneath: 'Duchess of Cambridge gave birth without recourse to powerful painkillers'.

Websites such as 'GivingBirthNaturally.com' and 'NaturalBirthWorks.com' abound; the kidshealth.org site (hosted by the American paediatric health care provider Nemours) tells women: 'You should be applauded for your willingness and enthusiasm to try to deliver naturally.' 'I felt inadequate and disappointed after my caesarean,' one mother wrote on the parenting website BabyCentre. 'I was made to feel even worse by people constantly harping on about the wonders of "natural" birth.' The British Pregnancy Advisory Service's chief executive Clare Murphy told me that while abortion once attracted highly charged debates, she believes there is now even less public support for elective caesareans.

When Katie Goodland, fiancée of England men's football team captain Harry Kane, used the hypnobirthing technique during her labour in 2018, Kane tweeted that he was: 'So proud' of her 'for having the most amazing water birth with no pain relief at all'. On this occasion, there was some public outrage, to which Kane responded 'any women can give birth however they would like', but his initial comment reflected a widespread view. It's perhaps not surprising, therefore, that epidural use has fallen in the UK – by 70,000, or 6 per cent, between 2008–09 and 2018–19, according to an NHS Digital report.

I believe women should be able to decide how and where they give birth: in a rainforest, in their living room, or via planned caesarean on a labour ward. It is not particular preferences that I question. It is the way that, amidst a rhetoric of feminist empowerment, self-determination, and an array of equally valued options, women are not cared for, supported or listened to in childbirth – one of the most momentous and potentially harrowing experiences of their life: their requests are either disregarded or covertly steered, and only one course of action – natural birth – is invested with moral worth.

Despite the overwhelming dominance of natural childbirth as an ideology, it is presented as the plucky outsider, fighting for recognition in the teeth of the powerful white-coated establishment. It is also viewed as the woman-centred option, with midwives helping women avoid the medicalised 'default' and achieve the authentic experience they supposedly really want. Natural childbirth is portrayed as virtuous and brave, medical birth as necessary only if you're weak or your birth is a failure.

Not only are these characterisations inaccurate; they also restrict women's real autonomy. Labouring women are being denied medical help, including anaesthesia, in the name of feminism. The violation of women's rights is dressed up as progress.

As early as 1989, the influential sociologist Ann Oakley described in a lecture how childbirth is governed by a series of binary oppositions: 'Midwives/obstetricians; Women/men; Subjective/objective; Practice/theory; Emotion/reason; Intuition/intellect; Nature/culture; Family/work; Private/public; Soft/hard'. These oppositions still govern the way we talk about, think about, prepare for and manage birth. Although historically the male, medical, rational camp has prevailed, I believe that the pendulum has now swung too far the other way.

These categories are deeply unhelpful – for all women. As I'll argue, they make one group of women feel bad about themselves, and perpetuate racist and classist attitudes towards other groups. And as well as being punitively judgemental, they are simply inappropriate terms with which to deal with the highly unpredictable way in which childbirth unfolds.

NORMAL OR PATHOLOGICAL?

What does it mean to say a birth is natural? Does it mean no medical interventions? No pain relief? Lots of pain, or none?

In 2018, the World Health Organisation issued new recommendations attempting to reduce the number of 'interventions', stating that 'childbirth is a normal physiological process that can be accomplished without complications for the majority of women and babies'. So-called 'normal birth' has been widely promoted, not only by organisations like the WHO, but by national governments, antenatal classes and parenting advice books and sites. The International Confederation of Midwives issued a position statement in 2014 entitled 'Keeping Birth Normal', and the UK's Maternity Care Working Party produced a consensus statement, 'Making normal birth a reality' in 2007, which was supported by the Royal College of Midwives (RCM) and the Royal College of Obstetricians and Gynaecologists (RCOG). There has been a recognition in recent years that this language is problematic: the RCM has now stopped using the term 'normal birth' and removed all references to it from its website. But the positive connotations of the concept have lingered in our culture.

I am sympathetic to the view that childbirth should be thought of as a life event rather than a medical emergency. But high rates of maternal and infant mortality and injuries in communities with scarce medical care are also 'natural'. According to the United Nations, more than 300,000 women a year die during pregnancy or childbirth, most from preventable complications; 94 per cent of those deaths occur in lower-income countries, about two-thirds in Sub-Saharan Africa. Our World in Data has estimated that if we still had the living standards of 1800, maternal mortality would claim 1.26 million lives a year. Save the Children has estimated that nearly a million babies die on their first day, with the vast majority of these in lower-income countries, and mostly in rural areas, where there are fewer skilled birth attendants and more limited access to medical facilities.

The cause of most of these infant deaths is complications during birth. A 2017 report by the RCOG found that three-quarters of the babies who died or were brain damaged during or soon after birth in the UK in 2015 might have been saved by better medical care – that amounted to 863 babies. 'Natural' birth carries a 90 per cent risk of a tear or cut to the genitals, and over a 5 per cent risk of tearing through the anus in a woman's first birth.

I spoke to David Bogod, a consultant obstetric anaesthetist who has a specialism in ethics and law, and has been a vocal supporter of women's rights to pain relief in labour. 'We're actually trying to achieve an *abnormal* outcome here,' he told me; 'we're trying to achieve a much lower maternal and neonatal morbidity and mortality than would occur naturally – and we're achieving it. But to do that we have to act unnaturally.'

The question of whether childbirth is a 'natural' or a medical event has preoccupied obstetricians for centuries. 'It is an enigma of modern obstetrics,' noted American doctors Purvis Martin and Steward Smith in 1961, 'that what passes in the record as a normal labour and delivery may be bitterly remembered by our patients as a terrifying experience.' As the American historian of nursing Margarete Sandelowski observes, psychologists have found it especially difficult to separate 'normality from deviance' in childbirth because there are so many aspects of it that 'border . . . on the pathological'. It is almost a philosophical question, and one that has been answered differently in different cultures. 'There is enormous diversity in the way birth is thought about, treated, and understood,' wrote the anthropologists Margaret Mead and Niles Newton in 1967. 'In some societies births are considered physiologically normal and in others pathological.'

Traditionally, this question has also divided midwives and doctors, with midwives characterising birth as normal, and doctors pointing to the frequent need for medical management. Some proponents of the natural style have attributed the 'pathological' characterisation of birth to Joseph DeLee, a Chicago obstetrician – yet he argued that 'everything depends on what we define as normal'. As he explained, employing a vivid metaphor: 'If a woman falls on a pitchfork, and drives the handle through her perineum, we call that pathologic – abnormal, but if a large baby is driven through the pelvic floor, we say that is natural, and therefore normal.'

The way childbirth is managed is subject to national norms and customs. In the UK just under a quarter of births are caesareans; in Germany, the US and Australia it's just under a third. In the UK, the epidural rate is surprisingly low: less than 20 per cent; in the US it is about 60 per cent. 'Talk to a French woman about giving birth without an epidural and they'll look at you as if you're completely and utterly mad,' David Bogod told me. 'They cannot understand it.' In Greece and Italy epidurals are rare – there's a misperception, Bogod explained, that they can paralyse women. In Switzerland, the rate splits along language lines. 'It's entirely societal,' he said.

THE ENIGMA OF PAIN

If childbirth is natural, why does it hurt so much? In all other circumstances, pain is an alarm system, signalling danger and triggering the fight or flight impulse. The idea of productive pain is counterintuitive. And in a significant minority of cases, women are right to worry. But why is childbirth uniquely painful for humans?

I spent an enlightening day with the Emeritus Professor of Obstetrics and Gynaecology, Philip Steer, at the Chelsea and Westminster Hospital. He started from the beginning. Mammals have existed on earth for 100 million years, but our ancestors only started walking on two legs 3 million years ago. Bipedalism is efficient: you have your hands free. Only the top of your head is exposed to the sun. Standing upright led to a narrower pelvis. But at the same time the human brain quadrupled in size. The part of the brain that has grown is the frontal lobes, which are responsible for abstract thought. Interestingly, it is this part that natural childbirth advocates advise women to 'switch off' during labour. 'Human labour is an uneasy compromise between our need to run and our need to think,' Steer told me. This is why babies are quite a challenge to look after – they are effectively born premature. If they waited until they were ready, they would get stuck every time. It's a fine balance, and women take the strain.

There are different perspectives on what is known as 'the obstetrical dilemma hypothesis': the American anthropologist Holly Dunsworth argues that babies are born just as their metabolic needs outstrip what their mother can provide in the womb. Either way, evolution does not seem to be working so optimally in this instance. Nature can get away with making birth so painful because women will still go ahead and do it anyway, time after time. Before contraception and pain relief, they had little choice. Nowadays they can use pain relief, or just grin and bear it: either way there is no evolutionary incentive to make it more tolerable.

The baby's head is, in fact, even bigger than the pelvis. Human babies have to turn themselves around in the birth canal to get out, so if all goes well they emerge with their head facing backwards, unlike other primates, who are born facing to the front. This means that human childbirth is a social process: even in 'natural' settings, humans generally need birth attendants to catch their babies.

In the nineteenth and early- to mid-twentieth centuries, commentators speculated that it was only in 'civilised' societies that humans had evolved to such an extent that women's pelvises had become too small, and babies' heads too big, for birth to not be painful. 'Primitive' or 'tribal' women, by contrast, had apparently not evolved from earlier times: their physiognomy had remained in a 'natural' state. 'We see then . . . an increase of the difficulties of labour as civilization is neared,' the American obstetrician George Engelmann wrote in 1882 in *Labor Among Primitive Peoples*; 'the squaws of the Madoc Indians – a tribe which has been little affected by the advance of civilization – suffer but an hour or even less' in childbirth. 'Refined women' had become 'languid', Engelmann complained. 'The system suffers from the abuses of civilization, its dissipations, and the follies of fashion,' he added. Another American obstetrician, Carl Henry Davis, wrote in *Painless Childbirth* in 1916 that contemporary women had evolved into 'hot-house products'; they were 'physically less fit to perpetuate the race'. Here we see the early stirrings of 'too posh to push'.

The roots of our modern preference for natural childbirth lie in these historic attitudes, therefore, first clearly articulated in the eighteenth-century concept of the 'noble savage'. Enlightenment philosophers such as Rousseau and Diderot may have been highly cerebral men, but their ideal woman was rural, hard-working and uneducated: closest to 'nature'. The French politician and physician Jean-Emmanuel Gilibert advised mothers: 'Look to the animals for your example: even though the mothers have their stomachs torn open . . . they forget themselves, little concerned with their own happiness,' he declared. 'Woman, like all animals, is under the sway of this . . . instinct.' Voltaire was refreshingly sceptical: 'No one has ever used so much intelligence to persuade us to be so stupid,' he wrote to Rousseau. Reading his work, Voltaire continued, 'one feels that one ought to walk on all fours'. But Rousseau-mania flourished in the culture at large – and we are still living with its inheritance.

These stereotypes are not only sexist and racist, they are also incorrect. African women – long idealised by primitivist thinkers for their supposed natural ease in giving birth – actually have on average narrower pelvises than European women: this is a factor in the higher rate of maternal mortality in African countries and also among British women of African descent. As the campaigning group Fivexmore has highlighted, black women in the UK are five times more likely to die in childbirth than white women, and they have the highest rates of emergency caesarean births. There are other factors at work here, such as inadequate hospital care, poor communication, and insufficient understanding of specific cultural needs and expectations; but physiology plays a part, too.

Charles Darwin pioneered the study of 'variation under domestication' – how species could be altered over time through breeding. Bred pigeons change quickly, because their generations are brief. The appearance of British bulldogs has also been transformed. Research published in 2016 led by Philipp Mitteroecker of the University of Vienna suggested that the success of caesareans since the early twentieth century has led to bigger heads, and therefore up to 20 per cent more obstructed childbirths. If that is the case, is it wrong, asks Philip Steer, to allow more C-sections? There's no point in saying childbirth should be natural, he argues; we are already dependent upon technology: 'the genie', he says, 'is out of the bottle'. By placing the whole issue in such long-term biological perspective, Steer is suggesting that we should take a pragmatic, rather than a moralistic, approach to 'what works' in childbirth.

There's a live debate among scientists about whether humans are still evolving, or if we have attained such safety and comfort that we are no longer exposed to the life-and-death conditions essential for evolution by natural selection. If women can give birth for the most part safely with the help of interventions, is natural selection no longer acting upon childbirth, or is it that the baby's head can safely grow? These questions are profound: are humans natural, or not? Has civilisation removed us from nature? Or are medical interventions local actions within its broader sphere? However, when it comes to childbirth, they are rarely asked: it's as if nature is fixed and women just have to deal with it.

Attitudes towards nature and civilisation have fluctuated over the centuries. For Francis Bacon, the seventeenth-century father of scientific method, Nature – of course figured as female – was to be mastered for the benefit of all. 'The mechanical inventions of recent years do not merely exert a gentle guidance over Nature's courses,' he wrote, 'they have the power to conquer and subdue her, to shake her to her foundations.' By contrast, the Industrial Revolution prompted many to fear civilisation's corrupting influence, and this anxiety became focused on childbirth. Even now that technology has evolved to the point where we can 3D print prosthetic limbs and perform nanosurgery on a single cell, there is an obsessive – perhaps compensatory – belief that a baby, the tabula rasa of humanity, should be born in an atmosphere of uncultivated innocence – whatever the cost to its mother.

THE EARLY HISTORY OF BIRTH

In pre-modern times, childbirth was mostly managed by women, though female birth attendants were treated with suspicion and contempt: 'midwives-cum-witches' were burned at the stake. With the rise of the medical profession in the seventeenth century, men began to take over. Obstetrics grew out of the guilds of barber-surgeons who had historically enjoyed exclusive rights to use surgical instruments. The (female) birth attendants had only tended to call in the (male) surgeons when things went drastically wrong.

That changed, however, with the invention of the forceps by the Huguenot Chamberlen family, who would conceal their precious innovation in a special box and blindfold the woman and her attendant before bringing it out. Since these tong-like instruments helped guide the baby's head out of the birth canal, they greatly increased the baby's chance of survival if it became stuck. So the surgeons began to assist with live births, too. A power struggle ensued over questions of expertise, knowledge and control. One seventeenth-century midwife, an Elizabeth Nihell, complained about her male counterparts' use of 'scientific jargon', and 'hard Latin and Greek words . . . to throw dust in the eyes of the ignorant'.

Because the hardware – and later, anaesthesia – was controlled by men, the feminist rejection of medical assistance during childbirth is essentially an accidental by-product of patriarchy. The implications of this are far-reaching: it should not be assumed that women automatically want to give birth in a way that – for circumstantial reasons – has come to be associated with women; not least because the majority of obstetricians are now female. What's more, it is wrong to conflate the control exercised by a woman giving birth to the control exercised by a female midwife. 'Providing pain relief in labour has been about empowering women,' David Bogod told me, 'and it's interesting that there's a feminist argument for disempowering women, because of an artificial divide which states that normal childbirth is a female-managed process and abnormal birth is a male-managed process.'

The hostile mistrust of medical assistance during birth – evident in common phrases such as 'cascade of interventions' – is largely attributable to a bizarre historical episode. Well into the nineteenth century, doctors were routinely – and unwittingly – killing women in labour. The Hungarian doctor Ignaz Semmelweis discovered that this was because physicians were transmitting an infection called 'puerperal' or 'childbed' fever by not washing their hands properly between dissecting corpses and delivering babies. But nobody believed him, and he died, frustrated, in a lunatic asylum.

THE FIGHT FOR ANAESTHESIA

If women are scared of labour pain, why not just offer them an anaesthetic? Pain relief is not a new-fangled solution, a modern woman's comfort: ancient Egyptians used opium, and ancient Greeks chewed willow bark, the predecessor to aspirin. But the Church came to regard pain in childbirth as a moral necessity. Thus in the King James Version of the Old Testament, in Genesis 3:16, God tells Eve: 'In sorrow thou shalt bring forth children'. In the Hebrew, and in Latin and English versions prior to the King James Bible, 'sorrow' is rendered as 'labour' or 'toil'. But Christian theologians began to routinely claim that painful childbirth was rightful punishment for Eve's sin.

A Scottish obstetrician, James Young Simpson, was the first doctor to administer an anaesthetic in childbirth in 1846; one of his patients was so delighted with the results that she gave her baby girl the middle name of Anaesthesia. The clergy were less pleased, however: during the religious furore that ensued, a rabbi was enlisted by medics to give his interpretation of the original Hebrew. In a lengthy response, drawing on biblical scholars for proof, the rabbi judged that Eve was cursed with toil not pain, and anaesthesia did not therefore contravene the word of God. When the obstetrician John Snow gave chloroform to Queen Victoria during the delivery of Prince Leopold in 1853, it helped popularise the method in Britain. Yet resistance remained: as one doctor claimed in 1929, 'the very suffering which a woman undergoes in labour is one of the strongest elements in the love she bears her offspring'.

Another barrier was expense. 'If rich women were as common as rich men,' wrote Virginia Woolf in her 1938 novel *Three Guineas*, 'you could provide every mother with chloroform when her child is born.' A letter to *The Lady* in 1942 noted that: 'one of the most cruel class divisions yet remaining in this country is that rich mothers need not suffer in childbirth as though we were still in the Stone Age, while poorer ones far too often do.' Anxious to redress this inequality, as early as 1928 a group of socially and politically influential women led by Lady Baldwin, wife of Prime Minister Stanley Baldwin, formed the National Birthday Trust Fund, an organisation dedicated to the improvement of maternity care for poorer women – including access to anaesthesia.

In her 1936 novel *Honourable Estate*, the writer, nurse and pacifist Vera Brittain has a Victorian patriarch say: 'The trouble with women nowadays . . . was that they were too pampered; they made such scenes about these natural processes that you'd think having a baby was a major operation.' The novel's heroine regards hospital birth as a triumph over 'the feeling of helplessness, of being completely under Nature's control'. Many of these robust statements were more critical of the promotion of natural childbirth than our culture is today.

I'm highlighting these historical examples because it is hard to imagine now that there was once such a powerful campaign in favour of pain relief, with official support. The 'sufferings of women', noted one 1940s local government committee, are 'a question of great national importance', and 'methods which can be adopted to alleviate such suffering' should receive 'earnest consideration'.

The suffragette movement promoted 'twilight sleep', a mixture of morphine and an amnesiac. It was a slightly bizarre method: women were placed into padded 'crib-beds' where they could thrash about in labour without hurting themselves – they would forget it all afterwards anyway. Doctors liked it because it left them free to do other things: 'I catch up on my reading and writing,' admitted one. Even though women were not fully conscious during the treatment, its proponents viewed it as a way to maintain control. One described her birth experience prior to discovering twilight sleep in memorable terms to her doctor: 'It bursts your brain, and tears out your heart, and crashes your nerves to bits. It's just like hell, and I won't stand it again. Never.'

While some enthusiasts were, it should be said, keen to promote this method primarily to upper-class women, others sought to broaden its appeal: the journalist Hanna Rion urged her readers to 'take up the battle for painless childbirth,' adding that every woman should 'have the choice of saying how she will have her child'.

Twilight sleep remained in use until the 1970s. Gas and air was first used in 1933. Pethidine was developed in 1939; by 1948 it was used in most hospital cases; now its use is limited, at least in the UK. Pethidine is an interesting case: it can cross the placenta, and occasionally causes babies to have breathing difficulties, but it is not classed as an intervention and can be administered by midwives: this may be why it has stayed in use at all – an instance of natural birth ideology trumping a small, but real, risk to babies.

Despite these valiant efforts, childbirth remained a gruelling and often unpleasant experience for women in the UK and the

US. In 1900, the vast majority of British babies were born at home, but by 1950, a typical woman would give birth in a hospital ward, after being shaved, given an enema, and strapped into stirrups. Episiotomies were routine. In 1958, the American magazine *Ladies' Home Journal* published an article on 'Cruelty in Maternity Wards'; it received responses from across the country. Some women objected to the imposition of drugs, 'used for the convenience of the doctor, not to spare the mother', wrote one. '"They give you drugs whether you want them or not, and strap you down like an animal",' another woman wrote.

Birth Story, a 1997 film stored in the Wellcome archives, features interviews with the first generation of women to experience childbirth in hospital: their testimony is often bitter – describing brutal, inconsiderate treatment under a hierarchical ward regime that failed to consult them or take their preferences into account. Women giving birth at home in 1935 were five times more likely to die in childbirth than women in hospital in 1950, but this is no excuse for cruel or high-handed treatment by nurses or doctors.

It's not surprising that there was an appetite for change. The problem lay with the direction that change took.

THE MOVEMENT GETS UNDERWAY

While I was still pregnant, I'd started looking into the history of natural childbirth in the Wellcome Library in London, self-consciously hauling my bump up the stone staircase in the old reading room. I was aware of the irony. There I discovered a remarkable archive. The National Childbirth Trust started life in 1956 as the *Natural* Childbirth Association, and its first president was a British physician named Grantly Dick-Read. Dick-Read is a hero of the natural birth movement, but the figure that emerges from the archive is rather more controversial.

He was born Grantly Richard Read in 1890, and was known as Dick Read for most of his life until, aged sixty-eight, he hyphenated his middle and last names, presumably to sound more grand. He was something of a maverick: at odds with the British medical establishment, and forced to close his obstetrics practice after allegations of unprofessional conduct, he left his wife and children in England and emigrated to South Africa, but was initially refused a medical licence there.

Early in his career, Dick-Read was a kind of male *Call the Midwife* character, attending births in east London as part of his training. It was on one of his home visits to a 'low hovel by the railway arches' off Whitechapel Road that he saw the light. 'The bed had no proper covering and was kept up at one end by a sugar box. My patient lay covered only with sacks and an old black skirt. The room was lit by one candle stuck in the top of a beer bottle on the mantelshelf.' Yet despite the unpropitious setting, there was an atmosphere of 'quiet kindliness'. In due course, the baby was born. 'There was no fuss or noise,' he described, approvingly. 'Everything seemed to have been carried out according to an ordered plan.' When the head appeared, he offered the woman some chloroform, but she refused. '"It didn't hurt,"' she explained afterwards. '"It wasn't meant to, was it, doctor?"'

Dick-Read was to repeat this story many times, in his lectures, articles and books. It was as if he'd found, hidden away, the real, authentic woman who had not been corrupted by 'lies' about childbirth being painful. Dick-Read believed that worldly and refined women had become scared and tense during labour, and this produced the pain they were expecting: what he called the 'fear-tension-pain cycle'. In reality, he claimed, there was nothing to fear except fear itself. 'The more civilised a people becomes,' he wrote in his 1942 bestseller, *Childbirth Without Fear*, 'the more intensified this pain appears to be.' But with a 'perfect labour', he wrote, 'anaesthesia is unnecessary because there is no pain.'

If 'primitive' women gave birth naturally, it appeared that 'civilised' women had to be taught how to do it. 'The mother is the factory,' Dick-Read wrote in 1942, 'and by education and care she can be made more efficient in the art of motherhood.' The irony here was noted by one doctor: 'Does childbearing require special training to be natural?' he asked.

The Whitechapel story acquired the ring of truth; but we only have Dick-Read's word for it. And it's an odd kind of story: looked at one way, it's about normality; looked at another, it's an egregious curiosity. It brings to mind travellers' tales that hover on the boundary between truth and falsehood – Thomas More's *Utopia*, or the outlandish depictions of cannibals in the essays of Michel de Montaigne.

In 1953, Dick-Read journeyed 6,000 miles by caravan through the continent, recording birth practices along the way. He described African women giving birth as if it were, in his words, a 'normal and natural defecation': 'probably whilst even yet at her work, labour commences,' he writes. The woman 'isolates herself, and, in a thicket, quietly and undisturbed she patiently waits'. Dick-Read seemed unaware that in many African societies, women have traditionally given birth in silence because of strict modesty rules. These were extraordinary tales about 'ordinary' women, uncomplainingly taking birth in their stride.

What about the high rates of maternal mortality in these so-called 'tribal' societies? Dick-Read explained that this was simply to be expected. He wrote that for African women, 'natural birth is all that she looks for; there are no fears in her mind; she has no knowledge of the tragedies of sepsis, infection and haemorrhage. To have conceived is her joy; the ultimate result of her conception is her ambition.' Read continued: 'two, three or four per cent of some tribes [die in childbirth] without any sadness . . . realising if they were not competent to produce children for the spirits of their fathers and for the tribe, they had no place in the tribe'.

The fact that birth practices actually vary widely across different countries and cultures reveals them to be a human and cultural rather than a uniformly 'natural' process. Margaret Mead and Niles Newton described how birth is regarded not only as both 'an event of illness or of normal physiology' but also as 'an open sexual event or one fraught with shame or secrecy, as meriting pay or praise, dirt or defilement, and/or supernatural involvement'. Any talk of women's 'maternal instinct', they added in their classic study, 'must reckon with this great variety in the handling of childbirth'. Non-industrialised peoples use naturally occurring drugs to hasten labour, and operations that enlarge the birth passages, including episiotomy. If women in these societies were able to give birth naturally, anthropologists have pointed out, they wouldn't need artificial interventions. Nor is it the case that non-Western women find birth painless: this was debunked in a 1950 paper by psychiatrists Lawrence Freedman and Vera Ferguson.

Not everyone was convinced by Dick-Read's thesis. One of his articles, published in 1946 in the *Sunday Pictorial* under the headline 'The Miracle of Childbirth', provoked a flood of responses. Some wrote to express fervent admiration for his methods: how they transformed birth from ordeal to triumph. Others were furiously reproachful: 'Even a pedigree cow enjoys analgesia when its owner is a humanitarian,' wrote one woman to the magazine. 'In this age of progress and research, don't you think that something should be done to relieve the ordeal of childbirth?' asked another. 'It is no use doctors saying that it is a natural event when we live highly civilised lives.' And another: 'You have been marvellously lucky in finding all the "animal" women,' who have their children 'while cooking dinner – in a bus – etc – painlessly.' The experience of another was refutation in itself: 'I had no fear,' she wrote, 'and yet I certainly had pain.'

PEDESTALS AND PREJUDICE

While Dick-Read appeared to praise East End working-class and African women for being able to give birth easily, what is generally absent from histories of the NCT is that he was motivated by eugenics. At the same time as idealising these women, he wished for them to be bred out of the human race. Dick-Read's aim was to convince more of the 'better sort' to procreate. Dick-Read targeted women from the middle and upper classes by placing articles in the upmarket *Times* and *Telegraph* newspapers. He wrote in 1943: 'If we are to survive as a people, and as an Empire, we must constantly be alert to improve our stock.' Likewise, Prunella Briance, the founder of the Natural Childbirth Association, which would become the NCT, wrote in 1957 that 'we urgently need in Britain a race of good quality men and women'.

Dick-Read and Briance were of course products of their time. Britain's heavy losses in the first and second world wars led to interest in what was known as 'positive eugenics', or encouraging the 'fit' to multiply, rather than preventing the 'unfit' from reproducing: a more acceptable ideology, perhaps. Those inclined towards positive eugenics aimed to transform childbirth into a more comfortable experience – for the right kind of women. Even after eugenics lost its acceptability, these attitudes were to influence the natural childbirth movement for many years to come. The fact that natural birth advocates still idealise non-white and non-elite women has ramifications not only for the women who are being 'taught a lesson', but also for those held up as examples: they are romanticised, but simultaneously stigmatised – and all while they actually endure worse birth outcomes.

Fuelled by these demographic concerns, the natural birth movement contributed to the post-war effort to persuade women back into the kitchen. In a speech to the Eugenics

Society in 1945, Dick-Read warned that if women did not embrace their vocation as mothers, 'our country will, within a few generations, cease to be a power or even an influence among nations of the world'. In *Motherhood in the Post-War World*, published a year earlier, he denounced the paradox of the woman who rejects her natural destiny. 'Woman fails when she ceases to desire the children for which she was primarily made,' he wrote. 'Her true emancipation lies in freedom to fulfil her biological purposes.'

Natural childbirth became intertwined with 1950s 'feminine mystique'. By 1960, an article in *Good Housekeeping* headlined 'How to Know When You're Really Feminine' noted that 'it is definitely more feminine to deliver one's child without the aid of drugs than to ask for an analgesic during delivery'. A male contributor to *Woman's Home Companion* enthused after witnessing a natural birth that even though the woman had had her baby within the hour, 'every hair was in place. Powder and lipstick were on just so. Her eyes were shining.' Women giving birth 'naturally' in the 1950s were expected to be quiet and compliant. An audio recording was made of a woman giving birth according to Dick-Read's method: even during the delivery, she just moans softly.

Although well-to-do women were Dick-Read's target reader-ship, his entreaties to them became increasingly impatient; not least, I believe, because those women were also the ones most likely to seek an education and employment outside the home. Dick-Read is quoted in A. Noyes Thomas's 1957 biography as saying, with curious alliteration: 'Single women of thirty and over should all be pitied, I'm told. But my experience is that they are impetuous, imprudent and impertinent. Their impenetrable minds are as impervious as their impassioned bodies and, for the sake of mankind, they should all be either imprisoned or impregnated!' If a woman felt pain, it was her fault. 'A tense woman,' he wrote, 'is closing the door against her baby.'

In fact, Dick-Read's hostility towards emancipated women appears to have prompted him to reveal, unwittingly, that his true attitude to pain in childbirth was highly inconsistent. Although he is well known for declaring that childbirth is not inherently painful, in an article in the *Sunday Pictorial*, he advised doctors to remind women that childbirth, 'is Nature's first hard lesson in the two greatest assets of good motherhood. Children will always mean hard work and self-control. Tell her the truth: motherhood is not fun, it is not a hobby.'

Such attitudes are perennial. In 2008, Belinda Phipps, then chief executive of the NCT, said: 'If we just dropped babies like eggs without noticing, what would that say about the responsibilities we're taking on for the next 20 years? Birth marks you out as a mother and a carer for a very long time.' Her comments were echoed a year later by Denis Walsh, a senior midwife and Associate Professor in Midwifery at Nottingham University. 'More women should be prepared to withstand pain,' he told the *Observer*. 'Pain in labour is a purposeful, useful thing, which has quite a number of benefits, such as preparing a mother for the responsibility of nurturing a newborn baby.' Phipps's mention of eggs recalled for me the late-nineteenth-century French physician Joseph Gerard, who wrote in a popular book on child health: 'When a hen lays an egg, she does not yet claim to qualify as a mother . . . the hen's real virtue emerges when she begins conscientiously to sit on it, depriving herself of her dear freedom.'

I thought about this history often as I sat in my NCT classes. 'Doing' NCT is regarded by many as a rite of passage, and an expensive one: the courses cost around £250 – although discounts are offered to those on low incomes. I'd signed up partly because, like many working mothers-to-be, I was worried about the imminent transition to domestic isolation. Chatting to the other women in the breaks, I found that all of us were in the thick of our careers. Early on we were asked what kind of birth we were planning on having. If I'd have said I'd quite like to book in an elective caesarean and then organise sufficient childcare to get back to my desk pretty sharpish, that would not have gone down well. It isn't what I wanted, but still. I was the only one who said I wanted to give birth on a labour ward.

We sat in that north London hotel function room feeling self-conscious and apprehensive. It was a kind of humiliation, having to buy friends because our real ones were not having babies at the exact same time, being encouraged to crouch on all fours and groan like wild animals, our partners awkwardly massaging our lower backs. It was like an excruciating corporate icebreaker, but this was no elite leadership course: we were preparing to exit the world of work. For our partners, the hiatus would last a fortnight; for us, the renunciation could prove permanent.

Of course, it is not now the mission of the NCT to persuade women to put their ambitions aside. But the institution has a history, and some ideological elements of that history are still at work. Get with the programme, it felt like we were being told. Where you are going, your professional airs and graces can't help you. But you have your breathing exercises. And remember to relax! It's nearly time for nature to take its course. Just give in. You can try to mitigate its force if you like, but really, pain relief is just for wimps. And also, it might harm your baby, and you wouldn't want that, would you?

MIND OVER MATTER?

Pain is a notoriously subjective experience. It is impossible to measure definitively. We only access our body through our mind's perception of it. Doctors ask patients to rate their pain on a scale of one to ten, but it's hard to know what ten feels like. Looking at the brain with an MRI scanner doesn't really help, because that just provides a picture of what the brain is experiencing: it's just an image of the act of perception.

Pain varies from person to person, according to interpretation, context, and state of mind. I'm sure that if I'd been supported to really feel that my contractions were 'taking me closer to my baby', as the natural birth advocates have it, I'd have been able to contain them, rather than them overwhelming me. A 2017 study by Australian researchers suggested that 'when women interpret the pain as productive and purposeful, it is associated with positive cognitions and emotions, and they are more likely to feel they can cope'.

That doesn't mean, however, that the pain is a figment of women's imagination. The Australian historian Clare Monagle writes of her own birth, during which she suffered a fourth-degree tear from sphincter to vagina, that the experience was one of 'abject horror, and the destruction of self. In the pain, I could find no bridge to anything I recognised; there was no familiarity and there was no language . . . The pain felt like it was my being now and I was outside of time.' Although the pain can almost defy description, it is also, Monagle acknowledges, 'subject to discursive construction' – yet it is also 'desperately entirely real'.

Rather than being a modern, Western foible, ancient writers repeatedly describe childbirth as the most dreadful pain endured in human life. Homer's *Iliad* refers to 'the sharp sorrow', while the Romans called it *poena magna* – the 'great pain'. In a 1984 lecture, 'The Myth of Painless Childbirth', the psychologist and theorist of pain, Ronald Melzack, concluded that whatever outlandish fables suggest, 'most women suffer severe pain during labour'. Melzack is well known for developing an 'objective' measure called the McGill Pain Questionnaire. But countless women would come to the same conclusion subjectively.

* * *

There is a tension running through the way we think about childbirth – with roots in history – that has profound implications for women today. Is childbirth a physical process that you just have to give yourself up to, or is it steered by your mindset? This tension is at the heart of attitudes still swirling unexamined in our culture: about educated women being asked to suspend their intellects when they procreate, about the disavowed hierarchical jostling between 'cerebral' male doctors and 'intuitive' female midwives, and about the idealisation of a version of motherhood that is down-to-earth and basic.

So what drives birth: head, or womb? In the mid-twentieth century, obstetrics and psychiatry were linked disciplines: one obstetrician, a certain W. C. W. Nixon, wrote that 'childbirth is a psychosomatic process par excellence, the mental state playing an important part in its progression'. Women's brains appeared to be important to Dick-Read primarily as receptors for his creed of painless childbirth: 'It is necessary,' he wrote to one doctor, 'to create the atmosphere that can give confidence in our teaching and that can allow us the influence essential for the control of their emotions.' For Dick-Read, childbirth was not merely 'a physical function', but 'a series of *spiritual* experiences, from fantasy to fact and from fact to fruition'.

For the natural childbirth technique to work, women had to believe in it – or at least, in its advocates. One mother described Dick-Read as a 'magnetic and persuasive' character. A rather critical obstetrician wrote to him in 1939: 'I think you are in some danger of failing to realise how much your own personality helps towards success'; another noted that 'patients wouldn't hurt just to please him'. Faith has played a central part in the movement's history. Dick-Read was an evangelical Christian. 'To me this work is no longer an obstetric practice only, but a mission,' he confessed. His aim in life was 'to give everything to spread the Gospel of sane and happy childbirth.' As well as being a member of a non-established church, Dick-Read was brought up believing in homeopathy, and natural childbirth was a similarly alternative tradition: it traded on its status as an underground method rejected by mainstream obstetricians.

Dick-Read's gospel of natural childbirth functioned as a kind of informal propaganda, disseminated through dozens of letters to obstetricians and midwives, an international lecture circuit, and his many newspaper and magazine articles. Dick-Read even presided over the first televised human birth in Britain, broadcast by the BBC in 1957. As we're about to see, a rather different kind of propaganda about painless childbirth was also being produced at the very same time, on the other side of the Iron Curtain.

PERSUASION

When my son was born I was given a zany colourful toy that clipped onto his buggy. The label said Lamaze. I had no idea that Lamaze International, a multi-million-dollar organisation, grew out of a mind-control technique developed in Soviet Russia. It all started with Pavlov's dog. The Russian doctor Ivan Pavlov rang a bell and then gave his dog some food, and when the dog saw the food, it started to salivate. The dog began to associate the bell with food, and after a while, it would salivate when it just heard the bell. This is known as a conditioned reflex, and it earned Pavlov the Nobel Prize in 1904.

Like Europe and America, the Soviet Union was looking for inexpensive ways to boost their population after the First World War, and the Politburo seized on a theory rather similar to Dick-Read's. Like Pavlov's dog, pregnant women were to be trained out of the idea that labour would hurt. This method of persuasion was known as psychoprophylaxis, and it was instituted in every maternity unit in the Soviet Union. 'The expectant mother must be convinced' that, like any normal physiological act, childbirth 'will be painless,' wrote the psycho-therapist Konstantin Platonov, one of the authors of the 1954 book *Painless Childbirth Through Psychoprophylaxis*. He called for 'the re-education and re-shaping of a mental attitude in which for centuries a fatalistic belief in pain has found roots'. As the obstetrician Anatoly Nikolaev put it, 'if the head is in any way responsible for labour pain, it is not the head of the foetus but that of the mother'.

In 1950, Nikolaev visited Paris and gave a lecture on the method; in the audience was an obstetrician named Fernand Lamaze. He was enthralled, and the following year, visited the Soviet Union as part of a delegation of left-wing doctors. He begged to witness the fabled technique of natural, painless childbirth first-hand, but his guides initially refused; when he threatened to denounce it as a sham, he was finally taken to Nikolaev's clinic in Leningrad, where, he said, he wept with happiness at seeing a thirty-five-year-old typist give birth to her first child 'without pain and with joy'.

Lamaze himself was not much of a role model. He cheated on his wife with numerous mistresses and went out drinking while she was having their first baby. When she requested a divorce and he refused, she killed herself. He contracted syph-ilis from prostitutes and passed it on to her replacement. Personal life is not always relevant, but it's ironic that women have through the centuries taken advice from such men (I'm also thinking of Rousseau, who as we'll see, was a less than perfect role model, and, to some extent, Dick-Read).

In his ideas at least – and the dramatic framing of his 'discovery' of the miracle of natural childbirth – Lamaze was in many ways a parallel figure to Dick-Read; and Dick-Read fought a long battle to prove that he had arrived at his method independently. Like Dick-Read, Lamaze was a charismatic figure and in France this helped to popularise his technique, which involved breathing exercises and other relaxation techniques. It also resonated with a live tradition of medicine and philosophy concerned with the relationship between mind and body, first propagated by René Descartes.

Lamaze's 1956 book *Painless Childbirth* went on to become a bestseller in the US, but not before the technique was freed from its associations with Soviet mind control. As Elisabeth Bing, one of the founders of the American Society for Psychoprophylaxis in Obstetrics – now Lamaze International – noted, mentioning the method's Soviet origins 'was not a very good public relations move, given how Americans were feeling about Russians in the late 50s'. It is for this reason, as well as the force of Fernand Lamaze's personality, that psychoprophylaxis became known as the Lamaze method. And in a final irony, natural childbirth as a way of boosting population numbers was cited in post-war America as a defence against the 'Red Menace'.

THE SECOND WAVE

When I was pregnant, I was gently instructed to relinquish my intellectual mind to my instinctual body. This had the opposite effect. My body was being assailed by novel symptoms, from twinges to cramps to piles, forcing me to focus on my physical self as never before. But at the same time, my mind fought a kind of rearguard action, aware of its vulnerable plight. In the teeth of the pacifying advice and immersive distraction, I was determined to rationalise what was happening to me. I didn't want to be ruled by my biology.

However, in the cult of natural childbirth, the body is boss. The natural birth writer and practitioner Michel Odent set up a *'salle sauvage'*, or 'primitive room', at his maternity clinic in France. Odent argues that the key to an easy birth is the suppression of the neocortex, the part of the brain that performs higher cognitive functions such as conscious reasoning and language.

A labouring woman should, he has said, avoid 'thinking too much'. Yet at the same time, many natural childbirth proponents claim to champion conscious choice, control and empowerment, in contrast to what they present as doped-up medicalised birth.

The work of Sheila Kitzinger, one of the leading lights of the movement, and who notably described giving birth as like having a multiple orgasm, illustrates this ambivalence about mind, body and control. 'One pushes exactly when and as long as and as strongly as each [contraction] indicates,' she wrote in 1962. 'It is a little like the orchestra responding to the conductor's baton.' The conductor is the uterus. Yet apparently this approach means the birthing woman is 'no longer a passive, suffering instrument.' She no longer 'hands over her body to doctor and nurses to deal with as they think best'. She retains the 'power of self-direction, of self-control, of choice, and of voluntary decision.' The authority of medical practitioners is replaced by the unthinking authority of the womb – as well as the advice of the natural birth guru. The labouring woman must, above all, 'have learned to trust her body and its instincts', Kitzinger wrote, a form of harmony that 'to a few civilised women comes naturally, but which most of us have to learn painstakingly.'

Kitzinger's approach illustrates how the natural birth movement merged, in the 1970s, with second-wave feminism. The manicured 1950s housewife gave way to the grunting, squatting, feminist earth mother. As Dorothy Thomashower, a New Yorker who herself opted for a hospital birth, wrote: 'it wasn't until women were burning their bras and letting their hair grow under their arms that they really all went for natural childbirth'. Although this incarnation seemed a far cry from the mid-century artificiality of household appliances and 'just add an egg', it was in a sense a continuation of the feminine mystique. As Betty Friedan understood, that mystique was as much about nature as it was about lipstick: 'it says this femininity is so mysterious and intuitive and close to the creation and origin of life that man-made science may never be able to understand it'.

In 1970, the natural birth advocate and practitioner Ina May Gaskin set up an eco-hippy commune known as the 'Farm' in rural Tennessee that still hosts birthing women today. During a Farm birth, Gaskin described in her 1975 book *Spiritual Midwifery*, there is no anaesthesia and few medical interventions. Gaskin declared that labouring women did not experience pain; they had 'interesting sensations'. A woman who asked to be taken to hospital for an epidural – the only such case in the Farm's history – was dismissed by Gaskin as a 'princess'. The complicity of these branches of feminism in perpetuating misogynistic attitudes is an apparent paradox.

Ina May Gaskin liked to draw parallels between labouring women and animals. She got through her first labour without any medication, she wrote in another book, *Birth Matters: A Midwife's Manifesta*, 'by pretending that I was a mountain lion'. She continued: 'One of my specialties during the early days of cultural development at The Farm was teaching "civilised", "educated" women how to behave like indigenous people – actually, like any other mammal . . . "Let your monkey do it" became the phrase I used to say to those intelligent, often competitive women who, by force of habit, used to try to "think" their babies out.'

Being told to 'let go' can be liberating, but it's also philistine, regressive and sexist. I am quite wedded to feeling in control, it's true, but at the same time men do not get asked to embrace their inner animal, to put aside their public, cerebral persona. While some women genuinely want to have a natural birth, it is uncomfortably ironic that women are now applauded for choosing the same painful birth their ancestors only endured because they had to. It is unfair that only affluent women had access to medical care during childbirth in the past, but curious that this demographic later came to passionately eschew it.

* * *

The brand of natural childbirth we have now is suspicion of airbrushed, upgraded 1950s domesticity and a 1970s new age yoga-and-candles ethos. Women drink raspberry leaf tea and prepare to open up like a lotus, but it is no longer socially acceptable to leave your bikini area unwaxed. Natural birth has become more of an industry, too – with a proliferation of hypnobirthing classes, doula services, and self-care products – and it's all packaged in the language of 'empowerment'.

The history of the natural childbirth movement shows that many of its advocates were genuinely striving to reclaim women's autonomy from patriarchal medical control. Compared with doctors, midwives have been routinely disrespected. The movement was an understandable reaction to this hierarchy, and also to what it was like to have a medicalised birth in the mid-twentieth century. The first manifesto of the Natural Childbirth Association set out its opposition to this 'conveyor belt' approach to birth. But in many respects, this wasn't really a women's movement at all. Its early proponents were men, and they wanted to work with doctors, not circumvent them.

Childbirth in the early to mid-twentieth century was often such a ghastly experience that the movement gained much value simply by emphasising the importance of a present and kind birth attendant, as well as arguing that partners should be in the room too. One woman wrote in response to an article by Dick-Read: 'I have had four babies, and I'm not scared of the pain, but they are pains of hell you ask any mother . . . But I do agree with the sympathy you want at the time from a nurse, if they would only stay with you, and hold your hand at times, half the battle is won, but I saw a nurse smack a woman's face once, and the woman was not histirical [sic], she only kept telling the nurse her baby was being born which it was.'

Just being supported goes a long way. But natural childbirth does not deserve its reputation as the automatically feminist choice.

THE SCIENCE BIT

So much for historical attitudes and campaigns: what does the evidence say? Cochrane is a charitable organisation that pulls together and assesses medical research: it provides a critical overview of the existing knowledge. In 2012, Cochrane reviewed the available data from around the world and found that epidurals work the best by far, followed by gas and air. Water birth, relaxation, acupuncture and massage may work. For hypnosis, TENS, aromatherapy, and Pethidine, there is not enough evidence to say either way.

Cochrane has shown that epidurals are very safe. They have no adverse effect on the baby: they do not alter Apgar scores, the indication of health straight after birth. There is no evidence that they make caesareans any more likely. They don't lengthen the first stage of labour. They may lengthen the second stage (the delivery bit), but only by about thirteen minutes. They do increase the chance of an instrumental delivery such as by forceps or ventouse, but this may be because the women who ask for epidurals are more likely to be having a complicated birth, which in itself increases the likelihood of instrumental delivery. To put this into perspective, for every twenty women who have an epidural, one extra woman would need delivery assisted in this way. Forceps and ventouse increase the risk to the mother of vaginal tears or cuts, but are safe for babies.

As Philip Steer explained to me, there is one other effect of epidurals that is not harmful in itself but needs monitoring: they raise the temperature of the mother, and this can produce an abnormal heart-rate pattern in the baby. Steer's team is conducting ongoing research into this. I was told in my NCT classes that the problem with epidurals is that they require you to be wired up to a foetal heart monitor so you are immobilised on your back, the worst position in which to give birth. But women could be offered wireless monitors as standard. It is also not widely known that women lying on their side are just as able to give birth as women remaining upright or crouching on all fours.

What about caesareans? As with pain relief, there is suspicion that these 'interventions' are carried out not for the baby's sake, but for the mother. The 'debate' about the safety of caesareans is really a debate about elective caesareans, but the decision is often not about convenience, but trauma the first time around: this was my reasoning with child number two.

There is no difference in terms of babies' survival rates between caesareans and vaginal births. It is possible that caesareans may increase the chance of the child developing asthma or allergies later in life, but the evidence here is unclear: there could be other explanations for this, for example, babies born by caesarean are slightly more likely to be premature and have low birth weights. It is hard to separate the risks generated by the C-section itself from the conditions that necessitated the C-section. The vulnerability to allergies may be due to the fact that babies born by C-section do not receive the inoculating effects of being exposed to the mother's bacteria during delivery; a quick swipe by hand could remedy this.

Another widespread myth is that pain in childbirth – and indeed vaginal births as opposed to caesareans – create an especially close bond between mother and baby. In *Childbirth in the Age of Plastics*, Michel Odent acknowledges that labour pain is real. But he traces a chain of causation from pain, to the production of endorphins, to the production of prolactin, the 'motherhood hormone', to lactation, essential for breast-feeding. 'Any attempt to eliminate electively the pain will neutralise the whole chain of events,' he warns. Having had a caesarean under a general anaesthetic and another under an epidural, I know that this is not true: I breastfed both my children easily right after birth, and I rode the full-on roller-coaster of maternal hormones from all-encompassing love to uncontrollable tears. Caesareans have been associated with lower levels of breastfeeding, but this could be down to other factors, such as not enough skin-to-skin contact after the birth – rates have been boosted by facilitating this.

As for the mother, whose health and welfare often seem to be at the back of the queue when it comes to assessing risks, some studies have found that C-sections raise the risks of infection, postnatal depression, future infertility and a longer hospital stay. But NICE has judged many of these studies to be of low quality, and also found that women who had a planned caesarean described 'a significantly better birthing experience'. I found recovery even from my emergency caesarean relatively straight-forward compared to other impacts of giving birth, but when I was deciding to have a second, planned one, I was informed – often by men in fact – that abdominal surgery is 'not trivial'. Sometimes women are warned away from caesareans for being risky, other times for being just offputtingly unpleasant. I am suspicious of the dual approach.

Caesareans reduce the risk of heavy blood loss and injury to the vagina, and vaginal birth also carries a higher risk of lifelong urinary incontinence. But women are not told about the 'risks' of vaginal delivery, because it is seen as the 'natural', default choice. Vaginal birth after a caesarean, or VBAC as it's known, results in an emergency caesarean for 28 per cent of women (nearly double the background rate).

The influential 'Birthplace in England' cohort study,

published in 2011, found that doctor-led birth units increase interventions without an improvement in outcomes. But for a substantial minority, things can go very wrong, very quickly. I sat in on Philip Steer's training afternoon for midwives and doctors on monitoring babies during labour. Steer explained that inadequate foetal monitoring is often responsible for injuries or deaths. Aside from sessions like these, which are funded by charitable donations, midwives and doctors receive surprisingly little training in monitoring, he told me. In the US, by contrast, a fully trained obstetrician is present at every birth. Steer showed slides of heartbeat traces. Turning points were marked with pencil arrows: from there, regular, healthy patterns gave way to hectic zigzags, juddering downwards. The NHS pays out billions each year in compensation for births that go wrong – about half of all litigation claims in monetary terms. The sum has risen greatly in recent years. The high-value claims are made by parents whose babies have died, or who are left caring for children with cerebral palsy as a result of being starved of oxygen – often while caesareans were put off.

As for home births, there have been no randomised controlled trials here. Those who choose to give birth at home tend to be at lower risk anyway, partly because statistically they tend to be better off financially – so it is hard to compare like with like. The Birthplace in England study found that first-time mothers who give birth at home are nearly three times more likely to have a dead or damaged baby, and 45 per cent of women who attempt to have their first babies at home are transferred to hospital either during or shortly after birth. For 'low-risk' women having their second or subsequent baby, giving birth at home appears to be safer. But in contrast to the notion that birth is a 'normal' event, more than half of women have, or will develop, risk factors that make home birth risky. About 50 per cent of women have complications in pregnancy, and a further half will develop them in labour: only a quarter are low risk. I am not arguing that women shouldn't be allowed to give birth at home; but the statistics on home birth highlight the fact that interventions are sometimes necessary.

'EMPOWERMENT'

When they decide where and how to give birth, the vast majority of women are driven by an intense desire to ensure a healthy outcome for their baby. But most also mistakenly believe that this trumps all other considerations, including her own well-being. In fact, in the UK, until the child is born, women are not legally obliged to take the interests of their unborn child into account in their choices. Of course, doctors and midwives have a professional responsibility to inform her of the relative risks to herself and the baby of taking a certain action. But ultimately, no matter what the science says, the woman is in charge. And she may legitimately act in her own interest. Mothers matter too.

The landmark Montgomery ruling of 2015 reinforced the principle of informed choice (Nadine Montgomery was not told the risks of a vaginal delivery, and her son was left with cerebral palsy as a result). Yet the paternalistic way in which childbirth (and, as we'll see in a later chapter, pregnancy) is still managed suggests that, even now, that ruling is only blurrily implemented.

A 2020 survey of 1,145 mothers by Mumsnet and the charity Birthrights, which champions women's autonomy in childbirth, found that a quarter of women felt their birth preferences had not been respected, and a further third were not asked for them at all. The 2016 NHS England 'Better Births' report found that despite some improvements in consulting women over the previous five years, 15 per cent said they were not offered any say in where they had their babies.

Rineke Schram is the lead obstetrician for Lancashire and

South Cumbria; she works with Birthrights, training other doctors about the law and how it should be applied in practice. 'It's no different from consenting someone to have an operation on their hip; discussing the pros and cons and alternatives,' Schram explained. 'And yet in a maternity setting it's often presented as different because of the baby: "a healthy baby is all important". And of course it is important, but how important it is in the context of that woman's experience, and what that particular woman wants or doesn't want, or how she accepts risk: that may differ according to the individual, and that's where choice and autonomy comes in.' She added: 'A woman is not a piece of luggage, just there to carry the baby.'

I also wanted to hear some midwives' perspectives. Simon Mehigan, who has been a midwife for over twenty years, is now director of midwifery at the Northern Care Alliance NHS Group. Mehigan is one of seven children, half of whom were born at home: 'I have a very positive view of the physiology of birth,' he told me; but 'I haven't got a bias either way.' He disagreed with my perception of the cultural dominance of natural birth: 'so many celebrities have elective sections and planned births', he said.

The fact that Mehigan and I perceive the social pressure so differently may have something to do with the fact that the picture is somewhat contradictory: caesarean rates are rising, creating the impression of increasing medicalisation. Yet social attitudes have, I believe, run in the opposite direction. This is also true in the US: 'At the same time as the rates of caesarean section are soaring, the use of midwifery care is also soaring', writes the American researcher Alexandra Fowler Dalton about the situation there. 'At the same time that medical intervention has become a standard part of childbirth, some women are questioning the necessity of these interventions.'

Mehigan also works with Birthrights, training other midwives to better protect women's rights. 'To me the most important thing is that a woman comes out of a birth experience feeling that she made decisions that were right for her,' he said, 'whether that be a beautiful uncomplicated home birth or a very straightforward elective section that went perfectly to plan.' He believes, however, that women are not being told enough about the risks of a C-section: 'It's just making sure that women understand all the risks without it being loaded one way or another.'

Schram and Mehigan's stated objective – and I agree with them – is to provide the clearest and most balanced information possible, and then leave it to the woman to decide. Delivering informed consent should also reduce concerns about liability among health professionals – leading to fewer unwanted interventions.

Yet as Rineke Schram observed, communication is not just about simply presenting the evidence. First of all, there may be a difference between guidelines and what is right for an individual: 'Guidelines are there for populations,' she told me. 'You use the guideline to have the conversation with an individual, but the individual makes the decision.' Second, sometimes the data is just really hard to crunch, particularly during a stressful labour. As Mehigan told me: 'You can give women all this information, and sometimes they'll still say, what would you do?'

And third, 'it's not just about risk,' Schram told me, 'but also about the judgement and the experience of the health practitioner, and the principles held by the woman.' According to the philosopher of medicine, Elselijn Kingma, 'we should focus less time debating the evidence and more time considering the values that play a role in discussions about birth. Those values are at present disconcertedly lop sided, paying attention almost exclusively to the harms done to babies, but not to those done to women.'

It is possible to give women apparently neutral statistics, while still communicating a preference. Saying to a woman:

'I've given you all the information on risks, but if you still decide to go ahead, then you are free to do that' conveys a subtly judgemental message. In the chaos of labour and delivery, informed choice is a complex and fraught concept that requires careful thought if it is to be meaningfully enacted. Doing so requires practitioners to acknowledge their values, priorities and agendas.

It is true that labouring women are sometimes rushed into medical procedures in the crowded wards of cash-strapped hospitals: induction is a particular problem. The situation is also very different in Britain and America. In the US, obstetricians largely took over from midwives; in the UK midwives are ostensibly in charge. British hospitals may unofficially limit epidurals and other 'interventions' on the grounds of cost: according to NICE, a planned vaginal birth is approximately £700 cheaper than a maternal request C-section, although it acknowledges that other costs down the line such as that of managing urinary incontinence may make it less clearly advantageous. In the US, there is a perverse financial incentive to carry out more procedures, but this context doesn't justify the disapproval directed at those who have them.

Caesareans are becoming more common not only because of bigger baby heads but also because of risk factors such as rising obesity and maternal age. But there is resistance – traditionally on the part of public health authorities, and in the culture at large – to this trend. Until recently, the WHO recommended that only 10 to 15 per cent of babies should be delivered by C-section. Women should not be browbeaten into agreeing to a caesarean by risk-averse doctors fearing litigation, a shortage of one-to-one care, or the compulsion to keep nether regions intact. But the setting of a somewhat arbitrary low target communicates judgement.

NICE guidelines clearly state that women have the right to an elective section, even without medical need. Birthrights found in 2018 that only a quarter of women who requested a caesarean were granted one without 'judgemental attitudes, barriers and disrespect', and in 2020 they found that only a quarter of trusts in England were following the guidelines. There are some signs that attitudes are changing – in 2018 the Care Quality Commission instructed hospital inspectors to stop assessing maternity wards on the basis of how few caesareans they carried out, explaining that it sent the wrong message about 'normal' and 'abnormal' births. Yet those attitudes still persist.

Some women feel they shouldn't ask for pain relief; others ask but don't get. In 2020, a government report found that, again contrary to NICE guidelines, women were being denied epidurals, sometimes through deflection or deferral. 'I know this happens because I've encountered it in my own trust,' David Bogod told me, 'you will see it in the records: a prime cause of complaint is a woman who requests an epidural but is told the anaesthetist is not available, and you go back to our records and there are anaesthetists sitting around with their feet up, and you see this in other units too.'

Related to this is the management of early labour, or the 'latent phase'. As Rineke Schram told me, many adverse birth outcomes begin with women's requests to stay in hospital being refused. I was nearly one of those cases. It is invariably midwives – as in my case – who send women back home: they are the first point of contact. I believe attitudes play a part: midwives not regarding one or two centimetres' dilation as sufficient grounds to stay. But there are also, of course, a limited number of beds. Simon Mehigan told me that 'latent phase is one of the biggest challenges we face in maternity services'. Because early labour is not a medically acute state, the rationing is allowed to continue, but given that it's a time of such anxiety for women, increasing provision should be a priority.

Women are routinely told they cannot have an epidural if

their labour is not advanced enough, and then that they cannot have one because it's too late. I was told in my NCT classes that there is a strict 'window' of possibility: between four and six centimetres' dilation; but as Bogod told me, 'this artificial window is complete and utter craziness' – he is glad that NICE is now debunking it – 'there's no science to it whatsoever'. Clearly there are financial implications for a resource-poor health service, but there's an attitudinal dimension too: according to Hanz Peter Dietz, obstetrics and gynaecology professor at the University of Sydney, 'there is a lot of anti-epidural bias amongst midwives, and women are even lied to because some midwives think they know better'. I asked Simon Mehigan about the 'window', and he acknowledged that a minority of midwives hold outdated views: 'It takes a long time to change culture,' he told me; 'it's not a quick fix.'

BEYOND CHOICE

The notion that women have agency and control in childbirth is enshrined in the birth plan, the wish list a pregnant woman is encouraged to compile before labour. Would she like to give birth on a labour ward, or in a natural birthing unit? Would she like an epidural? Gas and air? Or will she try the birthing pool?

I support the rights of all women to try for the births they want. But as the American historian Paula Michaels has noted, there is something fundamentally unhelpful about the entire framing of childbirth in terms of 'choice'. When the researcher Alexandra Fowler Dalton interviewed pregnant women about their birth preferences, the majority didn't fall into distinct 'camps', but wanted the 'best of both worlds': a natural as possible experience, with staff on hand if needed. Choice is an important element of autonomy, but it's not sufficient, and sometimes hollow. Most of the time, women simply want the best care.

Yet hospital architecture separates women into two distinct ideological pathways. There's the ward, with its bright lights and hi-tech equipment; and there's the midwife-led birth centre, with its 'home-from-home' ambience, birthing pools – and just one catch: no anaesthesia. As I've argued, a choice is not free when a particular course of action is framed as morally superior: this subtle privileging is illustrated in the furnishings.

It is a good idea for women to go into the process with a sense of possible scenarios and how they'd ideally like them to be managed, but if things do not go as planned, they can find themselves segueing rapidly from the natural to the medical for reasons of expediency. At the same time as women are denied self-determination, therefore, they are forced to take sides in an impractical and divisive debate. Why not just have the full range of alternatives, from pools to pain relief, available in a single room? Simon Mehigan would not recommend anaesthesia being offered on the midwife-led unit, but suggests instead that labour wards have a homelier atmosphere.

NHS England's Maternity Transformation Programme, arising out of the 'Better Births' report's findings, will hopefully lead to some real improvements. But that will only happen if there is official recognition that 'empowerment' and 'choice' sometimes means receiving, rather than resisting, 'interventions'. 'The natural childbirth lobby has had quite a lot of power within and around government,' David Bogod told me, 'and to some extent still does.' He identifies the association between 'feminism, empowerment, and normal birth' as 'the toxic link, but then you ask women what they actually want and discover, Oh my god, they want an abnormal birth – and then what are you going to do?'

Over the last few years, an investigation into failings at Shrewsbury and Telford Hospital NHS Trust has revealed the biggest maternity scandal in the history of the health service.

The senior midwife Donna Ockenden, who has led the inquiry, told MPs on the publication of an interim report in 2020: 'We have spoken to hundreds of women who have said to us they felt pressured to have a normal birth.' She also said that lives were lost as a result of caesareans not being offered early enough. The report called for urgent changes to all hospital trusts, including formal antenatal risk assessments and twice-daily consultant-led maternity ward rounds.

Another inquiry, the Morecambe Bay Investigation into deaths at the Furness General Hospital in Cumbria, found that midwives there were determined 'to pursue normal childbirth "at any cost"'; in fact they were so cavalier they dubbed themselves 'the musketeers'. An official review has since found that the Nursing and Midwifery Council (NMC) was slow to respond, and regarded James Titcombe, whose nine-day-old baby son died from a mishandled birth in Furness hospital, as a campaigning nuisance – even monitoring his Twitter feed. Titcombe said in 2017 that lessons had still not been learned, including around 'an overzealous pursuit of normal birth'. Cases like this keep emerging, but there is a resistance to joining the dots: the result, I argue, of a residual sense that midwives are the undervalued champions of labouring women.

Not being listened to has different resonances for different demographics. I am a relatively self-assured woman, but I was cowed into accepting what I was told when my legitimate concerns were laughed off. Indeed, I felt like a prima donna for even complaining at all. Luckily I came back into hospital before it was too late. In Rochdale, where Simon Mehigan works, 30 per cent are of an Asian ethnic background: there are language barriers to accessing services and ensuring informed consent. There are underlying risk factors in some minority ethnic communities, which also tend statistically to be more socioeconomically deprived – this increases risk still further. Some communities may be less likely to challenge health professionals, who in turn could be more culturally sensitive to specific needs.

Birthrights carried out a study with another charity, Birth Companions, which found that women who suffer from one or more disadvantages – whether they are living in poverty or poor housing, have mental health problems, or are asylum seekers – are less confident in articulating their wishes and are often not listened to or taken seriously when they do. A Canadian study published in 2010 found that less educated women on lower incomes are more likely to give birth on a hospital ward, but less likely to ask for epidurals, mirroring findings from other countries. All mothers, therefore, to a greater or lesser extent, have to navigate a gulf between rhetoric and reality when it comes to being treated with dignity and respect.

OUT IN THE OPEN

It is time we recognised the subterranean ideologies and disavowed power dynamics that underlie the act of giving birth. I have focused so much on historical debates in this chapter in part because the themes of those debates – pitting animal nature, primitivism and self-sacrifice against civilisation, medicine, and women's lives outside the home – tell us something about the evolution of retrograde attitudes that still prevail today. These attitudes will reappear through the chapters that follow.

Childbirth is a tumultuous, agonising process, but also a wondrous event; yet too often it is aggravated by these opposing agendas battling inexplicitly beneath the surface: natural versus medicalised birth, doctors against midwives, midwives against 'uppity' vocal mothers, mothers who achieved normal birth versus mothers who resorted to interventions, and the false zero-sum game between mother and baby. I would love to see genuine cooperation between all these parties and interests, working to make childbirth into a joyful, joint enterprise: but that will only happen, I believe, if we are honest about our different positions and beliefs.

Despite its iconoclastic origins, natural childbirth has been gradually incorporated into mainstream hospital practice: in the 1902 Midwives Act, which formalised what had previously been regarded as traditional folk wisdom and practical know-how, and in a 1993 Department of Health White Paper, *Changing Childbirth*. Some midwives have expressed ambivalence about what they have perceived as capitulation to patriarchal officialdom. As the editors of an anthology compiled from the archives of the Association of Radical Midwives stated in 1997: 'We think that the main battle area, the area of discontent, is over the realm of "professionalism".' There has been a contradictory desire for institutional recognition on one hand and countercultural independence on the other.

We should critique the power attached to knowledge, but not knowledge itself. To me, the slightly pointed emphasis on the jurisdiction of midwives felt like an ideological statement: the medical establishment agreeing to respect the primacy of normal birth. But my birth was not normal, and my wishes were not respected.

The practitioners I spoke to all emphasised that cultures are changing, and the all-important working relationships between doctors and midwives – involving good communication and mutual trust and respect – are becoming the norm. But there is still more to be done. Ted Baker, the Care Quality Commission's chief inspector of hospitals, said in an email seen by the *Guardian* in 2020 that inspectors had witnessed 'a cultural division between midwifery and obstetrics (or "normal" vs "interventional" approaches)'. He called for more work to create 'an effective multidisciplinary culture'.

Simon Mehigan told me that while constructive relationships

are the norm, some tensions still remain. 'I can think of some colleagues I have across the country who have worked in units where the power dynamic is very, very challenging,' he said, 'and where whatever the obstetrician says goes, and you wouldn't dare challenge them.' Rineke Schram concurred: 'There's something about power relationships and that continues,' although, she added, 'these are less gender-based than they were.'

David Bogod stresses that 'in the majority of trusts there is not a pitched battle between doctors and midwives,' and that most midwives are fully signed up to a multidisciplinary approach to childbirth'. But some midwives still regard themselves as 'guardians of normality'. 'I once described midwifery,' he adds, 'as the last bastion of paternalism in the NHS, which didn't go down very well, but I do think there are still a lot of paternalistic midwives out there.' He wants to see – and I think there is a consensus here – a properly funded maternity service, a genuine respect for maternal preferences, and one-to-one midwifery care. While there isn't a shortage of anaesthetists on maternity wards, he says, there is a clear shortage of midwives.

Although attitudes have been largely reformed, history reveals that the promotion of so-called 'normal' birth evolved hand in hand with some highly questionable and decidedly non-progressive agendas. Women have been told they *should* feel pain. But they have also been told they needn't feel pain and will only do so if they are culpably sophisticated – this argument relies, as I've shown, on inaccurate primitivist stereotypes.

It is time to restore proper perspective to discussions about 'medicalised' and 'natural' births, recognising which attitudes are actually – yet covertly – powerful. Women should not feel guilty, selfish or a failure if they have an epidural or a caesarean. Being bullied or cajoled into having a natural birth because of trumped-up risks to 'baby' is not what I call feminism. As we will see, however, the moral weight attached to certain styles of motherhood governs the whole process from beginning to end. And it's to the very beginning that I'll now turn.

2

TICK, TOCK

Before I got pregnant I was sure I wanted to have children, but I didn't particularly like children as a category. I found them uninteresting and intimidating. I babysat as a teenager, but I soon realised I was not 'good with kids'. Asking my charges what their bedtime routine was would have betrayed my ignorance, so I remember nonchalantly inserting a toothbrush into the two-year-old's mouth, wondering if she even had teeth to brush, and then into the eight-year-old's, wondering if this was as inappropriate as helping a twelve-year-old into a swimsuit. If you are with children every day, you become an expert through repetition, but the competence is age-specific: if someone handed me a stinking baby to change now, my approach to the task would be not far off that of a well-meaning childless person in their early twenties – I would hold my breath, and not be sure which way to wipe.

Even now I find being left alone with a child – especially one that's a different age to mine – a bit terrifying. It's even worse if I'm being observed. Most questions – how's nursery, what's your teddy's name – wither drily in the mouth before they are even uttered, or fall flat like pathetic stand-up. There's a one-word answer if you're lucky, then another mile of conversational wasteland to traverse. You can't reach for adult social skills with kids – charm, flirtation, drinking, or making acute observations about politics or literature. Those can't help you now. Children smell your fear. And so you struggle weakly on until the parent comes back in, looking cheerfully for signs that you've bonded. Instead, the child runs and clings to their legs.

It is getting easier now that my own children have reached an interesting and – though it's not their job – entertaining age. Sometimes I even prefer talking to kids than to adults. But going for a walk with an acquaintance and their new dog reminds me of that earlier stage (it turns out that getting puppies is what many people do when their kids get older; I on the contrary, grateful finally for a bit of peace and quiet, have drawn the line at a hamster). 'Oh sorry, are you alright with dogs?' they ask considerately as it jumps up at me. I stand there stiffly, feeling churlish for not letting it lick my face.

Despite looking after kids evidently not being my natural calling, from my late twenties onwards I started to feel pressure to 'settle down' and have them. I was led to believe that as a woman, I needed to become a mother. But I also had the strong impression that being a mother would 'break' me, or 'break me in': 'life will never be the same again', I often heard people say. It's a cruel combination, to be told to do something or else feel existentially lacking, and yet to be warned that that thing is more arduous than you can possibly imagine, especially while you're gadding about like that. Cycling to an absorbing job every day, and going out most nights, the messages felt jarringly discordant. I was surrounded by warnings that – in their frequent use of the phrase 'career women' – seemed to be pointing a finger directly at me.

'Should you have your baby now?' was the pointed question headlining one typical *Newsweek* story, from 2001, when I'd just got my first real job: 'Women today have grown up with the expectation of "having it all": material wealth, career success, marriage and children,' the writer explained, but they've neglected one small but crucial detail: their age. In 2014, the TV presenter Kirstie Allsopp warned women that their fertility would 'fall off a cliff' when they hit thirty-five. If she had a daughter, she told the *Telegraph*, she would say to her: 'Darling, do you know what? Don't go to university. Start work straight after school, stay at home, save up your deposit – I'll help you, let's get you into a flat. And then we can find you a nice boyfriend and you can have a baby by the time you're 27.'

When a thirty-seven-year-old Meghan, Duchess of Sussex announced that she was pregnant, the *Mail* was one of many newspapers to refer to it as a 'geriatric pregnancy' – the clinical, but surely journalistically unnecessary term (can't doctors use a different one too?). The *Mail* has cliché status on this topic, but deservedly so: an article from 2003, headlined 'Career women's baby hunger', carried a caution for 'well-educated women' who 'put off motherhood'. 'Desperate to conceive? Then give up that high flying job as research shows stress causes infertility', ran another of its headlines, in 2014. That phrase 'high-flying' suggests Icarus-like ambition – time and again, a successful career is framed as a hubristic prelude to an inevitable fall.

The *Daily Mail* is not the only culprit, however. 'Childlessness doubles as career women put off starting family until "too late"' announced the *Telegraph* in 2013. '"I couldn't have it all" – choosing between my child and my career' was the headline to a personal piece from the same year in the *Guardian*, illustrating the fine line between critique and reinforcement. In 2019, after the singer Rihanna tweeted about neglecting her family and friends because of work, *Grazia* magazine set out to explore 'why we prioritise career success over our actual happiness' (suggesting that 'career happiness' is an oxymoron). 'Career versus motherhood' was the dilemma headlining a *City A.M.* article in 2020, which blamed a global 'fertility crisis' on 'the higher number of women in education and work'. Also in

2020, *Forbes* was still reporting that 'Millennial Women Are Delaying Having Children Due To Their Careers'.

There's an unexamined knot of attitudes bound up in the phrase 'career women'. Its ubiquity – even now – indicates a pointed desire on the part of the patriarchy to take down women with the potential to succeed in worldly terms – and may reflect the fact that while the average age for a British woman to have her first child is thirty, it's thirty-five for university-educated women. There's also a curious investment – recalling the attitudes of the Dick-Read era – in the 'right sort' having more babies. One *Evening Standard* piece from 2005 presenting 'new evidence about how British career women are waiting longer than ever to have children' went on to spell out what the phrase 'career women' often really means: 'Figures from an official study show only 27.5 per cent of women born into middle-class families have given birth by the age of thirty. This compares with 54 per cent of women from working-class homes.' In the same year the *Telegraph* reported that 'Middle-class French mothers will be paid to start *le baby boom*': cash incentives were to be provided to persuade these women to have third babies, 'amid growing concern that too few children are being born to professional couples'. Family lobbyists, apparently, were 'dismayed by a fall in the number of babies born to better-educated women'.

A familiar metaphor in these stories is of course the bomb-like ticking clock. It apparently originated in a *Washington Post* story from 1978 headlined: 'The Clock Is Ticking for the Career Woman' (note the double meaning: the career woman's days are numbered). It was no accident that the article appeared at the same time as second-wave feminism, the development of contraceptives, the legalisation of abortion, and a declining birth rate. In 1957, the average American woman had 3.5 children; by 1976, that number had dropped to 1.5.

As the American writer and academic Moira Weigel has

noted, the idea of the biological clock was originally developed by the US Air Force, who were exploring the use of drugs to minimise the influence of circadian rhythms (pilots could be made to fly at any time of the day or night); but when it comes to motherhood, the emphasis is on obeying, rather than controlling, nature. If the ticking clock is mentioned at all, Weigel observes, it should describe the elimination of mothers' leisure time, as they put in a full working day, and then have to tackle the housework. The clock ticks so loudly because they are doing it all, not having it all.

The temporal alarmism is not restricted to the press: it is reflected in public attitudes. A commercial survey of 2,000 British women in 2017 found that 79 per cent believe having children should come before a career. In 2018, ITV's *Loose Women* asked its female viewers 'Did Your Biological Clock Panic You Into Having a Baby?' Almost a third said yes. 'Women have a biological clock. Men have a financial clock' is an oft-repeated maxim on Twitter. As the campaigner Jody Day notes in her 2017 TEDx talk on the subject, childless women still have to contend with being called 'crazy cat woman', 'witch', 'hag' and 'spinster' – not to mention 'bunny boiler'.

Psychologist Jordan Peterson, whose polemics are dispiritingly popular with many young men, argues in his YouTube talk 'Women at Thirty: Jordan Peterson's Advice for Young Women Choosing Careers Over Motherhood', that since most women will have not a career, but a rather less satisfying 'job', they would be better off seeking fulfilment in motherhood and domesticity, understood by what he regards as right-thinking women 'as the most important things in their life'. Peterson's appeal exemplifies how antiquated beliefs can appear fresh and countercultural when feminist equality is mistakenly assumed to be the dominant mainstream.

You might expect the medical advice underpinning these stories and attitudes to be more measured, but it is often just as dramatic. In 2005, three obstetricians, Susan Bewley, Melanie Davies and Peter Braude, wrote an editorial in the *British Medical Journal* (*BMJ*) declaring that 'women want to "have it all" but biology is unchanged; deferring defies nature and risks heartbreak'. In 2009, the American Society for Reproductive Medicine (ASRM) ran an ad campaign about age-related infertility, accompanied by an upside-down baby bottle in the shape of an hourglass. 'It's kind of like issuing a warning,' said the ASRM president Michael Soules. 'It's our duty to let people know.' In 2013, the journal *Reproductive BioMedicine Online* published an article entitled: 'Cassandra's prophecy: why we need to tell the women of the future about age-related fertility decline and "delayed" childbearing'. By employing the figure of Cassandra – who resisted Apollo's advances – as a metaphor, the article both positions itself as a Cassandra, counselling women not to leave it too late, and also seems to imply that women who 'resist' potential partners because they are holding out for a better prospect will suffer a similar fate.

By the time I was thirty-three, I had been living on my own for nearly a decade. I was trying to get beyond a junior grade in a shrinking media industry. The fertility fearmongering was like having an alarm clock waved in front of your face while trying to negotiate a twisting road. A few years before that, not yet out of my twenties and thoroughly single, I was told by a friend who'd already got married and had a baby to 'hurry up'. I'm not doing this on purpose, I thought. Good men seemed hard to find. When I wasn't single, I was either being messed around by unreliable heartthrobs, or uneasily dating men I knew were not quite right. Actually having children seemed as unlikely as developing a maternal instinct.

A killer combination of factors and expectations – biological constraints, demographic imbalances, rigid, stereotypical working patterns, the novel promises of science making it harder for those who don't succeed to tolerate disappointment, and the residual idea that fulfilment resides in becoming a mother – hits women at precisely the time when they have the best chance of achieving equality with men in the workplace. What a coincidence!

SOME PERSPECTIVE

It would seem from media portrayals that the 'heartbreak' of childlessness is a relatively new phenomenon, the consequence of women 'putting off' motherhood by entering higher education and the workplace. Yet difficulties conceiving are not new. In previous centuries, women sought all kinds of remedies for childlessness. Roman 'solutions' were particularly colourful: eat the eye of a hyena with liquorice and dill, or – something of a physical feat, this – pluck three hairs from the tail of a she-ass while she is being mounted, and then knot them together during intercourse. Medieval English women were sent off on pilgrimages or instructed to drink potions brewed from animals' sex organs (some still do). In the sixteenth century, Catherine de Medici consulted magicians, astrologers and quacks in her failed attempts to produce an heir for Henry II. In eighteenth-century Europe, women were encouraged to 'take the waters' in spa towns to prevent 'spasms of the womb', a supposed cause of infertility.

Late motherhood is also not an exclusively modern development. While pregnancy rates for women over forty have more than doubled since 1990, the stereotype of the contemporary career woman who chooses to have her children later in life is cast in a different light by the fact that older mothers were common before the arrival of reliable contraception. In the 1920s, the average age a woman had her last child was forty-two.

Another modern impression is that women are increasingly defying their natural maternal instinct. But a glance at the historical sweep reveals that such instinct was far from universal: if anything, it was less assumed than it is now. The warfaring Spartans bumped off puny boys. Roman children were sold to circuses, prostituted, or castrated to produce eunuchs. Infanticide was so common in the Holy Roman Empire that Pope Innocent III ordered the installation of revolving-door contraptions that enabled an infant to be donated anonymously to a convent. Unlucky medieval boys were disposed of at monasteries. One of the less illustrious achievements of Renaissance Europe was the sheer number of foundlings: a single home in Renaissance Florence took in almost a thousand children a year. In France by the mid-nineteenth century, 5 per cent of all babies were abandoned. Of course, none of this prompts any kind of nostalgia for this era before the welfare state. Very many of these terrible practices were driven by economic expediency, and without maternal consent. Some were reluctantly given up for their own good. But it tempers the accusation that modern women are uniquely selfish for prioritising their working lives over procreation.

We might also think that since women now have a life outside the home, they are eschewing motherhood for the first time in history. Yet as the American historian and author of *How to be Childless*, Rachel Chrastil, has documented, it was only in the baby boom after the Second World War that an over-whelming majority – 90 per cent – of women became mothers. Previously, a surprising 20 per cent of women in Europe and North America never had children. These were mostly urban women, and they often articulated that decision explicitly as a conscious choice undertaken to maintain their independence.

In 1928, the birth control crusader Margaret Sanger published *Motherhood in Bondage,* a collection of letters she had received over the years from women desperate to avoid pregnancy. In the Seventies, even after access to contraception, second-wave feminists campaigned for the right to remain childless. The National Organisation for Non-Parents (NON) was co-founded by the activist Ellen Peck in 1972; her *The Baby Trap* (1971) appeared, alongside similar titles such as *Childless by Choice* by the sociologist Jean Veevers, published in 1975. No Kidding! International, which runs social clubs for the childless and childfree, was set up in Canada in 1984.

In our era of crude scientific fundamentalism, we tend to assume that maternal instinct is biologically innate, yet many twentieth-century thinkers framed it as a questionable social construction. 'There is no such thing as maternal "instinct",' Simone de Beauvoir wrote in 1949; the term does not 'apply to the human species.' In her 1974 book *Housewife*, the sociologist Ann Oakley concurred: 'There is no biologically based drive which propels women into childbearing or forces them to become childrearers once the children are there.' These statements have a curiously historic feel: there may be more public acceptance of child-free existence – I'm thinking of Sheila Heti's 2018 exploration of whether or not to have children, *Motherhood*, and in decisions to forgo parenthood driven by concern for the environment. Yet despite these exceptions, childlessness is today widely regarded as an anomaly – and a blight; a great irony at a time when we are supposed to be governed by enlightened, feminist choice.

Women are still perceived as egotistical if they choose childlessness (the bestselling 2015 essay collection by the American writer Meghan Daum, *Selfish, Shallow, and Self-Absorbed: Sixteen Writers on the Decision Not to Have Kids,* is an illustrative, if satirical, title) and tragic if they can't conceive. 'A lot of women feel it is their fault,' comments New Zealand grief counsellor Lois Tonkin, author of *Motherhood Missed: Stories of Women who are Childless by Circumstance* (2018), even though 'it wasn't about their choice but the outcome of the choices that they had made. Because of this they felt they were not eligible for other people's support.' A 2017 study by researchers at Purdue University in Indiana found childlessness in America is considered not only abnormal and surprising, but also morally wrong: perceiving those without children as less fulfilled, the researchers argued, acts as a way of 'punishing' them for violating this still strong social norm. And scientific progress in fertility treatments has the unintended side-effect of making those who 'fail' feel even more anomalous.

Women have always been blamed for infertility: in 1873, the Harvard doctor Edward Clarke advised women that their baby-making 'machinery' must be 'carefully managed': 'Force must be allowed to flow thither in an ample stream, and not diverted to the brain by the school, or to the arms by the factory, or to the feet by dancing.' At least in pre-modern times, however, chance or God's will were also cited as factors in the failure to conceive. Now, in a supposedly feminist era, women are held even more responsible for their fate – and for similar reasons: education, work, social life. The positive aspect to this modern agency is that women have been able to make use of developments such as contraception to enter public life: they have shaped their lives with the help of science and culture. Yet patriarchal society has responded with the 'news' that women are in fact determined and constrained by nature.

THE FACTS OF LIFE

Physiological limits are presented in the media as hard and non-negotiable. The science behind them is more complicated, however. I went to see Yacoub Khalaf, a consultant gynaecologist who runs the Assisted Conception Unit at Guy's and St Thomas's Hospital in London. Dressed in scrubs, he excused himself repeatedly to perform some life-changing, life-creating procedure. Seeing the couples waiting in the corridor was a sobering reminder of real people facing real problems. As women get older, their fertility does, of course, decline, said Khalaf – but he calls for perspective. 'People refer to a cut-off age: 35, or 38. And those women will then assume that the day after their birthday their fertility will fall off a cliff. But biology is not that categorical,' he told me.

The oft-repeated statistic that one in three women in their late thirties will fail to get pregnant after a year of trying is based, as the American psychologist Jean Twenge has pointed out, on French birth records from the eighteenth century: from a time before electricity, antibiotics or fertility treatment. More up-to-date research on fertility is surprisingly sparse. Natural conception rates are hard to establish, mainly because people do not reliably record when they have sex. And even if we were able to gauge fertility on average, this would be of limited use to individual couples, since the range is so large. In general, the information we have on fertility rates comes from couples who seek treatment, which may skew the results. It's also hard to know how many women are not conceiving out of choice.

The few modern studies that do exist are more reassuring. A 2011 study by researchers at the Institute of Education's Centre for Longitudinal Studies found that previous studies which suggested that fertility declines with age had not taken into account the rather obvious fact that couples have sex less often when they've been together a long time. With this in the equation, the decline in fertility for women between their late twenties and early thirties was 'very modest and of little prac-tical importance'. As far as women in their late thirties are concerned, two studies – one led by David Dunson of Duke University, North Carolina, in 2004 of 770 women in a number of European countries, and another led by Kenneth Rothman of Boston University in 2013 of nearly three thousand Danish women – found that around 80 per cent of the women in their late thirties conceived within a year, compared to only a slightly higher proportion of women (around 85 per cent) in their twenties and early thirties. There was still a significant propor-tion – around 15 per cent – who failed to get pregnant even within the younger age group – a problem less often highlighted in the media.

While it's seldom made clear that the studies underpinning the advice are sometimes centuries old, rates of age-related infertility can be established by examining data from the era before birth control. Emily Oster, the economist and author of two myth-busting books on pregnancy and childcare, points to research from the nineteenth century which found that the chances of having children were pretty much the same for women who got married at any age between twenty and thirty-five. Women who got married between thirty-five and thirty-nine were 90 per cent likely to have a child. For women marrying between forty and forty-four, this dropped to a still substantial 62 per cent; 14 per cent of those who got married between forty-five and forty-nine had a child. The numbers haven't changed very much since then.

Fertility does decline fairly rapidly after the age of forty, mainly due to a deterioration in egg quality, but babies born to women in their forties still account for only 3.4 per cent of all births: the media focus on this age group is disproportionate. The average age of mothers is rising not only because women are having children later but also because of a drop in teenage pregnancies. Most fertility problems are the result not of age, but of conditions such as blocked fallopian tubes and endo-metriosis, which affect both older and younger women.

Rates of IVF success do also decline over time. The typical chance of a single cycle working is 20–35 per cent; the cumu-lative probability of three cycles is 45–53 per cent. According to the Human Fertilisation and Embryology Authority, in 2018, birth rates per embryo transferred were 25 per cent for patients aged thirty-five to thirty-seven, 19 per cent for patients aged thirty-eight to thirty-nine, and 11 per cent for patients aged forty to forty-two. Success rates for the over-forties are soberingly low. But only about 1 to 2 per cent of babies born each year in the UK and the US are the result of IVF.

Infertility affects a relatively small proportion of women, therefore, but it is important not to gloss over the pain they – and their partners – suffer. Twenty per cent of women born in the 1960s turned forty-five without having children; of those, 90 per cent are involuntarily childless, and of that 90 per cent, only 9 per cent know the medical cause – although this percentage is likely to decrease with advances in reproductive technology that I will discuss later on. We should also not forget the women who found a partner too late to have a much-desired second child. But nor should we ignore the fact that these eventualities are less common than some sections of the media would have us believe, and – despite all those moralising headlines – are neither the straightforward result of women's free choices, nor their fault.

Media warnings about fertility declining with age are invariably directed against women. I have never heard the phrase 'career men'. Yet the American Society of Reproductive Medicine estimates that of couples seeking fertility treatment in the US, 40 per cent discover the problem lies with the woman, 40 per cent with the man, and 20 per cent of the time they cannot tell. Fertility problems in men appear to worsen with age – although the effect is less pronounced than in women. There is a reality, here, but also a diffuse yet powerful agenda encouraging successful women to settle in both senses of the word: settle down early, and settle for a man who is available.

FACTS VERSUS REALITIES

The effort to make sure couples are aware of the statistics is made in good faith by bodies such as the UK's Fertility Education Initiative, who cannot control the headlines. But too often, warnings about age-related fertility are founded on an assumption that women are blithely ignorant of the facts. 'What science tells us about the aging parental body should alarm us more than it does,' claims a *New Republic* cover story. 'Know What You're Doing If You Decide to Delay Childbirth', runs a headline in the *New York Times*. I understand the public health imperative to spread knowledge, even if it's scattergun. But very many women are already alarmed – perhaps more than some health professionals realise. The ticking is clearly audible.

In fact, so many women are convinced that they are reproductively dysfunctional by the time they are in their late thirties and early forties that they become careless about contraception (or are spooked into ending pregnancies by the media's exaggeration of risks): in 2014, the Department of Health revealed that abortions among the over-35s had risen by 15 per cent since 2001. The British Pregnancy Advisory Service's former chief executive, Ann Furedi, put this down to 'scaremongering' about age-related infertility. BPAS's research showed that abortion is now more common among women over thirty-five than among teenagers. In 2015, they surveyed over a thousand women and found that 'far from sleepwalking into infertility, women are aware of their reproductive window', and more than 60 per cent felt 'there is now pressure on women to have a baby before they are ready to do so'. Most were 'acutely aware of their reproductive window, with younger women needlessly concerned about infertility'. Women's complacency is overstated.

I believe this anxiety is a problem that also needs to be addressed – especially if women cannot do much to change their situation. In 2016, researchers from Aix-Marseille University in France studied the experiences of women over forty going through IVF. From the start of their treatments, the researchers found, the women perceived a 'race against the clock': 'This feeling of urgency,' they continued, 'accompanied their experiences and was related to the desire to not be too old for their future child.' Their study illustrated, they wrote, 'a growing gap between biological and biographical temporalities' – a technical phrase which encapsulates the mismatch between bodies and circumstances.

In 2013, researchers at the University of California spoke to women undergoing fertility treatment: nearly half the women said that 'even if they had possessed better information, their life circumstances would not have permitted them to begin childbearing earlier'. The researchers concluded that lack of knowledge 'is not sufficient to explain' the phenomenon of delayed childbearing. Women know that fertility declines with age yet they defer motherhood anyway, because of structural factors they cannot control.

There's a perception that contemporary women have become more 'wilful', independent and focused on their own desires and ambitions. They are doing what they want, when they want. Take this nugget from the start of one of those *Daily Mail* articles on age-related infertility, written by a nutritional therapist, Marilyn Glenville: 'Elizabeth sweeps into my consulting room bearing all the hallmarks of the successful career woman – designer handbag, expensive hairstyle, iPad in one hand and mobile in the other.' Privileged and carefree, runs the subtext: little does she know!

In reality, women are not delaying motherhood; they are just struggling to create the necessary conditions for it to happen at all. Many twenty-somethings are saddled with student debt. The average age to buy a first property is now thirty-five. In the UK, one in three men and one in five women aged between twenty and thirty-four still live with their parents. In many competitive industries – once realistic options for graduates – it takes decades to get beyond the precarious early career stage.

Then there's the fact that women's earnings take a huge hit when they have children: in 2006, the Institute for Public Policy Research estimated that an average mid-skilled woman who has her first baby at twenty-four will miss out on up to £564,000 over her lifetime. This compares with losing £165,000 if she delays motherhood by just four more years, let alone into her thirties. Women returning to work after maternity leave end up earning a third less than men, partly because their twenties and thirties is the time when wages rise fastest. In 2016, researchers from Washington University in St Louis even concluded explicitly that women should wait until their thirties before having children, in order to minimise the impact on earnings. The much-cited gender pay gap should really be renamed the motherhood penalty. It's a powerful illustration of the fact that having children is the biggest obstacle to achieving feminist equality.

That's even before we get on to the prohibitive cost of child-care. The Trades Union Congress revealed in 2018 that childcare costs have risen three times faster than wages over the last decade. Women routinely give up work on grounds that it hardly makes financial sense for them to return, since their wages would only just cover the cost of childcare – or they'd even end up with a net loss. Childcare is not generally regarded as a cost to be borne jointly by partners, like food shopping: a 2016 post on Mumsnet, 'Is it worth going back to work if all my wages will go on childcare', attracted a full fifty replies, and another on Netmums – 'I barely have anything left after paying nursery fees' – had responses running to five pages. The UK government claims to provide 'free' nursery care for three- and four-year-olds, but this is a lie: in well-off neighbourhoods, parents typically pay top-up fees to cover the real cost; in less affluent areas, scores of nurseries are going bust – since the Covid-19 crisis, the entire sector is on the brink of collapse.

And then there's the fact that so many mothers don't end up coming back to work at all, or find returning a daunting battle. As I'll discuss in a later chapter, employers put barriers in the way of many mothers returning, which are often subtle – there are laws against discrimination after all – and often mothers' exclusion from the workplace will be classed as 'voluntary'. The charity Pregnant Then Screwed surveyed 20,000 women in 2020 in the wake of the first months of the Covid crisis; 46 per cent of those who were made redundant said a lack of childcare played a role. This was an acute manifestation of a broader trend, exacerbated by shrinking industries which are not hiring any new staff, ever again – even, and especially, if they are old staff. Those who do keep a foot in the door pay a price in lost years with their fast-growing children, or end up on the 'mummy track', humiliated by the fact that younger male colleagues are bounding up the ladder while they tread water in a two- or three-day mid-career role.

The lion's share of media attention on this issue is focused on parental leave arrangements, but that six months or a year is relatively unimportant in the long span of a working life. The real problem comes several years down the track, when many women realise that school holidays and the gap between 3.30 and 6.30 are stubborn design flaws in the modern industrialised economy. When BPAS asked the women they surveyed what was preventing them from starting a family, almost three-quarters cited the difficulty of combining one with work.

But there is another factor outweighing all of these: the choices and inclinations not of women, but of men. BPAS found that this was the biggest single reason cited for 'delaying' motherhood, at 82 per cent. Susan Golombok, director of the Centre for Family Research at Cambridge, agrees. 'It's not about careers at all,' she told me: 'it's about not being in a relationship with someone who wants to commit. By the time women need to get pregnant because of their biological clock, men of a similar age don't want to settle down. Women are feeling the partner they're with is not the right one to have children with, or they do think that, but their partner doesn't want to do it.' Yet this factor is much less often mentioned in the media and public discussion. A 2019 Office for National Statistics report on conception rates for women, showing the big increase in women having children over forty, cited a number of drivers including increased participation in higher education and the workforce, as well as the rising costs of childcare. Yet, bizarrely, relationship circumstances weren't mentioned at all.

I spoke to Danny Dorling, Professor of Human Geography at Oxford University, who specialises in demographic trends. He explained that the problem of single women unable to find a suitable partner is 'getting more pronounced all the time'. In the Nineties, this was known, rather pejoratively, as 'the Bridget Jones effect' – yet despite being a bit of a retro cliché now, the numbers haven't become any more favourable. According to Dorling, the problem is worse in cities: alongside the decline in traditionally male-dominated manufacturing, 'service sector jobs, publishing, civil service, lecturing are all female dominated'; whereas outside of the cities, 'everywhere has electricians, plumbers, farmers, men in white vans'. For urban, educated women in particular, therefore, there is a limited supply of similarly successful, equally well-educated men – despite the rise of professions like IT. 'There is no sign of a slowdown in this trend,' Dorling told me, 'but it has become taboo to talk about it.' The pressure on women to 'settle' is made even harsher by this demographic disparity. Why shouldn't women reasonably expect to be with someone of similar status?

The situation is particularly unfair on women, Dorling continued, since they consistently outperform men – in IQ tests and school examinations. For centuries, our society tactfully corrected for this curious gap with public schools and grammar schools for boys. But as those counterbalancing forces have tapered, it has begun to show. 'We're beginning to see differences in degree results,' Dorling told me; 'more women are doing masters courses, and then you see the gap most strongly in people's twenties.' But when women have kids, the advantage abruptly disappears.

Settling down out of panic is not great for women, men or children. As BPAS's Clare Murphy told me, the common perception that 'if only women had more information, they would do things differently' is particularly irksome in relation to this issue of finding the right partner: 'the messages are completely divorced from the realities of women's lives and the contexts in which women are making fertility decisions'. The mismatch leads to 'poignant situations', Murphy continues, 'where women are, say, in their early thirties, and they're with someone they are not necessarily sure they want to be with, but thinking "is this my last chance to have a baby?": they're making potentially life-changing decisions on the basis of not very good science'.

I got together with my husband just before my thirty-fourth birthday, and in the years leading up to that unforeseen *deus ex machina* (he was perfect, and not just because of the timing) I would sit in my flat on Sunday afternoons calculating if I had enough years in which to meet a suitable partner before my ovaries dried up. The odds seemed increasingly dicey. In the event, events took a swift, natural course. But I still can't quite believe my luck. All those disingenuous Seth Rogen films about gorgeous successful women settling for schlubs have a sobering effect on women who have the temerity to believe they could end up with their equal.

We are surrounded by examples of late fatherhood. Mick Jagger became a dad at seventy-three, Richard Gere at sixty-nine; Rod Stewart was sixty-six, as was Clint Eastwood – and of all the things said about Boris Johnson becoming a father again at the age of fifty-six, his age was not the most prominent. 'Delaying also affects partners: semen counts deteriorate gradually every year,' that 2005 *BMJ* editorial commented, as if men are clamouring to have babies earlier. As the ONS showed in 2018, the average age of first-time fathers has risen by about a year a decade for the past forty years. But nobody seems to ask why that is. The rising age of first-time mothers is put down to greater educational and professional opportunities, but that cannot be the case for men. They can't be worried en masse about children disrupting their careers, as they generally take just two weeks' paternity leave. Men who have degrees tend to be older when their first babies are born than men who don't. Yet I do not hear commentators musing about educational aspirations leading men to 'put off' having children. Financial insecurity may well be a factor. But many men also appear to want partners who are younger than them; as the age of women settling goes up, men's rises in lockstep (the ONS estimates the average age of first-time dads to be about three years older than that of first-time mums). Or maybe it's just extended adolescence.

At the very same time that the science of the biological clock is being pressed upon women, the pseudoscience of evolutionary biology is being invoked to justify why men sleep around more than women: men want sex, the theory goes, while women want *protection*. Stereotypes about men being 'programmed' to maximise their genetic legacy let evasive bounders off the hook. The American anthropologist Cora Du Bois revealed such theories to be bunk way back in 1944: among the Alor islanders of Indonesia, then still a hunter-gatherer society, men were more eager for offspring than women. This retrograde ideology has recently been given a turbo boost by online dating culture, which ramps up unrealistic expectations and creates an impression of endless consumerist options, reducing men's desire to commit still further. On my second date with my husband, he asked me if I wanted children. I was struck by the novelty of a man cutting to the chase (it was a huge mark in his favour). Finding out the score early on shouldn't be that unusual.

Rather than ignorance and conscious delay, women are generally conscious of the time pressure but powerless to act. Yet the language in which this issue is couched assumes active decision-making ('Should women delay motherhood?' asks the

New York Times). 'I'm just giving you the facts,' women are rather maddeningly told. This is about facts, but it is also about a glaring injustice in the way society is organised. Why not issue dire warnings to government, employers, and men?

I understand that women should not be offered false hope by US senator Tammy Duckworth having a baby at fifty, and Brigitte Nielsen having her fifth at fifty-four. But when the *Daily Mail* worries that 'the number of older mothers has soared', these warnings stray into the territory of disapproval beyond concerns for children that their mothers will be 'tired old ladies' when they are teenagers (what about the tired old dads?). There's a logical contradiction here: bemoaning just how many older mothers there are, and then warning older women how hard it is to become one.

TECHNOLOGICAL FUTURES

Our culture appears ambivalent about the use of science to enable older mothers: it sometimes feels as if this counts as 'defying nature' as much as the brinkmanship of 'delaying'. That aside, future medical advances may help to resolve some of the paradoxes I've been discussing. But there are economic, practical and scientific hurdles. Tests to predict how many years still remain on a woman's fertility clock were debunked by researchers in 2017. Egg freezing has attracted a lot of recent publicity, and companies such as Apple and Facebook offer the service to employees as a perk – 'The "Egg whisperer" helping Silicon Valley career women defy time', as the *Telegraph* put it. But it's still hard to determine success rates, and there are downsides. If your eggs are frozen when you are young, it's more likely to work. This may be set to change, but currently, unless you can prove you are infertile, eggs have to be used within ten years, although no good reason is provided for this (perhaps it is to stop women exercising too much licence). Yacoub Khalaf also pointed out that egg freezing is an expensive and invasive procedure and there are side-effects. Given the relatively low chances of needing the eggs, he says (the vast majority of women never use them), it's not worth it. It's a highly commercialised business. There is a lot we could be doing as a society to just make it easier for women to have babies in the usual – cheaper – way.

IVF is also cripplingly expensive. A single cycle costs on average between £3,000 and £5,000. Our culture cannot decide if fertility treatment is a medical treatment or a luxury, and whether it should be provided to the deserving (younger) or the needy (older); and this ambivalence is reflected in stark variations in its availability on the NHS in different parts of the country. NICE guidelines state that women should be offered three full cycles up to age forty, but the HFEA has found that just one in eight regions in England follows them. Many only provide treatment up to thirty-five.

This is often referred to as a 'postcode lottery', but in 2002, researchers from Flinders University in Australia found that women who discontinued fertility treatment hated the phrase as it pathologises those who 'fail' to become pregnant as 'losers'. The ideology of consumerist choice and self-determination, the idea that you can have whatever you want, as long as you pay for it or try hard enough, personalises misfortune and places it heavily on individual women's shoulders.

Doctors such as Susan Bewley and Melanie Davies are right to critique the commercialism of the fertility industry, and the unrealistic promises dangled by some providers. But these companies also have an incentive to scare women into under-estimating their chances of conceiving naturally. Yacoub Khalaf concurred that this profit motive may lead some clinics to make statements about ageing that cause unnecessary alarm.

The panic is often misplaced or counterproductive; particu-larly around supposedly fertility boosting or limiting behaviours. 'If couples go on the internet and consult Dr Google, they will find advice that makes them feel hounded,' Khalaf says. 'This particular food is bad – exercise is good or bad. They are walking on eggshells.' He reminds them that in poor countries where even food is limited, 'people are breeding like rabbits. So there's no need to get yourself into a state.' Khalaf told me that private clinics offer add-ons to their treatment, many of which are unnecessary and deprive couples of financial resilience. He is angry that couples anxiously grasp around in the dark, paying for treatments – like acupuncture, hypnotherapy or astrology – whose effectiveness here, be believes, is 'utter tosh. Totally unfounded.' His advice is simple: 'If a woman over thirty-five has been trying for six months and hasn't got pregnant, the couple should go and see their GP.'

Israel is the only country in the world to provide free, unlimited IVF to women up to age forty-five. Research in 2015 which compared the Israeli experience to other national approaches found that women with ready access to IVF are more likely to marry, to complete their university education and to pursue postgraduate qualifications later on in life. Israel is the only country that regards resolving the tensions I'm talking about as a practical necessity and therefore a state responsibility, and in doing so, destigmatises them. The Israel National Bioethics Council recommends egg freezing because it 'considers age-related fertility decline to be a medical problem' – rather than, as the British and American media often put it, a lifestyle choice.

THE POLITICAL PRESENT

Technologies such as egg freezing – alongside more exotic biotechnologies, such as growing babies in glass wombs – may in future ease the pressure on women. But complex scientific solutions come with their own drawbacks, and offer convenient pretexts for policy-makers to avoid providing more straightforward solutions. Are there more accessible, creative, inexpensive remedies staring us in the face: co-parenting with friends, queer parenting, living in a modern commune? In her book *Full Surrogacy Now*, the feminist writer Sophie Lewis argues that surrogacy should be a metaphor for a new kind of shared parenting that sees bringing up kids as something citizens can do for each other, regardless of family connection.

Some people, meanwhile, are choosing to not have children altogether in the face of our bleak environmental outlook – although, as Danny Dorling argues, 'having a child has a negligible effect on the environment: it's about the behaviour of families' – their carbon footprint. I'm all for diversity in living arrangements, but we also need to acknowledge that new ideas coexist with a surprisingly intact and rigid romantic fatalism. Even speculative and futuristic films are shot through with traditional values – *Gravity* (2013), *Arrival* (2016) and *Proxima* (2019) all feature women uncomfortably defined by their identity as mothers: it seems, to adapt a saying by Fredric Jameson, that it's easier to imagine the end of the world than to imagine the end of the nuclear family.

It is important to get out of our bubbles and see that attitudes and practices are changing in communities on the ground. Grassroots radical innovations can be hard to scale up, however, especially now in an age when the big state is out of fashion. In the Sixties and Seventies, progressive local authorities like Camden Council in London funded experiments in collective childcare. But as Danny Dorling points out, it may be that even if we were able to restart the community playgroup movement, the Anglo-American world view has become so individualist that it would be hard to sustain. There would be unseemly squabbles about nappy duty. The Nordic model of universal, state-provided childcare – of which a great deal has already been written – seems the obvious way to go; if we are prepared to pay for it. It's time we stopped asking women to bridge the gap between reasonable life aims and both biological and societal constraints, and recognised that this is a holistic social and political responsibility.

What about the supposed rise of women choosing to 'go it alone'? It appears from the avid press coverage that there has been a huge increase in lone women having children through artificial means – 'A generation of women are choosing to have a baby on their own through IVF', bellowed the *Daily Mail* in 2018. But the numbers are still small. Fertility treatments for lone women have risen in recent years, but are still only 3 per cent of IVF cycles: just 2,279 women tried to start a family on their own (through IVF or with donor insemination) in the UK in 2017. As Susan Golombok notes, the rise of egg freezing suggests that, despite the supposed normalising of lone parenthood, most women are still holding out for Mr Right. She also told me that, in contrast to media stereotypes of air-punching independence, some mothers who have children alone by donor insemination report sadness: 'This isn't how I wanted to have children – it's not right to call it a choice,' they say. 'Time is running out for me, so unless I do it this way, I'm not going to be able to do it at all.'

The outcomes for children in non-traditional families – those born to lone mothers, or to lesbian or gay parents, or to parents not in a romantic relationship – are generally positive, illustrating that it is other forms of disadvantage such as poverty which make the difference, not family structure. Studies have suggested that children born to lone women over forty have better physical and emotional health than those born to partnered women in their twenties. Golombok told me that researchers took a while to come to this conclusion because they had traditionally read across from single-mother families, where children had experienced negative effects from conflict, divorce, or a mum who saw her income drop or became depressed post-separation. They had assumed that these negative effects would also be seen in children whose mothers had them alone. But in fact, the children of these lone mothers are often brought up in conditions of material comfort; their mums do not usually experience mental health difficulties, and the children do as well as, or even better than, those in traditional two-parent families. The suspicion with which these women are represented in the media is therefore particularly unjust. We need to lessen the stigma and decouple finding the right relationship from having children.

One final aspect to all this is that having children later, and with costly and painful treatment, makes them more hard-won, and it therefore makes ambivalence towards motherhood more difficult to acknowledge. You wanted this baby, so now enjoy it. If you say you love being a mother, then that makes women who can't have children feel worse, and if you say you don't like aspects of the experience, there's a risk you'll seem ungrateful, because those women don't even have the luxury of complaining. The more difficult it is to have children, the more motherhood is idealised. And as we will see in the next chapter, idealisation is also what leads pregnant women to believe that – whatever the cost to themselves – they must protect their unborn child as diligently as they possibly can.

3

DOWN TO EARTH WITH A BUMP

I found out I was pregnant in the toilet at work. As I watched the second red line come into view through the oval window, I felt joy and relief. I'd been sure I was destined to end up childless in my forties. But the binary certainty of the result contrasted with other, more mixed feelings. It was as if a portal had opened up from that small window, through the walls of my work building and out to a different future. A gap had emerged between work and motherhood that was set to grow until it prised open my life and forced work out; and even if it returned, I already knew the child would be a constant subtext, detracting from the perceived seriousness of my commitment. That afternoon, I walked around the office feeling silently special, but also now just another member of an infinitely receding series of faceless bodies. My own history seemed to dissolve in the here and now, but I was newly aware of being part of a long tradition of pain and patriarchy. The grinding machine of maternal sacrifice had somewhere been launched, and was heading steadily in my direction.

This chapter is not going to be about the relentless series of symptoms that came marching through my body as they have all those other women's bodies, some of which I didn't even know existed until I typed them in and discovered reams of time-consuming message-board testimonies: tugging twinges that were apparently my uterus being stretched into the right position, as if by some briskly unconcerned stage managers; cramps in my calves that woke me up at night, as if my tendons were being electrocuted; crippling nausea and sudden intolerance of my little treats in life, alcohol and caffeine; overwhelming tiredness that sent me to bed at eight, like a child; the haemorrhoids, the constipation; the unsettling limbo of being overdue.

Those aspects of pregnancy are well covered elsewhere, in the numerous almanacs that catalogue the stages. This chapter is about the politics of pregnancy; how it transforms a woman overnight from autonomous individual to responsible carrier and carer of a being who seems infinitely vulnerable and therefore infinitely valuable – certainly more valuable than her. It's about how she is encouraged to regard her relationship with that being as a zero-sum game in which any gain to her is the baby's loss, and so there is only one allowable direction for that equation to run. As the economist Emily Oster notes, 'this idea – that what parents need or want will play a role in choices – can be hard to admit'. In a sense, she writes, 'this is at the core of a lot of the "Mommy War" conflicts.'

This chapter is also about the shadows that pregnancy casts: the very real possibility of losing the baby before term, the darker intimations and dawning implications, the restrictions and fears that coexist with the optimism and cheer. Since these aspects are less socially acceptable, they multiply underground, leaving the mother-to-be feeling egregiously and culpably uneasy.

The pregnant woman is a canvas onto which other people project their investments. I could barely get my head around what was happening to me, but I saw in other people's faces how my body had meanings for them that I couldn't control. Yet rather than talk about what these meanings are openly, our culture prefers to discuss the more practical aspects, such as the dietary prohibitions. To some extent, these are arbitrary placeholders for psychological, social and political agendas: the protection of optimism, and the control of women. It is only by recognising these agendas that women can truly both acknowledge pregnancy's downsides, and enjoy its delights.

THE ADVICE

While I was writing this book, I revisited those pregnancy and babycare manuals – shelves and shelves of them, but tucked away in the back of bookshops. Social media may be increasingly dominant, but where the re-education of women is concerned, the classic titles are still on prominent display: *What to Expect When You're Expecting*; *The Baby Whisperer*; the Dr Sears books. I approached these tomes – with their pink and blue colour schemes and playschool fonts – as my own school-age kids would reopen their first ABC: with amused and incredulous recollection. Defamiliarised, the condescension was striking. And even when I was at that stage, I didn't want to be addressed as if my brain had turned to mush.

The patronising miasma of pregnancy extends into the advice. 'Is it safe to drink a little during pregnancy?' asks the NCT's FAQs. 'The advice is – no, not really. Research has shown that even drinking small amounts of alcohol could potentially be harmful for your baby.' 'How about after the first trimester?' the fictional questioner persists, as if hopefully fingering the corkscrew. 'Again, unfortunately not,' comes the infuriatingly sympathetic reply. The bestselling *What to Expect When You're Expecting* recommends complete abstinence from alcohol, and a diet strictly tailored to the needs of the unborn child. 'Every bite counts', women are told in a section entitled the 'Best-Odds Diet'. 'You've got only nine months of meals and snacks with which to give your baby the best possible start in life . . . Before you close your mouth on a forkful of food, consider, "Is this the best bite I can give my baby?" If it will benefit your baby, chew away. If it'll only benefit your sweet tooth or appease your appetite put your fork down.'

Sometimes the popular advice goes further than official advice, but the guidelines themselves are draconian. Many countries including the UK, the US, France, Canada, and Australia advise pregnant women to avoid alcohol altogether. The UK's Chief Medical Officer has recommended women should not drink at all while trying to conceive or while pregnant, on the grounds that it is 'better to be safe than sorry'. In no other adult context would you encounter such a phrase. One widely quoted Texas obstetrician warns that a single 'sip of wine may be one sip too many'. In 2017, even the German brewery industry launched a crusade against maternal drinking, claiming that 'every sip of alcohol during pregnancy can severely affect the health of an unborn child'.

The list of foods pregnant women are instructed to avoid extends from blue cheese to soft cheese, pâté (including vegetarian pâté) to game, sushi to bean sprouts. They are told, as noted by the authors of a 2009 article, 'Risk and the Pregnant Body' in the American journal *The Hastings Center Report*, to sleep 'in a specified position (avoiding stomach and back, with left side preferred to right)'; to avoid paint, cat litter, and sitting in the bath 'longer than ten minutes'; to not 'sample the cookie dough'; not listen to loud music; and even 'to keep a laptop computer several inches from their pregnant bellies'. They should steer clear of new household items from cars to frying pans, pesticides to painkillers. Sometimes the advice is contradictory: peanuts are cited as both increasing and decreasing the risk of their child developing an allergy. There are frequent reports of pregnant women being denied coffee by baristas, especially in the US.

Male partners often become informal policemen, too, as if protecting their investment. While a large majority may mean well, the disciplining of pregnant women can shade into much darker behaviour. Pregnant women are particularly vulnerable to domestic abuse, including coercive control and violence: the Confidential Enquiry into Maternal and Child Health has found that 30 per cent of domestic abuse begins in pregnancy. Viewed in the round, it appears that as a society we are less benignly protective of pregnant women (and indeed their babies) than we may think.

The avoid list is particularly stringent in a 2013 Royal College of Obstetricians and Gynaecologists paper – widely questioned, it should be said – entitled 'Chemical Exposures in Pregnancy: Dealing with Potential, but Unproven, Risks to Child Health'. It advises pregnant women to stay away from food packaging, household chemicals, cosmetics and family medicines; anything, in other words, modern and manufactured. We live in an increasingly artificial world, yet pregnant women must live in an archaic bubble. 'The mother is the guardian of her baby's development and future health,' the RCOG paper stressed, and she must ensure it has 'the best possible start in life'. As the American sociologist Evelyn Glenn puts it, mothers are 'seen as all-powerful – holding the fate of their children and ulti-mately the future of society in their hands – but also as powerless – subordinated to the dictates of nature'. Mothers are also subordinated to the dictates of these medical author-ities and must avoid any risk to the baby, however small and debatable, and however large her sacrifice.

THE EVIDENCE

The weight of the advice contrasts with a paucity of evidence. This is partly because pregnancy health falls between the disci-plinary cracks: David Williams, one of only four consultant obstetric physicians in the UK, has referred to maternal medicine – the care and treatment of pregnant women – as a neglected 'Cinderella subject'. I asked Eric Jauniaux, Professor of Obstetrics and Fetal Medicine at University College London Hospital, to help me tease out fact from fiction – particularly on the subject of alcohol consumption. He told me there's a lamentable lack of research in this area 'because it's a woman's problem – rather like the menopause – so men don't care; and they generally hold positions of power'. And then there are the methodological problems.

Studies have been carried out on animals – such as testing the effects of giving alcohol to pregnant rats and sheep – but as media reports often fail to note, animals have very different physiognomies. For example, as Jauniaux told me, miscarriage is much more common in humans because our placenta is more complex and delicate. So more recently, scientists have tended to rely on observational studies, looking at trends in large populations. It is hard to draw conclusions from such studies, however: some don't effectively control for other behaviours, such as drug use. Another issue is the accuracy of reporting: participants won't necessarily tell you if they drank or smoked while pregnant. And small long-term effects of certain actions are hard to measure, unlike in the case of Thalidomide, which produced severe birth defects. Given the scale of that scandal, the reticence of researchers and drug companies is understandable.

Yet as we will see, these qualms are causing great anxiety for the sensible majority. If mothers are given an inch, they really won't take a mile. But most stories in the media and posts on internet forums – 'even low-level caffeine consumption during pregnancy (even chocolate!) may be detrimental to your baby's health'; 'I accidentally ate some Brie today and now I'm in a right flap!' – are firmly in splitting-hairs territory.

The ethics of research on pregnant women are complex, themselves the subject of journal articles. First, there's the issue of consent: pregnant women can grant it, the unborn child cannot. No scientist is going to undertake randomised controlled trials of drinking alcohol in pregnancy, but the blanket excuse that it is unethical to do any research involving pregnant women doesn't wash. The authors of a 2013 article in the American Medical Association's *Journal of Ethics* concluded that, since there are adverse consequences for pregnant women of not conducting trials, 'we can no longer hide behind claims that ethics precludes the inclusion of pregnant women' in research. Rather, they continue, 'ethics – and to be more precise, justice – *demands* that we move forward with their responsible inclusion'. Pregnant women 'have not benefitted fairly from the research enterprise. It is well past time that they do.'

Common sense dictates that pregnant women should avoid binge-drinking; Eric Jauniaux contrasted this Anglo-American habit with the much more moderate drinking culture of Continental Europe. The NHS states that drinking heavily, meaning more than six units of alcohol a day, throughout a pregnancy, can cause a baby to develop foetal alcohol syndrome disorder (FASD). Drinking more than a glass of wine a day in the first trimester – relatively speaking, probably the riskiest period to drink – may be linked to slightly lower birth weights and a slightly higher chance of preterm delivery. But there is no clear evidence that light drinking harms babies. The existing research – including a large Danish study in 2012 measuring its impact on children's cognitive performance, and a 2010 Australian study exploring the effect on children's behaviour – is either contradictory, shows no damage, or even suggests positive outcomes for babies of light-drinking mothers. All these studies have been compromised to some extent by confounding – the inability to eliminate muddling factors such as education and income. The upshot, as Emily Oster concludes, is that 'there is virtually *no* evidence that drinking a glass of wine a day has negative impacts on pregnancy or child outcomes'. Nevertheless, note the courage required by the mother to not check her behaviour despite these sane counter-statistics: the censorial power of the whispering 'what if . . .?'

In 2017, the *British Medical Journal* acknowledged – citing an analysis of the available data in its online journal, *BMJ Open* – that the evidence for the potentially harmful effects of light or occasional drinking in pregnancy is 'surprisingly limited', but recommended that 'women are still better off avoiding all alcohol while pregnant, just in case' (another grating phrase, that, and again rarely deployed in medicine outside this context). Statements such as 'no amount of alcohol has been proven safe at any time during pregnancy' can be found all over the internet, yet they misleadingly suggest a negative where there is just an unknown; as the *BMJ* notes: 'Women often ask about "safe" levels of drinking during pregnancy, but there are no clinical trial data on this issue.' Despite the 'distinction between light drinking and abstinence' being 'the point of most tension and confusion for health professionals and pregnant women,' the *BMJ* continues – '"But one glass is OK, isn't it?"' – 'our extensive review shows that this specific question is not being researched thoroughly enough, if at all.' I believe that couples should be told about the research ambiguities and then left to make up their own minds. Conscientious mums who fancy a tiny tipple are worrying unnecessarily. As Jauniaux puts it, to ban alcohol completely is to take the 'robotic approach'.

There is little evidence that drinking coffee has any ill effects. A Cochrane review of the evidence has even found that drinking three cups of coffee a day early in pregnancy is probably fine. The NHS website – among many other authorities – advises women to avoid sushi. As far as I know, I'm the only one among my acquaintances who ate it. Sushi exemplifies the great discrepancy – as I probably informed someone at the time, between slightly guilty mouthfuls – between the topics that obsess women and those that are studied by scientists. 'Sushi and pregnancy' produces over six million hits on Google; on

PubMed, the repository of medical research studies, the result is zero. Eric Jauniaux told me that he is asked about sushi more often than anything else on the 'avoid list' and bemoaned the prevalence of what he called the 'myths and fake news of pregnancy' – particularly online. As he explained, it's not the sushi itself that's the issue, but the bacteria carried by it: the result of poor hygiene in preparation or packing.

Similarly, outlawing blue or runny cheese on the basis that it may contain listeria is arbitrary and nonsensical: the very rare cases of foodborne illness from listeria in the UK have come from an unpredictable variety of foods, including pre-packaged sandwiches, pork pies and butter. Jauniaux did sound a note of caution on toxoplasmosis, a rare but increasingly common infection caused by a parasite which can be damaging to the baby. Here he thinks the NHS could usefully introduce screening. But the bottom line is – once again – a sense of proportion and the application of good sense: the risk can be largely eliminated by washing fruit and vegetables, and, if you like your meat rare, freezing it first.

COUNTERPRODUCTIVE

Beyond the injustice of being bound by bad science, obeying the zero-tolerance directives may actually be harmful. Many pregnant women exist in a state of hypervigilance and self-restraint. The rational weighing up of risks and benefits, derived from the evidence, has been replaced by an extreme enforcement of the precautionary principle. As well as detracting from pregnant women's mental wellbeing, this heightened nervousness can lead to difficulties in dealing with real-life grey areas and imperfections.

The journey from research to guidelines may be complex, and public health authorities have their eye on small changes across big populations; but questionable blanket bans may cause parents to stop trusting edicts. As the New Zealand medical legal expert Colin Gavaghan argues in the *Journal of Medical Ethics*, the authorities should 'consider whether they are in danger of "crying wolf", with the attendant risk that genuine warnings of real dangers will be treated less seriously'. There is evidence that this is already happening: on social media, anxious women post questions about what they can and cannot eat, suggesting that they know there's an official answer and a real answer. But the internet is not a trustworthy arbiter either. Gavaghan notes that while we might think we've moved beyond a time when high-handed doctors withheld information from patients for fear they'd make bad decisions, 'a paternalistic exception is permitted in the case of pregnant women'.

Research by the WRISK project, a collaboration between BPAS and Cardiff University, has found that – as with age-related infertility – women are well aware of concerns around drinking in pregnancy. 'I see this all the time,' BPAS's Clare Murphy told me: 'the idea that woman are ignorant of the risks. If anything, women are hyperaware, to the point where they consider ending pregnancies because they're so worried about the odd night of binge drinking before they found out they were pregnant. If a pregnancy is unplanned, that doesn't mean it's unwanted.'

Society takes it upon itself to protect the rights of foetuses, because they are so defenceless. But as I showed in the first chapter, such attempts to constrain women's autonomy do not follow the law – at least in the UK (attempts to prosecute pregnant women who drink or take drugs have been more successful in the US, though these have been challenged by women's advocacy groups). And in fact, while a bump can be prodded by total strangers, the foetus floats in a padded and buffered chamber. Why else do we fantasise about returning to the safety of the womb? Yet 'the dominant idea of a "good mother"', the authors of the *Hastings Center Report* article argue, 'requires that women abjure personal gain, comfort, leisure, time, income, and even fulfilment': during pregnancy, this 'expectation of self-sacrifice,' is 'even more stringently applied'. They continue: 'the idea of imposing *any* risk on the fetus, however small or theoretical, for the benefit of a pregnant woman's interest has become anathema'.

This is especially illogical when the apparent avoidance of risk is actually detrimental to mothers – for example, medication that brings a very slight increase in the risk of cleft palate, but treats a woman's severe allergies; treatments for epilepsy; or the vexed issue of antiemetics. In the wake of Thalidomide, those authors argue, 'the pendulum has now swung from over-confidence back to overanxiety': medicines and interventions that should be seen as therapeutic or lifesaving 'are instead seen as frightening or poisonous in the context of the pregnant body'. But the admonitions continue, because – as Gavaghan notes – 'the quality of life of the pregnant woman is so far behind the interests of the future child in any scale of ethical relevance as to be beneath consideration altogether'. As Clare Murphy told me, work is being done to improve clarity on medication in pregnancy, but public health guidance is still failing to take into account both clear-sighted proportionality and the law as it stands: 'it's one step forward, two steps back'.

Furthermore, abstinence messages rarely work. 'I'm not for a moment suggesting that FASD doesn't exist,' Murphy stresses. 'But there's good evidence to suggest that policing women just causes anxiety for those who are low risk, while doing nothing for genuinely problematic drinkers.' The single biggest cause of foetal growth restriction is not alcohol, but crack addiction. It is, of course, common knowledge that crack is bad for you, yet telling pregnant women not to use it hasn't worked. As the columnist and author Zoe Williams has pointed out, such messages are commonly regarded as evidence of a 'nanny state', but they are in fact the opposite: the state washing its hands of responsibility for the individual: You were warned!

Poor pregnancy outcomes are mostly not the result of eating certain foods or drinking alcohol or coffee, but rather factors beyond women's control, such as genitourinary tract infections and genetic conditions, as well as smoking, poor nutrition and obesity. While we should be tackling the drivers of smoking and obesity as a society-wide issue, this fact should not mean that individuals should be singled out for blame.

Obesity and poor nutrition are not simply a matter of poor choices, but are correlated with low levels of income and education. A 2017 study by researchers at Bielefeld University in Germany found that pregnant women who 'have a low education' appear to be 'at higher risk of inadequate dietary intake', and a 2020 study by Belgian researchers published in the European journal, *Obesity Facts*, noted that the prevalence of maternal obesity was 'strongly related to social, educational and ethnic differences'. These women, often demonised in the media, are dealing with multiple forms of disadvantage, as well as experiencing the poorest care during pregnancy, with the most deprived being 60 per cent less likely to receive any ante-natal care as compared with the least deprived, according to a 2014 study by researchers at Oxford University. Murphy told me that women with high BMIs 'are told they shouldn't be getting pregnant, are made to feel that if anything goes wrong during pregnancy, it's their fault, and are deprived of particular birth options. We need to think about the lived experience of the women who are on the receiving end of these messages.'

PURITY AND DANGER

The modern catalogue of banned items – alcohol, coffee, sushi, household chemicals, and the rest – contains novel items, but it is also part of a long tradition of advice, both authority-driven and folkloric. As the French historian Jacques Gélis notes, there was once a superstition against pregnant women engaging in any kind of circular rotation, as this was thought to cause the cord to become wrapped around the baby's neck – no coffee grinding, therefore, or winding skeins of wool. The seventeenth-century physician Jacques Duval advised pregnant women to avoid 'beef, hare, eel', and salty or spicy meats such as 'venison pate, saveloys', or 'Mainz ham'; also 'vegetables, cheese, garlic, onions, quinces both wild and cultivated, hazelnuts, walnuts, medlars and hard-boiled eggs'. It is hard to see what was left. The eighteenth-century obstetrician François Deleurye advised pregnant women to avoid 'immoderate laughing and shouting', and to keep away from 'loud sounds and noises, such as thunder, artillery and loud bells'. According to the French writer and historian Elisabeth Badinter, such prescriptions were routinely cheerfully dismissed. Yet mothers now seem to have lost their confidence to resist them.

Anthropologists have also identified diverse pregnancy prohibitions in cultures around the world. A 2019 paper by researchers from Rhodes University in South Africa found that pregnant isiXhosa women from the Kat River Valley communities of the Eastern Cape are forbidden from eating meat products, fish, potatoes, fruits, beans, eggs, butternut and pumpkin: valuable sources of nutrition. In 2012, researchers from the Polytechnic Institute in Macao published a study exploring Chinese taboos around eating ice cream, watermelon, mung beans, bananas, prawns, mango, lychees, and pineapple.

I'm not claiming that what is banned is entirely arbitrary, that there haven't been scientific advances in our knowledge of what is safe, or that anything goes; but we don't hear so much about the way the advice has changed over time and across space. The very irrationality of some of the foods 'banned' highlights the fact that symbolism sometimes trumps substance, and the sheer variety of rules shows up the common denominator: the desire for control. Perhaps we should attend more to the underlying forces driving the prohibitions, and not assume that because we in the modern global north are so 'advanced', superstitions have disappeared.

In her classic book *Purity and Danger*, the anthropologist Mary Douglas describes fears of contamination that accompany 'liminal' states such as pregnancy – regarding the womb as dangerously permeable and the woman as a vessel to be carefully supervised – which can be traced from seventeenth-century midwifery texts, through twentieth-century parenting advice, to our own febrile age. If anything, these fears have intensified as a response to modernity: the spread of pollutants prompts an impulse to curate pregnancy as a zone of hygienic exception, which does not sit well with the fact that pregnant women are ordinary human beings, at a stressful time in their lives, and often with heightened appetites and eccentric desires.

MAGICAL THINKING

It is understandable that magical thinking should be so prevalent in pregnancy, this frail state of uncertainty. The unborn baby is half physical fact, half theoretical possibility. Magical thinking is – in the absence of evidence – what turns an innocuous sip of beer or coffee into poison. It's tempting to believe that if we follow a set pattern of behaviour, then this precious being will come to no harm. If you do miscarry, it's easy to recall an instance when you 'broke the rules' – and therefore it must be your fault. Clare Murphy gives the example of a scare story on the front of the *Daily Mail* in 2020 about caffeine causing miscarriage: the science has been roundly disproved, but the damaging ammunition for self-blame lingers.

The risk of harm to the future child is relatively small, but it is talked about all the time; the chance of having a miscarriage is quite high (though this is hardly ever the consequence of the mother's behaviour), yet that is hushed up, especially in the presence of a pregnant woman. It is the outcome of around one in four pregnancies; in the UK, around 650 babies are miscarried every day. Some scientists even think that most pregnancies end this way, without women even being aware of it. Around 80 per cent of miscarriages occur in the first three months. The taboo attached to telling anyone during this time serves no one except the embarrassed acquaintance who doesn't have to hear that you were pregnant, but now you're not. A retrograde superstition insinuates hubris at trumpeting good news. And it means you lack support. Women are regarded as public property when it comes to telling them how to behave and what to eat, but are expected to deal with pregnancy loss in private.

The silence around miscarriage is further proof of the idealisation of motherhood. It also makes it seem less common, and therefore even harder to deal with as an event. If it were more integrated into everyday conversation, it would be less egregious and lonely. It may help a little when celebrities – for example, the Duchess of Sussex, Lily Allen, and Beyoncé – talk about their experiences, but the normalising effect is tempered by the fact that they are exceptional individuals.

In previous centuries, losing babies both before and after birth was a regular reality. As I said in my introduction, before modern medicine, a quarter of children died before adulthood. These grim odds did not necessarily mitigate parents' grief, but life events are always experienced in cultural context. Contemporary culture has adopted a subtly contradictory position on losing a child. We either avert our eyes from it as a reality, or we make it into a tragedy so huge that it is barely mentionable. Babies are now so few, so longed-for and so prized, it's also possible that losing them can be felt as even more traumatic than in times past.

Elisabeth Badinter looks at this from a different angle. She notes that it could seem, from historical accounts, as if some mothers in history showed a relative lack of interest in their babies – giving them away, wet-nursing them, suffering them to be 'brought down' for just an hour a day. Badinter interprets this as an emotional defence against the high incidence of childhood mortality. Yet, as she adds, this can in turn serve to explain away the more difficult fact that women could sometimes appear to take the loss of a baby in their stride. She cites the example of one English woman who, 'having lost two of her children, pointed out that she still had a baker's dozen in her'. Badinter argues that we should replace our mistaken belief in a universal and automatic maternal instinct with a different concept: maternal love. 'Maternal love is a human feeling. And, like any feeling, it is uncertain, fragile, and imperfect.' She continues: 'When we observe the historical changes in maternal behaviour, we notice that interest in and devotion to the child are sometimes in evidence, sometimes not.'

As the anthropologist Margaret Mead has shown, responses to miscarriage and stillbirth vary greatly across cultures – some consider even newborn babies as not yet real humans – and the status of foetuses is subject to an extensive, live debate about abortion and the increasing viability of preterm babies. 'How closely is emotional commitment related to the probability that the infant will survive?' Mead asks, and calls for more research. This question would be highly unusual now, surrounded as it is by piety and taboo.

In the era before birth control, miscarriage was often regarded as nature 'doing its work'. The American historian Shannon Withycombe has found that in nineteenth-century America, miscarriage produced a wide range of reactions – from horror and dread (it could be life-threatening, and still is) – to being seen as an unpleasant but relatively minor inconvenience. Another historian, Leslie Reagan, has documented that – in American magazine coverage of the issue during the twentieth century – the way pregnancy loss was talked about shifted dramatically, from a medical hazard, to something of a blessing (fewer children to feed), to how it's framed now: as a tragedy.

It remains an open question whether we in the modern age do women a disservice by gravely mandating a certain reaction, or whether we are finally giving this immensely upsetting event – with considerable mental health consequences – its proper due. Certainly shrouding the entire issue in denial and awkward silence deprives women and their partners of the vocabulary with which to articulate their distinct experiences. As the psychoanalyst Julia Bueno has eloquently described in *The Brink of Being*, losing a child before term deals a double blow. Not only does it entail the loss of a baby; it also embodies thwarted hope.

BE HONEST

I didn't take my own pregnancies for granted, but neither did I enjoy them straightforwardly. Fearing both loss of self and an unimaginably painful event, I was faced with the question that underlies so much discussion about motherhood: when you have a baby, does something 'have to give'? Society does not take care of a pregnant woman, but relentlessly monitors her. The denial of adult pleasures such as alcohol positions her as both child and impeccably responsible adult. She must actively cultivate, yet passively incubate.

Earlier representations of the pregnant state can be surprisingly radical. In her classic study, *Of Woman Born*, Adrienne Rich writes that under patriarchy, 'the mother's life is exchanged for the child; her autonomy as a separate being seems fated to conflict with the child she will bear'. Rich describes how the 'Good Mother' is defined as 'self-denying, self-annihilative' and 'linked implicitly with suffering'; this new persona replaces 'the woman or girl who once had hopes, expectations, fantasies *for herself* – especially when those hopes and fantasies have never been acted on'. The second-wave feminist Shulamith Firestone called pregnancy 'barbaric'. And in *The Second Sex*, Simone de

Beauvoir cites the Freudian psychoanalyst Wilhelm Stekel who believes that vomiting as a result of morning sickness 'always expresses a certain rejection of the child'. I love that confident 'always'. It would be rare nowadays for anyone to interpret those physical symptoms in such an unguarded and figurative way.

A woman experiences pregnancy, wrote de Beauvoir, as both 'enrichment' and 'mutilation'. She 'feels as vast as the world; but this very richness annihilates her, she has the impression of not being anything else'. The coming baby will 'justify her own existence', but she also feels 'like the plaything of obscure forces'. Finally, she 'experiences the satisfaction of feeling "interesting", which has been, since her adolescence, her deepest desire'; her friends and family respect her; 'even her caprices become sacred': this is what encourages her, she writes, 'to invent "cravings"'. These imaginative and understanding interpretations stand in refreshing contrast to the stifling literalism of modern pregnancy chat.

In his 1965 textbook of obstetrics, the American psychiatrist Stuart Asch wrote that pregnancy 'will shake the most mentally healthy person' – some sort of disorder is always present, he argued, whether in the form of phobias, depression or psychoses. I felt pride and excitement in the early months, but also a curious darkness. The difficulty of the first trimester is greatly underestimated – and that's the one you have to endure silently. When I went to meet the perinatal psychiatrist Gertrude (Trudi) Seneviratne at the Maudsley Hospital to ask her about postnatal depression, the subject of my next chapter, she told me that depression during pregnancy affects between 7 and 10 per cent of women, a large and underreported proportion; this is sometimes the result of hormonal changes: oestrogen, progesterone and cortisol levels can be up to a hundred times higher than usual. In 2018, researchers from King's College London found that as many as a quarter of pregnant women suffer from mental health problems during those nine months.

The sense of hope for the future that pregnancy embodies – for women, couples, and society alike – is a genuinely wonderful thing, but it also has a slightly manic quality. It brooks no dissension from unalloyed happiness, cannot countenance the possibility of failure (although the fear of failure fuels the absolutist advice), and represents a quixotic attempt to compensate for deficiencies, sweep away imperfections, and cleanly start again.

4

IS IT NORMAL TO FEEL LIKE THIS?

When my son was a few days old, the health visitor came round with her forms and bible-like 'red book' to document his length and weight and my daily diet and who else was in the household. It seemed to go on for hours and felt pretty perfunctory. But then there was a final question: how was I feeling? I started to cry. The health visitor put down her pen. I could sense cogs turning in her head. Was this just baby blues, or something more serious? I was also torn: I wanted the care, but not the categorisation. My principles were colliding with my pride. I was already outraged by how widespread postnatal depression is, but I wanted to be marked down as well able to cope. And I didn't want to be stigmatised for finding it hard. It was hard!

There was something else, too: it seemed demanding and self-indulgent to 'complain'. When I saw other mothers pushing buggies around the high street, they looked more capable than I felt; or maybe they had more on their plate. It was hard to apply that useful dictum: never compare another person's outsides to your insides. There's an insidious hierarchy of hardship and toughness in motherhood: You have two children? Think what it's like with three! What about twins! While variations in material circumstances undoubtedly matter, there is a hint of internal-ised patriarchy about the way in which women refrain from acknowledging legitimate difficulties and asking for help – especially if they feel they don't deserve it. I was after all pretty well supported. And of course, millions of women had had babies before me and got through it, I couldn't help reminding myself.

While it's utterly ordinary to have babies, it's also extremely common to develop mental health problems. Postnatal depression (PND) affects up to one in five mothers. Suicide is the leading cause of death for mothers during their baby's first year in the UK. The NCT has estimated that fully half of British mothers develop a mental health problem of some sort before or after birth, including postnatal depression – the main focus of this chapter – but also anxiety, post-traumatic stress disorder and postpartum psychosis.

Some years ago, I decided to make a radio documentary about PND – and immediately found myself deep in controversial territory. It started when I approached a reporter to find case studies. I made the mistake of phoning her on her day off: she had young children and worked part time. She was understandably bristly: here was I, a childless full-time office worker, insensitive to the fine balance of combining freelancing with childcare. And then I outlined the thesis I wanted to explore. What if PND wasn't a physical illness, but a reasonable reaction to the way reproduction is managed today? Very many mothers get two weeks of help from their partners and then they're out the door. Motherhood is exhausting and lonely. Babies can be delightful, but also tedious and exasperating; looking after them involves maintaining cheerful one-sided conversations while you feel your public self drain away.

I got to the end of my speech, and there was a frosty silence which was hard to interpret. Who was I to judge the quality of a mother's life? Or perhaps I'd hit a nerve. The controversy continued when it came to the interviews. These women were deeply resistant to the notion that their depression had anything to do with their situation. Was I suggesting they weren't managing, or criticising their partners? What they were dealing with, they insisted, was an illness, and the appropriate remedy was medication. The majority of the experts I spoke to concurred with this account; nobody seemed willing to stray from the consensus that the condition was caused by genetic or hormonal factors. I understood their position: how could I, as an outsider, second-guess the testimony of sufferers and practitioners in the thick of it?

Yet despite my uncomfortable sense of blundering into taboos, my niggling suspicion continued, and it is still with me now. How can something so widespread always be defined as a medical condition? To follow that line of enquiry is to push against the prevailing ideal of the naturally contented mother, to appear to question women's life circumstances, and to imply that some women lack stamina and self-sufficiency. Yet none of this is the result of either fault or failing.

Health professionals and childcare manuals tend to draw a distinction between 'baby blues' and PND: in contrast to the few days of tearfulness when breastfeeding hormones kick in, the depression is of a different order. It is as if a line is being drawn between the ordinary and the medical. Yet the one can lead to the other. So what does the prevalence of PND tell us about motherhood as an intrinsic experience, and about the way it is organised in modern, Western society? This question cuts to the heart of profound dilemmas in sociology, psychiatry and the interpretation of everyday life: where is the boundary between normality and pathology? Are the problems that humans experience physical, psychological or structural? Should they be treated with drugs, talking cures or political action?

THE LIMITS OF SCIENCE

For a condition that's so prevalent, PND is very poorly understood. It has a lengthy but still little-discussed history. Mental maladies following childbirth were identified by Hippocrates, and after the sixteenth-century Portuguese physician, Amato Lusitano, documented a case of melancholy in a new mother, the condition was treated – but not formally identified – in the centuries that followed. In the nineteenth century, it became associated with that catchall term 'hysteria', and even now the Diagnostic and Statistical Manual of Mental Disorders does not identify it as a distinct condition – it is a subcategory of depression.

A 2011 study by Scottish researchers, tellingly entitled 'The enigma of post-natal depression', spoke of 'a vacuum in the evidence base'. Genetic predisposition, a history of depression and the influence of hormones are often identified as causes. Health authorities acknowledge that circumstantial factors – such as relationship difficulties – play a part, but medical explanations tend to be cited most prominently. For example, in 2013 there was news of a blood test that women could take in the early stages of pregnancy to identify specific genes that would make them more likely to develop 'the disease', so that they could be treated before giving birth. 'Postnatal depression blood test breakthrough' which 'could help tens of thousands of women at risk', reported the press. 'Experts hope that the test will be available within two years, with results showing it to be at least 85 per cent accurate.' The NHS's fact-checking website, Behind the Headlines, pointed out that the test was not yet ready for widespread use, and Kimberly Yonkers, a professor of obstetrics at Yale, warned of the potential to panic women: it would 'have to have very good predictive value', she said. 'We are just not there yet.' Even in 2018, the research was described as 'still in the early stages'.

In 2010, researchers in Leipzig, Germany, found another ostensible physical 'cause' of PND: as well as hormones dropping in the days after birth, an enzyme blocking 'feel-good' chemicals. 'Neurological cause found for the baby blues'; 'Enzyme behind baby blues found', ran the headlines. In 2019, there were reports of the first drug developed to treat PND, brexanolone – 'Drug that beats the "baby blues" in 48 hours' according to the *Daily Mail* – a hormone treatment which researchers said tackled the 'neurological root cause' of the condition. These studies – or at least the way they are represented in the media – reinforce the portrayal of PND as a physical illness.

Psychiatrist Trudi Seneviratne, who works with women who suffer from PND, is markedly holistic in her approach, explaining that what causes the condition is a mix of biological, psychological and social factors: the 'biopsychosocial model'. PND, Trudi told me, can be triggered by a traumatic birth, or a birth that does not go according to plan. 'Half of major postnatal depressive episodes' even begin 'prior to delivery', not least because pregnancy is 'incredibly tiring and hard work'. Depression is also closely linked with anxiety – about the ability to cope with a new baby, and its life impact. And then there's breastfeeding, which does not always come easily. Trudi spoke empathetically about the perfectionism and inadequacy that many mothers feel; about how they struggle to get their babies into routines, and then feel bad if they succeed; about how childcare manuals are easy-going towards babies, but exacting for mothers.

Trudi is a professional working at the coalface, but what she told me was more open-minded than much popular commentary. 'Not every woman feels a rush of love,' she said. 'There are mothers who feel uninterested in their baby, who feel it has destroyed what they had previously, their job or their relationship with their partner. They may have feelings of resentment or even hatred towards the child.' That leads to intense guilt, then, sometimes, on to depression. 'They are terrified of admitting that something is wrong; that the midwife will get social services involved and trigger a safeguarding situation.' Trudi explained that we are following a risk-averse pattern established in the US, stoking counterproductive anxieties about disclosure and referral. A 2018 Nuffield Foundation report revealed that the number of newborn babies removed from their mothers had doubled in the last decade. It is of course a difficult balance: we must as a society do our utmost to prevent harm to children. But at the same time, mothers who do not admit to difficulties for fear that their babies will be removed can find that their illness, untreated, only gets worse.

The mother's impulse, in fact, is often to protect her child, even if that is to her own – and ultimately the child's – detriment. For example, many women who take antidepressants come off their medication while pregnant, for fear of damaging the baby; but this raises the risk of PND, which can be much more harmful to babies than the medication. Unintended consequences are a recurrent outcome of ostensibly risk-averse parenting. A 2009 study by Janice Goodman, a senior psychiatric nurse in Massachusetts, found that only 35 per cent of a sample of over five hundred pregnant women indicated they would take antidepressant medication, even if recommended by their doctor.

The tendency to medicalise depression and regard genetic or hormonal tests as a holy grail may prevent health professionals from making the most of the already existing screening method: taking the time to talk effectively (not just with tick-box forms) to mothers. Trudi told me that proper 'MOT checks' on new mothers are still not being done – although she hopes this will improve with NHS England's drive to improve perinatal care. Alongside medication, she said, there also needs to be more use made of talking cures, whether that's cognitive behavioural therapy, or 'mother and baby' psychotherapy. What mothers need, Trudi concluded at the end of our conversation, is to feel nurtured – mothered – themselves.

I also spoke to the psychoanalyst Angela Joyce, who has worked extensively with mothers who are having difficult relationships with their babies. Psychoanalysis, she told me, regards mothers' ordinary imperfections as necessary, even beneficial, to children: their job is to 'let the world in in small doses'. Mothering is also about learning to cope with the baby's inevitable frustrations: it's a two-way process, and depression occurs when it goes wrong. In some cases, Joyce explained, the depressed mother tries to protect the child from herself because she feels she's failing; at other times the mother starts to regard the baby as an alien presence who is judging her. She feels guilt and grief for failing, or anger at the baby for revealing it. 'In the mother's mind the baby is imbued with some quality that she associates with her poor mental state, whether it's that the baby is being critical of her . . . or it might be the other way around, that she is damaging the baby with her mental state . . . and this might make her avoid the baby, or it might make her intrusively overprotective.' The depressed mother often has a flat, blank affect, Joyce said: 'her responses are dampened down; and this makes it really important to have other people around to engage the baby. But then the mother feels terrible, because she feels she can't give the baby what she sees somebody else giving it.' This reinforces the cycle of isolation and reluctance to seek help. Help may be exactly what she needs, but it exposes her 'inadequacy'.

CONTEXT MATTERS

Dig a little deeper into the research literature, and the social factors emerge: the change in status, the gap between the expectation and the reality of motherhood, isolation, and a lack of support. 'Women who suffer from postnatal depression are likely to have been competent and successful before their pregnancy,' the journal *Nursing Standard* reported; they also 'often try to hide their condition from nurses and midwives' – that resonated with my own encounter with the health visitor.

Having control in your former life doesn't necessarily help: in the turbulent unpredictability of early motherhood, the contrast can even make things worse. In 2014, researchers at Denison University in Ohio found an association between PND and the expectation that parenthood 'would be naturally fulfilling', and also 'the expectation that an infant's behaviour will reflect maternal skill' – the control fallacy again. Another study by French researchers from 2017 concluded that 'brooding rumination' and 'low maternal self-esteem' are factors. An Australian study from the 1990s found that women were at greater risk of PND if their 'spouses provided low care'.

A similar picture emerges from surveys. In 2015, Mumsnet asked 631 women what contributed to their PND: 65 per cent cited the 'pressure to be the "perfect mother"', and 46 per cent the 'pressure to bond with your baby and/or to feel overwhelming love for them'; 29 per cent considered 'the pressure to breastfeed, from other people' a significant factor, while 48 per cent blamed their own expectations of breastfeeding. A Netmums survey found in 2018 that around half of depressed mothers believed the main cause was isolation, and 40 per cent had had a traumatic birth; it also found that a full 30 per cent never tell a health professional. Another survey, this time undertaken in 2018 by the Co-op and the Red Cross, revealed that 82 per cent of new mothers under thirty reported feeling lonely some of the time, with 43 per cent saying they often or always felt lonely. In 2020, this isolation has been exacerbated by Covid-19.

It is worth dwelling for a moment on the perceived 'failure to bond' with the baby, which contravenes the 'natural' law of maternal instinct. In the 1970s, two Australian researchers, Marshall Klaus and John Kennell, extrapolated from studies of elk, goats, and Guatemalan women, arguing that if skin-to-skin contact was not established immediately after birth, the mother–infant relationship would be compromised in the long term. The importance of 'bonding' has been endlessly reinforced in advice to parents. Yet a 2016 NCT survey revealed that a third of new mothers find bonding difficult. The problem is compounded by widespread ambiguity about what the term even means. It is clear that many depressed mothers find it hard to establish a pattern of happy interaction with their baby, but the idea that there is an open-or-shut critical 'window' immediately after birth is both unhelpful and unscientific.

And then there's the small matter of sleep deprivation, as researchers at the University of Alberta in Edmonton found in 2018. Their study showed that not only does sleep training for infants solve sleep problems, it also improves maternal mood. Yet sleep training – also known as controlled crying, leaving children to cry for limited periods of time – is highly controversial and currently frowned upon by most parenting experts. According to the Ask Dr Sears website, controlled crying goes against a mother's 'basic biology'. Child psychologist Penelope Leach has warned that it can lead to long-term harm: 'One is talking about a baby that is crying hard and nobody is responding,' she writes. 'When that happens, and particularly if it happens over a long period, the brain chemical system releases cortisol and that is very bad for brain development.'

We never quite got around to mastering sleep training: we weren't against it, but it always seemed to require more organisation than my husband and I could muster. We'd either plump for half-asleep, short-termist instant gratification – give the baby some milk and a cuddle – or, when we had a new baby, and a toddler who wouldn't go to sleep, we tried leaving the toddler to cry in his cot: he promptly climbed over the bars and spent the next six weeks in the bed between us, thus demonstrating the enduring relevance of Sigmund Freud. No more new babies, thank you very much, he was effectively saying – as if that was on the cards. The sleep-training 'debate' is presented as if it's an either-or, but I think most parents muddle through the middle.

Like other parenting debates, only one side is morally sanctioned by society: Gina Ford's sleep-training manuals are still in the shops, but her methods are controversial – 'cruel and selfish' according to a typical Netmums poster; she only has the brass neck to impose them on other people's kids because she 'has never actually had one of her own', remarks another. Yet as Emily Oster has shown, the research on controlled crying does not suggest that it is harmful to infants, particularly if they are six months or older; in fact, it makes them more secure, not less. It's not just the lack of sleep itself that – I argue – contributes to PND: it's the harsh censuring of mothers trying desperately for rest.

I wasn't depressed, but I was often a bit lonely. On bad days I would eye up other mothers hopefully in the park; sometimes I'd be brave enough to strike up a conversation. It was like standing around awkwardly in a nightclub, minus the glamour: was I coming on too strong? Or maybe they were having a bad day too, and boundaries were somehow easier. To massacre Groucho Marx, mothers don't want to be members of a club that would expose their need for membership. Whether it's tact, pride, shyness, custom, or the influence of the smartphone, mothers exist in separate bubbles, fighting private battles. If I see a baby crying on the train, I try to resist an urge to 'help' by pulling faces or playing a lame game of peekaboo, as I can't even tell if that would be a welcome break for the mum or an annoying intervention, implying she can't cope. So I don't reach out either.

Natasha Mauthner is a social scientist who has collected and analysed PND testimonies. Part of the problem, she told me, is that the causes are mutually reinforcing. Loneliness produces shame and the impulse to reduce contact even more, and confinement can feel safe. Perfectionism heightens the perception of failure, which raises the stakes still further. Healthcare professionals may fear the contagion of suggestion, so the silence is cemented. In addition to cultural pressures, women themselves are very protective of maternal ideals, Mauthner observed interestingly. They equate not being happy with not being 'good'. 'Just being a mother,' Mauthner notes, 'is not enough.'

For some of the women Mauthner interviewed, the official sanctioning of their predicament as a mental illness seemed to come as a kind of relief. But it's important to state that PND *is* a mental illness. It's a serious condition, but it is sometimes brought on by societal factors, and even when it has a physical origin, it exists on a spectrum with difficulties all mothers can face. As it is too often framed, either you are depressed or you aren't, and if you aren't, you just have to get on with it. Just as we tend increasingly as a culture to pathologise sadness or anger as maladies to be treated rather than rational reactions to life events, there is a similar tendency to want to lift PND out of its social context. And this has political ramifications, as it prevents us from critiquing the way that motherhood is managed. Depression occurs when women are unable to process ordinary feelings of frustration, anger and ambivalence, and when those feelings are not validated by society. What matters is not just experience, but how it's interpreted. Traumatic emergency caesareans or difficulties breastfeeding are more likely to lead to depression if they are regarded as failure.

While I'm not blaming either doctors or the women themselves for medicalising PND, it's important to recognise that it is society, and not the mother, that is out of line. Mauthner believes that PND is an understandable response to the multiple losses that characterise modern motherhood: 'of self, occupational status and identity, autonomy, physical integrity, time, sexuality, and male company'. Yet she stresses that just because something is common doesn't mean it's inevitable, and indeed, this 'obscures the range of feelings women actually experience': after all, 'many find motherhood deeply satisfying, fulfilling and joyful'.

While medication undoubtedly works for some women, others find it helpful going back to work – although that can prompt further guilt and alienation. What Mauthner found to be the most powerful solution by far was solidarity and companionship. The turning point for very many depressed mothers, she told me, was when they were able to surmount the considerable obstacles – both internal and external – in the way of talking about the problem with other mothers in a similar situation, and discover that they were not alone in both senses of the word.

* * *

For all its advances, the 'developed world' in the twenty-first century is not very good at looking after mothers. 'During the twentieth century, for the first time in history, the majority of women have had, increasingly, to bring up their children virtually alone,' writes the medical historian and psychiatrist Ann Dally. She calls this 'an impending crisis of motherhood in the western world'.

In a widely cited 1983 paper, American anthropologists Gwen Stern and Laurence Kruckman analysed PND across national boundaries. They found that in industrialised countries, 50 to 80 per cent of women suffered from 'baby blues' and 15 to 25 per cent experienced PND. By contrast, in cultures where care for new mothers is routine, postnatal disorders were rare or non-existent. In Mexico and other Latin American countries, the postnatal period is known as *la cuarentena*, or quarantine – from *cuarenta*, forty in Spanish: the days of mandatory rest. In China, a common custom is 'doing the month': the mother stays indoors, looked after by relatives. In Japan and parts of India, it's traditional to move back to the childhood home and be cared for there. In Tanzania and Kenya, a new mother's only task is to eat, sleep and look after her baby; in parts of Nigeria she is placed in a special 'fattening room'.

In Britain until the 1970s, it was customary to stay in hospital for a two-week 'lying in' period. Newborns would sleep in the nursery to allow mothers to rest. I wouldn't have wanted my baby to stay in a different room, but this presents an interesting contrast with my first largely unassisted night after the emergency caesarean. Maternity hospitals were often brutal places, but the good aspects – the care and attention – fell away along with the bad during the second half of the twentieth century.

In the modern global north, pregnant women are given excessive attention, but after the birth the shutters come down and visitors are generally only interested in the little bundle. A popular book for new mothers, co-authored in 1989 by Arlene Eisenberg, describes this as 'the reverse Cinderella' – the 'pregnant princess' becomes 'the postpartum peasant'. When Meghan, Duchess of Sussex, announced her plan to have a doula after the birth of Archie, eyebrows were raised. But why not? The doula is as close as many women get nowadays to the kind of support that was once routine.

PND is found in non-Western countries, but usually in situations where the mother is isolated or has little support, reinforcing the importance of social context as a factor. Researchers from Liverpool University found in 2017 that in Pakistan, where – traditionally – women have strong family networks, the risk of postpartum depression is nearly seven times higher among women with little support from their husbands, and over six times higher among those lacking wider family help. A 2019 study of mothers in Ethiopia also found an association between PND and 'low social support'. A 1980s study of couples in Rio de Janeiro, Brazil, who were determined to cast off the traditional reliance on grandparents and nurse-maids, then found that the Western nuclear-family model made more of the mothers depressed. It's important not to draw patronising parallels between the historical past and non-Western countries today – particularly when, according to the Norwegian authors of a 2010 cross-cultural study, across the world many postnatal customs that were common before 1950 'are no longer existent. The focus on rest and assistance for the mother after delivery has gradually decreased.' But the modern West is particularly bad at abiding by the adage 'it takes a village to raise a child'.

BREAKING THE SILENCE

Amidst the airless jollity and perfectionism of modern motherhood, I want to open a window onto forgotten examples of tolerance and acceptance, or at least honest description. It's hard to 'diagnose' postnatal depression in the past and in works of literature, but Charlotte Perkins Gilman's short story *The Yellow Wallpaper*, which appeared in an 1892 edition of the *New England Magazine*, seems to resemble what we recognise as the condition today. It takes the form of a secret diary written by a young woman with a new baby who – according to her physician husband – is suffering from a 'temporary nervous depression'. The story is inspired by Gilman's own experience: five years previously, and severely depressed after the birth of her daughter, she was treated by the influential neurologist Silas Weir Mitchell. His treatment for this form of 'hysteria' was strict bed rest. After a month, Gilman writes in her autobiography, she was sent home with the following prescription: 'Live as domestic a life as possible. Have your child with you all the time . . . Have but two hours' intellectual life a day. And never touch pen, brush, or pencil as long as you live.' After a few months of this, Gilman 'came perilously near to losing my mind'.

The picture that emerges from Sylvia Plath's poetry, life and suicide is an ambiguous, potent combination of devoted, yet ambivalent and unsupported motherhood. Another important figure in this history is the writer and academic Hannah Gavron, who ended her life in 1964, aged twenty-nine, with two children and a new job as a lecturer. She had recently completed a PhD, published the following year as *The Captive Wife*, which describes how leaving paid work after childbirth stripped many women of their independence: a message still relevant now. It is worth noting (without judgement or inference) that Gavron had a nanny from nine to five, five days a week – an arrangement that nowadays would be barely socially acceptable now, let alone affordable. I am certainly not harking back to these difficult stories as positive precedents, but they throw light on how little progress has been made for mothers, and at the same time how unusual it has become to openly discuss motherhood's darker side.

When Rachel Cusk published her unflinching memoir *A Life's Work* in 2001, the public reaction was vicious, as if she was culpable for simply describing her own experience. I found it realistic, but where motherhood is concerned, realism is apparently unconscionably negative. The selfishness of the 'complaining' mother feels like a modern phenomenon, the consequence of women becoming more aspirational, ambitious and entitled. Yet as early as 1949, Doris Lessing famously left two toddlers with their father in Southern Rhodesia (she had already left them for a second husband), returning to London with her son from the second marriage to pursue a writing career and become a communist activist. 'For a long time I felt I had done a very brave thing,' she wrote in 1950 of her decision. 'There is nothing more boring for an intelligent woman than to spend endless amounts of time with small children. I felt I wasn't the best person to bring them up. I would have ended up an alcoholic or a frustrated intellectual like my mother.' Such decisions and candid explanations are simply forbidden today.

Reflecting on the reception of *A Life's Work* seven years on, Rachel Cusk wrote that this 'sanctimoniousness' was 'part of what I had found intolerable in the public culture of motherhood' itself, the 'childcare manuals and the toddler groups, the discourse of domestic life, even the politics of birth itself'. Intrinsic to new motherhood, Cusk continued, was the expectation that women 'should re-encounter the childhood mechanism' of 'suppressing her true feelings in order to be "good" and to gain approval'. Her 'own struggle', she wrote, had been to 'resist this mechanism. I wanted to – I had to – remain "myself"'. This resistance – even the analysis itself – is still highly unconventional.

Our culture has little time for women who are materially replete but socially, emotionally or intellectually starved. Yet in the Fifties and Sixties, the era of the suburban housewife was at least accompanied by mainstream critiques. *McCall's* magazine published articles like 'The Mother Who Ran Away' in 1956, and 'Is Boredom Bad for You?' in 1957, and in 1960, *Redbook* magazine ran an article on 'Why Young Mothers Feel Trapped'. It opened with the words of a generic husband and wife, representative of the time: 'It's wonderful to be a mother, but sometimes I feel like a pie being cut into six pieces and served to a dinner-party of ten,' wrote the 'wife'; 'I want status. I want self-respect. I want people to think that what I'm doing is important.' The article attracted thousands of confirmatory responses.

And then there was Betty Friedan's *The Feminine Mystique*, published in 1963, which explored 'the problem that has no name': the unhappiness of wives and mothers who did not work outside the home. We still have the problem, and it has even less of a name: Friedan's illuminating terminology has become retro (barely anyone self-identifies as a housewife these days, except ironically) and, in an age of supposed freedom, choice and empowerment, the issue is now shrouded in taboo. *The Feminine Mystique* sold a million copies in the year after publication and attracted extensive media attention, including a CBS TV special on 'The Trapped Housewife'. We tend to think of the Fifties as the last decade of purely devoted motherhood, before Sixties and Seventies feminism ushered women into universities and the workplace. Yet Friedan pointed to early American feminists who fought for women's rights to education and a career: the Fifties, she argued, was a blip.

These writers, critics and analysts untangled the double binds in which mothers are caught. The anti-war, anti-racist activist and author Grace Paley wove frank accounts of single motherhood into her short stories, published from 1959 onwards. Tillie Olsen, a socialist author and mother of four, tackled the intersections of poverty, race and feminism in her fiction: her 1961 story *I Stand Here Ironing* reflects on how work – including housework – gets in the way of looking after her daughter; her 1978 non-fiction work, *Silences*, explores the challenge of combining motherhood and writing.

In *Of Woman Born*, Adrienne Rich described mothers' 'powerless responsibility', and in *A Woman's Estate*, published in 1971, the feminist scholar Juliet Mitchell observed how 'the "freedom" of the housewife is her own isolation'. In 1983 the philosopher Sara Ruddick described how, as a mother, 'a single day' can 'encompass fury, infatuation, boredom, and simple dislike'. Jane Lazarre, who has explored themes of motherhood and race in her fiction and non-fiction, described in her 1976 memoir *The Mother Knot*, 'the strange and paradoxical way in which the infinite kind of love we feel for our children is locked into the dull, enervating routine of caring for them' – an observation that has particular resonance for me: when I'm out and I hear my children's voices on the phone, or when I look at photographs of them when I'm not with them, that infinite love is suddenly unlocked, and I wonder why I get so desperate for them to go to bed.

At the beginning of the 1960s, the psychoanalyst and paediatrician Donald Winnicott presented a series of extraordinary programmes on BBC radio, entitled 'The Ordinary Devoted Mother and Her Children'. His voice was calm, rhythmic, nasal, and rather high-pitched: some listeners even thought he was a woman; but this was perhaps because a man discussing motherhood was so unusual. Winnicott has been criticised by some feminists – Denise Riley among them, in her 1983 book *War in the Nursery* – for recommending that mothers should be entirely devoted to their children. 'Enjoy letting other people look after the world while you are producing a new one of its members,' he advised his readers. But although fathers have less prominence in his account, Winnicott acknowledged that mothering is a role that can be taken on by a different primary carer. He was, of course, also a product of his time.

Two of Winnicott's broadcasts – *What Irks*, and *More that Irks – and Why* – were surprisingly insightful about the downsides and difficulties of motherhood. When the baby is first born, he says, a special state of affairs prevails: this is the period of 'primary maternal preoccupation': the time when the mother – unless things go wrong – can't stop staring into her baby's face, smelling its head, checking it's alright. But then after a few months, the mother begins to re-establish herself as an adult. 'And now starts a tremendous struggle,' says Winnicott. The baby 'makes a claim on all your secrets'; it 'stakes claim after claim in a perpetual gold rush', but 'the gold is never enough, and a new claim must be staked'. As the mother becomes more and more independent, her 'gold mines' become 'more and more inaccessible' to her baby. Winnicott is both astute and forgiving. 'You don't quite recover,' he says of this fraught, gradual disentangling: 'if you did it would mean you'd finished with being a parent.' And of course if you have several children, 'the same process starts up again and again; and you're 45 years old before you can look around and see where you yourself stand in the world'.

Winnicott's language is down-to-earth, but it is also eloquent, poetic even: the 'gold rush'. And the image of the forty-five-year-old reaches through time to me now. When I first heard what Winnicott says next, however, it struck me with a mixture of sadness, envy and irritation. 'I do believe from talking to innumerable mothers and from watching their children grow,' he says, 'that the mothers who come off best are the ones who can surrender at the beginning. They lose everything. What they gain is that in the course of time they can recover.' This is because their children 'gradually give over this perpetual staking of claims and begin to be glad that their mothers are individuals in their own right. As indeed they themselves quickly become.'

I was not able to surrender at the beginning. I clung on with a panicked grip, taking on a big creative project during my maternity leave and giving my baby to my next-door neighbour and friend to be looked after when he was six weeks old for two hours a day, three days a week. I was desperate to keep my head above water. But I do also regret not letting go more. I did gradually succumb, but over many subsequent years, as the kids became more mature and more interesting, and I slowly exhaled with the knowledge that they'd won me over, but not taken me over.

For all his emphasis on maternal devotion, Winnicott is ultimately reassuring: 'So I feel rather hopeful about these mothers who describe their battle on behalf of the clock against the invading hordes of their children,' he concludes one of his broadcasts. 'In the end this battlefield is not strewn with corpses, but with individual children,' who are not 'deprived' or 'problem' children, but 'adolescents eventually, each able to stand up in his or her own right'. And it's when that happens, he says, rounding off his account almost like a filmic narrative, 'that you can afford to do so too. You can afford to be yourself – with your secrets – which brings you back, although with a difference, to where you were before you were invaded by your children.'

No amount of maternal self-sacrifice is too much for today's simple-minded cultural expectations, but Simone de Beauvoir understood its corrosive potential: 'Some mothers make themselves slaves of their offspring to compensate for the emptiness in their hearts and to punish themselves for the hostility they do not want to admit,' she wrote in *The Second Sex*. Cultivating a 'morbid anxiety' which prevents them letting their child 'do anything on his own', these women 'give up all pleasure, all personal life, enabling them to assume the role of victim'; her suffering is 'a weapon she uses sadistically; her displays of resignation spur guilt feelings in the child' which are 'more harmful than aggressive displays'. This analysis of the bitter consequences of being an endlessly 'good' rather than a 'good-enough' mother is still relevant. With 'hypocritical prudishness', she writes, society displaces the inevitable badness in mothers (they can't be all good) onto the fictional cruel stepmother.

'I got depressed,' wrote the writer and editor of the *London Review of Books* Mary-Kay Wilmers about the birth of her first son in 1972, 'because instead of maternal goodness welling up inside me, the situation seemed to open up new areas of badness in my character.' The only thing that seems to be 'eternal and natural in motherhood is ambivalence', wrote Jane Lazarre. One of the most helpfully clear-sighted writers on maternal ambivalence is the psychoanalyst Rozsika Parker, who described in her 1995 book *Torn in Two* the disorienting alternation between overwhelming love one minute and antipathy the next, and how negative feelings are brushed under the carpet by a society that expects a mother to be 'an icon of adult restraint, moderation and thoughtful control'.

In fact, as Parker writes, it's important for mothers to let the negativity bubble up, since it prompts them to pause and think about their relationship with their child. Yet our twenty-first-century intolerance of these inevitable feelings extends to the expectation that childcare should be characterised not only by restraint, but also abandon. The American psychologist Martha Wolfenstein observed in a 1951 pamphlet entitled 'The Emergence of Fun Morality' how government-issued childcare literature was now mandating mothers to 'make play an aspect of every activity', and as a result, play had assumed 'a new obligatory quality'.

The exhausting injunction to satisfy not only an infant's needs but also his wants – his desire for play – weighs heavily on tired contemporary mothers, and also raises the bar for children, who also need to just 'be'. The psychotherapist Juliet Hopkins has noted that there is such a thing as 'the too good mother': 'some sensitive, responsive parents may inadvertently "worse than castrate" their children by depriving them of an autonomous sense of agency', she wrote in a 2007 paper.

The widespread assumption that women now largely enjoy the power to self-determine is perhaps what leads us to pathologise PND: we can't reconcile it with modern progress. But feminist thinkers have long wondered whether PND is an integral part of being a mother, or a consequence of how it's managed. In 1971, the bestselling feminist writer Ellen Peck published *The Baby Trap*, which bluntly put the case against becoming a mother at all. Some Seventies second-wavers went even further, rejecting not only motherhood, but the nuclear family altogether: the activist and writer Shulamith Firestone was brought up in an orthodox Jewish family, but called for the abolition of 'the biological family' in *The Dialectic of Sex*, published in 1970: artificial reproduction outside the womb would free women, she argued, and children could be raised in collectives. For these writers, depression was an inevitable consequence of having babies.

The sociologist Ann Oakley articulates the alternative position: in a 2012 British Library oral history recording for the 'Sisterhood and After' project, documenting the Women's Liberation Movement, she noted that if you complain about your experience of motherhood, 'that is read as a complaint about the children'. But, she continues, 'I loved those children, I wanted to have those children'. What she didn't like was 'the position in which women then and still are expected to do this mothering'; the assumption of 'exclusive responsibility'. Oakley was diagnosed with PND, but says that this diagnosis 'which was handed out to me and continues to be handed out to thousands of women, is in most cases I'm quite sure, a misnomer'. She elaborates, building on the theme of this chapter, 'it's a medicalisation of normal human distress, the experience of sleep deprivation, the responsibility of a new job for which one has no training . . . loss of status, career change, not very much money often, and no social support. All of these things create a situation in which we wouldn't be human if we didn't have a reaction to that.'

Adrienne Rich describes a glorious summer spent alone with her sons in a friend's house in Vermont, away from 'school hours, fixed routines, naps'. One night, heading home at midnight after a drive-in movie, with three sleeping boys in the back of the car, she felt 'elated': 'we had broken together all the rules of bedtime, the night rules, rules I myself thought I had to observe in the city or become a "bad mother"'. Of course, she writes, when they returned home, 'my own mistrust of myself as a "good mother" returned'. It's a glimpse of what motherhood can be like as an experience rather than an institution, as Rich puts it. The absolutist management of motherhood – ostensibly designed to produce virtuous mothers and happy children – actually ruins the experience for all.

PND is both underdiagnosed and over-medicalised: in our idealisation of motherhood, we are reluctant to countenance the idea that it can sometimes be depressing; and we'd rather label women sick than address ways society could support mothers. Pharmaceutical prescriptions may help individual women, but they leave the broader context intact.

* * *

Now that my own children are at school, there are fewer days spent roaming around freezing parks, but it sometimes feels as if the froideur of early motherhood has given way to cliquiness at the school gates – a defence against loneliness that deflects it onto others, perhaps.

Can new technology provide the answer to solitude, perhaps the biggest driver of PND? The last five years have seen the launch of no fewer than five apps – Peanut, Mush, Mummy Links, Happity, and Buump Active (with a fitness focus) – enabling users to connect with like-minded mums in their local area – are you, Mush asks new joiners, a 'c-section sista', a 'baby-led weaner', or a 'routine parent'? Peanut has over a million users; Mush claims it has spawned 'over 2 million friendships'. Yet this cyber 'solution' is not a panacea. The apps are sustainable only by selling users' data or charging for premium membership. Like Tinder, mothers swipe left or right, and being rejected has the potential to compound the problem of alienation further. 'These social meet-up apps can put a lot of pressure on mums, especially if no one is connecting with you,' the clinical psychologist and author of *The Supermum Myth*, Rachel Andrew, told the *Sun*. 'When people don't connect, the temptation can be to think negatively about ourselves, and mentally this can lead us to feel low or anxious and cause us to isolate ourselves further.'

It is time these vicious cycles were broken once and for all. The measures which I believe would help reduce the incidence of PND are a microcosm of the solutions I propose all the way through this book. We need, first, structured ways for new mothers to meet beyond limited and informal NCT networks and the small number of opportunities currently provided by services such as breastfeeding drop-ins. Second, real equality within partnerships, driven by improved parental leave arrangements but more importantly changes to the structure of work itself: I'll come back to this in chapter 7. Third, proper monitoring by health professionals and increased access to psychotherapy. And fourth, heightened consciousness-raising among mothers of their right to be dissatisfied about the way motherhood is organised, leading, I hope, to stronger peer-to-peer solidarity and therefore greater impetus for change.

If such solutions appear daunting, let's remember – with the help of the liberating insights of Winnicott and the feminist critics I've highlighted here – that mothers today are labouring under a set of entirely unnecessary cultural strictures. Let's also remember that we already have the models and the infrastructure in place to deliver these solutions – such as the Sure Start family support programmes that are now so woefully, needlessly and counterproductively underfunded. And for those who prefer the grassroots to the top-down state, we could radically extend initiatives like Home-Start, the community network of experts and trained volunteers helping parents around the world. These human solutions are messier than an app or a pill, but ultimately more effective. The social and political prescription is waiting to be fulfilled.

5

NURTURE ON TAP

I was lucky. Both my babies did it within minutes of birth. With my son, it felt reassuring to breastfeed after the emergency caesarean, and with my daughter, it partly vindicated my elective one (I, too, have internalised those judgements). After my son's birth, I stayed in hospital for five days, which meant I received by accident the kind of free breastfeeding training that used to be more commonplace in the days of 'lying in'. I also enjoyed it, if 'enjoying' means the relief of being able to stop the unbearable sound of my baby crying, like switching off a fire alarm going off inside my head. And if enjoying means being flooded with hormones that are not as gentle as love but feel more like a powerful head-rush. I was grateful to be able to do something uncomplicatedly useful for my babies, looking down at their fists beating rhythmically on my chest like an overheated runner thumping the sideboard as he drinks a glass of water too fast – it was a rare moment when I didn't have to think: What now?

I would, however, invariably realise too late that, once again, I'd forgotten to put a pad in the other bra cup, and would watch my nice clean top develop a dark, sodden stain. And there were awkward moments, such as a rare conference trip when I was taken out to dinner by my twenty-something male host, blind to this kind of hydraulic pressure; I did my best to keep up my end of the conversation while my boobs started to throb, but eventually had to speed-walk to the toilet and milk myself into the sink.

I didn't have cracked and bleeding nipples, or a biting baby, or mastitis that turns your breasts swollen solid and raging red: a condition only relieved – partially – by feeding the baby, but that hurts so much you don't dare to do it. But I did get the pain of 'let-down': an unbearable hill you have to get over once the baby starts to suck. Breastfeeding, even at the best of times, is not problem-free. And when it's hard, it's really hard. One friend found feeding more painful than giving birth. Another had twins and had to arrange them into a two-handed rugby hold using a specially designed pillow – almost impossible to achieve alone. Another had blocked milk ducts – hard knots of pain that made feeding agony, and her baby was losing weight. The psychiatrist Trudi Seneviratne told me that stress can inhibit breastfeeding, causing a downward spiral. A 2019 BBC *Woman's Hour* poll found that half of new mothers struggle to breastfeed; those that do struggle feel a failure, and for one in seven, problems with breastfeeding negatively impact on their mental health.

In spite of these difficulties, mothers are told to breastfeed at all costs. And that's before we even get on to the issue of combining it with work. Some women find it hard to sustain a career while attached to their baby for the best part of every day, for half a year or more – especially if they live in a country with little or no maternity leave. Other women simply cannot afford to take that kind of time off. In the face of such a blatant mismatch between instruction and reality, one would think that the benefits of breastfeeding as opposed to formula-feeding must be significant and clearly demonstrated by scientific evidence. Yet they are not.

Like so many areas of motherhood, infant feeding is a highly controversial topic: several researchers I approached for this book declined to be interviewed on the record. Both the reticence and the antagonism are unhelpful to mothers, creating the sensation of picking one's way through territory full of dangerous pitfalls – for both babies and themselves. But to be 'for' or 'against' breastfeeding is to apply the wrong paradigm. The part that is missing is the real forces that shape women's lives: economic necessity and social norms.

There is a widespread assumption that good motherhood went down the tubes when women began to pursue education and employment – this is most commonly expressed in dismay at the advent of ready meals and junk food (code for maternal absence). Yet as I'll show in this chapter, the history of infant feeding reveals a surprising range of practices and habits, many of which didn't involve the mother at all. In presenting this history, I do not intend to advocate for formula-feeding or for mothers being apart from their babies. Instead, I will use it to expose the myth of a historic golden age of devoted motherhood, and to show how narrowly punitive attitudes have become today. I would like to see guidelines and advice that is scientifically proportionate, recognises women's lived realities, and promotes equality between mothers and fathers.

'BREAST IS BEST'

The UK government recommends that women breastfeed their babies exclusively for six months, and then combine breast with solid foods for up to two years. The government and the NHS are here following WHO guidelines, and the NHS has also signed up to promoting the Baby Friendly Initiative, launched by the WHO and UNICEF in 1991 as a global programme to 'protect, promote, and support breastfeeding'. The Baby Friendly Hospital Initiative's accreditation guidelines include the recommendation to 'give infants no food or drink other than breast milk, unless medically indicated'.

Breastfeeding is said to confer a whole host of benefits including reducing the risk of stomach, chest, urinary tract and ear infections, allergies, eczema, asthma, diabetes, obesity, meningitis, and cot death; boosting eyesight, IQ and behaviour; cementing an essential emotional bond between mother and baby; lowering the incidence of postnatal depression; and lessening the chance of women developing osteoporosis and breast cancer later in life.

This message is repeated and disseminated by NCT classes, midwives, health visitors, breastfeeding counsellors, advice books, news features and parenting websites. The tone and imagery can be dramatic and alarmist: one campaign by the National Breastfeeding Awareness Campaign in the US depicted a pregnant woman riding a bucking bronco in a bar, and taking part in a log-rolling competition, cheered on by spectators. 'You wouldn't take risks before your baby is born. Why start after?' ran the caption: 'Breastfeed exclusively for 6 months.' Posters produced by the global network World Alliance for Breastfeeding Action warn women of the '21 dangers of infant formula', which include, they claim, for the baby, infections, obesity, allergies, sleep apnoea, anaemia, dental problems and cancer; and for the mother, breast cancer, osteoporosis, obesity, diabetes and cardiovascular disease.

The NHS website informs women that formula 'does not give you any health benefits'. It also warns that it 'can contain bacteria, which is why it's vital to make it up with water that is hot enough' – in fact it is insufficiently cleaned bottles and teats that are the biggest risk here, rather than the milk. The WHO and UNICEF guidelines, from which the UK derives its advice, have been developed on the basis that some countries lack a clean water supply, good quality formula is not widely available, and formula is marketed to women who can ill afford it. That context is different to ours.

In the US, the strategy appears to be working somewhat: more infants are now breastfed there than at any time in the last forty years, although the numbers are still well below where the authorities want them to be. In the UK, breastfeeding rates are among the lowest in the world. In 2016 the *Lancet* found that only 34 per cent of babies are receiving some breast milk at six months compared with 49 per cent in the US and 71 per cent in Norway.

My contention is that this low rate somehow coexists simultaneously with a seemingly ineffective, poorly targeted and highly guilt- and anxiety-producing advice culture. Women I know who turned to formula as a desperate last resort were met with tight-lipped or explicit disapproval from postnatal midwives: one friend whose baby was losing weight was told that under no circumstances should she give up. In 2018, a hospital trust was criticised for addressing mothers who formula-fed their babies as feeding them 'artificially'. National guidelines recommend that health professionals provide mothers who formula-feed with the information they require. But a 2014 study entitled 'The midwives aren't allowed to tell you' found that a misinterpretation of the Baby Friendly Hospitals Initiative leads midwives to believe they are barred from discussing formula, including even safety precautions such as sterilisation. This in itself is risky: the instructions on the side of a tin of formula read as if the primary consideration is the avoidance of litigation.

A 2015 review of the NCT's 'Baby Café' breastfeeding drop-ins found that 'many women felt that they had been given unrealistic expectations of breastfeeding by professionals keen to promote the benefits', that 'this left them feeling unprepared when they encountered pain, problems and the relentlessness of early infant feeding', and this led in turn to 'feelings of guilt and inadequacy over their feeding decisions'. In 2016, after chef Jamie Oliver urged new mothers to breastfeed, singer Adele responded in colourful yet apt terms: 'all those people who put pressure on us, you can go fuck yourselves, alright?', she said. 'Some of us can't do it! I managed about nine weeks with my boobs (I mean I trip over them – I've got a very good push-up bra). Some of my mates got postnatal depression from the way those midwives were talking.'

In 2018, the Royal College of Midwives changed its policy. They reiterated that the WHO and Department of Health guideline was still the 'most appropriate' one. The RCM's chief executive Gill Walton emphasised that breastfeeding 'brings optimum benefits for the health of both mother and baby'. But she conceded that 'if, after being given appropriate information, advice and support on breastfeeding, a woman chooses not to do so, or to give formula as well as breastfeeding, her choice must be respected'. This was an improvement, but it was passive-aggressively conditional: we've told you the facts, but if you still decide to go your own way, well, we can't stop you.

At stake here is what it really means to respect women's autonomy and appreciate her situational constraints. The lexicon of infant feeding is dominated by these two seemingly innocuous words: 'support' and 'choice'. I'm certainly not against support, but it can be used to undermine the principle of choice (she is making a certain choice because she doesn't have enough support). It can also compound blame (if she gives up, it's because she's doing it wrong). 'Breastfeeding is a natural way to feed a baby and it should not hurt,' says the NHS website. 'If you experience pain in your breasts or nipples, it's usually because your baby is not positioned or attached properly.'

Humans are animals, but we can't give birth easily without the help of others; and the ability to breastfeed, likewise, is by no means automatic. In 2018, researchers from Denmark interviewed 1,437 women about their breastfeeding experiences; up to 40 per cent of the mothers had problems. Out of these, the most prominent was 'infant's inability to latch on' at 40 per cent (closely followed at 38 per cent by 'mothers having sore, wounded and cracked nipples'); these problems were 'associated with early cessation'. Anatomy may play a part: 'latching on' difficulties are often put down to 'tongue tie', although it's rarely as simple as that. Rather incredibly, for a topic that receives such vexed attention, it was only in 2014 that scientists – from Tel Aviv, Israel – found that babies deploy a suction seal rather than 'milk' the nipple like a calf. There are a number of reasons why the seal might be insufficient: some can be resolved through instruction, some not.

Formula-feeding is also not exactly a 'choice' when women are driven – for whatever reason – to work. Accompanying my husband on a research trip to the US one summer when the kids were young, I grabbed a couple of mornings to myself to sit in a quiet library, writing an early draft of what would become this book. Taking a wrong turn on the way to the ladies, I came across a grim, windowless cubicle with a sign on the door that read 'Lactation Room'. This bizarrely gothic but in American workplaces totally commonplace room is where women – if their employers permit it – sit for hours each day, pumping milk into bags. Parents in the US get zero paid maternity leave – a fact that deserves to be regularly shouted from rooftops. A third of mothers return to work within three months of giving birth; two-thirds return within six months. Lactation rooms are embarrassing symbols of a failed system, a form of institutionalised barbarism where women's solitary labour away from both desk and baby meets nobody's needs but employers'.

Then there are powerful cultural norms. In Britain, breastfeeding rates are particularly low among young mothers and disadvantaged socioeconomic groups. In the UK, 32 per cent of women in the 'routine and manual socioeconomic' group breastfeed beyond six weeks, compared with 65 per cent in the 'managerial and professional' group.

There is little research into why women on low incomes are less likely to breastfeed. I spoke to Alison Steele, a consultant paediatrician and safeguarding lead at Great Ormond Street Hospital. According to Steele, the two biggest determinants are whether your mother breastfed and the attitude of your partner. One 2018 study by researchers at the University of Sheffield conducted in an area with low breastfeeding rates found that decisions were influenced by the 'behaviours and beliefs' of 'family and friends' and 'socio-cultural norms' as well as by health and practical considerations. Others cite the fact that in some non-white communities, which often intersect with low-income groups, a wider family circle helps to look after the baby.

Andrea Freeman, the American law professor and author of *Skimmed: Breastfeeding, Race, and Injustice*, describes how not only ethnicity itself, but also attitudes towards minority ethnic groups, can inflect feeding habits. She told NPR in 2020: 'There's an assumption when [black] women give birth that they're not going to breastfeed, and they're not offered the same kind of assistance. They're offered formula right away.' She continued: 'Racial justice needs to incorporate these hidden oppressions that pretend that we're just making choices based on personal preferences, when in fact, we're all just responding to our circumstances that are set by forces greater than us.' There is also something askew in the fact that women demographically less likely to breastfeed are often given formula without question, while women whose social circumstances predispose them to try are subject to unremitting pressure.

Choice is also not the appropriate frame because for many women it's not an abstract either/or: they box and cox according to what they can manage. I did both: I breastfed my son and my daughter until they were eight months old, but from around five months I also used formula. I and many of my friends were warned off combining breast with bottle by midwives or breast-feeding counsellors citing the perils of 'nipple confusion'. To avoid the allure of the bottle, professionals often recommend using a cup or teaspoon instead. I can testify that this does not work. There is something gratuitous about this advice, that since bottle-teats resemble nipples, it's best to use something completely different, because then it's less of an easy jump.

The thing about a bottle – and even more so formula as it doesn't involve hours of expressing – is that it can be administered by someone else, including a father, enabling mothers to get a full night's sleep, take the day off, or return to work. Exclusive breastfeeding makes equal parenting more of a challenge, especially as it establishes enduring patterns of maternal primacy.

When my daughter was five months old, I was invited to South Africa for a four-day writers' festival. In the weeks leading up to my departure, I tried to get her to take formula. I feigned that I was easy either way, but inside, grew increasingly frantic. It was as if she knew something was up: she flicked her head from side to side as the alien liquid soaked down her front. As the day approached, I didn't know how I was going to leave her. But then a doctor noticed that she was slightly underweight and prescribed an enriched formula. She took to it as if it were double cream, and I felt guilty relief. But I was soon back – with my rocket boobs – and she merrily alternated between the two.

Time and again in modern motherhood, the medical and scientific community fails to perceive the cultural dominance of natural parenting at least in some demographic quarters, mistakenly believing it to be a countercultural underdog that needs championing. This misdirected approach results in the hammering away of a message that for many women is already thoroughly internalised.

There is a prevailing impression of stigma attached to breast-feeding, attributed to the difficulty of feeding in public and at work, and to the sexualisation of women's bodies. There are elements of truth here. Women are still told to do it in the loo. I had friends round to celebrate my birthday soon after my son's birth, and I'd put on a wrap dress without thinking through how much worse it is to have to access the boob over the top rather than discreetly from underneath. Even I, a committed feminist, found it weirdly surreal to be so exposed in a party situation. The virgin-whore dichotomy is very much in play in our culture's dual attitudes towards this area of women's anatomy: you never hear anyone say tit-feeding or even boob-feeding: it's always holy and wholesome 'breasts'.

'The odds are stacked against breastfeeding,' an anonymous NCT practitioner told the *Observer* in 2019. 'The formula industry spends millions on promotion. There's nothing comparable to support or promote breastfeeding.' Researchers at the University of Nottingham claimed in a 2017 study of representations of infant feeding in magazines that 'in many high-income countries breastfeeding rates are low and this may be a reflection of social norms which in turn may be influenced by the media'. But while popular depictions of breastfeeding may be rare, that does not mean it's not the moral default.

In 2016, researchers at Liverpool University studied the experiences of more than 1,600 new mothers. Among those who used formula, 67 per cent reported feeling guilty, 68 per cent felt stigmatised, and 76 per cent felt the need to defend their feeding choice. And researchers from Aarhus in Denmark reported in a 2013 study that the women they interviewed wanted to breastfeed, but gave up because of concerns that their baby was not getting enough milk. They 'always tried to do what they perceived was best for their child', the authors report, and, tellingly: 'it was difficult for them to face the world with a bottle'.

As with the issue of fertility and age at conception, there's a conflict between a sensible desire on the part of public health authorities to shift the dial towards breastfeeding in the population as a whole, and the need to avoid making women unnecessarily anxious – especially when the benefits are outweighed by losses in individual cases. As Alison Steele put it: 'It's difficult because there's a double message and it's slightly conflicting,' she told me: 'you're pushing all out for people to breastfeed, so that means they do feel they've failed if they can't. And that's true particularly for those women who have an idealised view of motherhood, and set themselves certain goals, and it's pretty demoralising if you perceive yourself to fail one of the first ones.' While some may not be aware of breastmilk's advantages, Alison went on, many are – and health professionals should not be piling on additional pressure. Many women who formula-feed are 'probably going to be feeling guilty about it anyway; they don't need anything else from you as a professional.'

WEIGHING IT UP

Study after study has been carried out to try to prove the advantages of breastfeeding, as if a needle is being hunted in a haystack, but so far the evidence has failed to substantiate many of the major claims. There is no clear evidence of long-term benefits for children. The only consistent finding is that breastfeeding reduces a baby's chance of getting a stomach bug in the first year. The protection only lasts for as long as you breastfeed (in contrast to the NHS statement that 'breastfeeding has long-term benefits for your baby, lasting right into adult-hood'). This is because, unlike other mammals, the antibodies in human milk do not enter the blood, just the gut. It's not even clear whether the protection comes from something in the breastmilk, or from not using dirty bottles. And what we're talking about is approximately four out of a hundred babies having one fewer incident of diarrhoea or vomiting in that first year.

All the other supposed boosts for babies have been shown to be either minor, evidentially dubious or statistically insignificant. There may be a small reduction in the risk of some breast cancers for mothers – around 2 per cent – but here too there is debate among scientists. As the economist Emily Oster notes, there are other advantages: environmentally, it results in less methane emissions and plastic pollution, and some women find breastfeeding satisfying and pleasurable – but these factors are hardly ever mentioned: the emphasis is invariably on 'benefits for baby'. 'The studies do not demonstrate,' reported one older but still respected meta-study, published in a 1984 issue of *Pediatrics*, that 'one method is superior to another in all instances'. They 'do not support making a mother feel that she is doing psychological harm to her child if she is unable or unwilling to breastfeed'.

On 'nipple confusion', there is no research evidence for its existence. A Cochrane review in 2016 found no reliable evidence overall to justify cup feeding. There is no good evidence that combination feeding (using both breastmilk and formula) reduces the likelihood a woman will continue breastfeeding, and the outcomes for children who are combination fed have never been studied. Once again, ordinary habits are beset by uncertainty and therefore anxiety.

In parenting circles there's a lively debate about the merits of feeding 'on demand' versus feeding on schedule. But like all the other pseudo-dilemmas, only one course of action is deemed morally acceptable: mum on tap. But what does 'on demand' actually mean? Babies don't state what they want, so their needs can be hard to interpret. Babies vary in the amount and frequency of feeding they require. A 2016 Cochrane review comparing 'baby-led' versus scheduled feeding found no benefit either way. There's also a big debate about whether to introduce solids at four months or exclusively breastfeed until six months: health authorities are split on the issue – and the controversy is played out on countless parenting blogs – but again there isn't much in it evidence-wise.

It's hard to do randomised controlled trials (RCTs) on infant feeding when there is already an existing belief that it's less advantageous to use formula. So the majority of research on infant feeding – as with other aspects of childbearing and childrearing – is observational studies, which analyse survey data or follow different cohorts and compare outcomes. Meta-reviews frequently highlight the pitfalls of asking women to recall their breastfeeding habits from years ago, when they may have given up after a few weeks, or combined breast with bottle at night – the stigma attached to formula-feeding may also prevent full disclosure. The British Pregnancy Advisory Service has noted that women from higher socioeconomic groups tend to overestimate how much they breastfeed.

Observational studies are also beset by the methodological problem of confounding: women who breastfeed tend to be well-off and better educated, so the more positive outcomes may be the consequence of those factors, rather than the breast-milk itself. A 2005 study by economists Eirik Evenhouse and Siobhan Reilly attempted to eliminate the confounding effect by tracking outcomes for siblings within the same family. The authors compared rates of diabetes, asthma, allergies and cognition between breastfed and formula-fed siblings. 'Almost all the differences turned out to be statistically insignificant,' they wrote; for the most part, the 'long-term effects of breast feeding have been overstated'. Another 2014 sibling study, 'Is breast truly best', by researchers at Ohio State University, also found no significant differences.

A particularly well-respected study led by Michael Kramer of McGill University in Canada attempted to eliminate confounding in a large study in Belarus. The researchers began with a sample of women who intended to breastfeed. Half of this sample was randomly chosen to receive breastfeeding help and encouragement; the other half left to proceed as they were. The assistance made a big difference to breastfeeding rates, so the researchers were able to measure the effects. Kramer has since stressed his support for breastfeeding, but his study shows that – yet again – many of the supposed benefits disappear under scrutiny. Kramer found that breastfeeding does not reduce obesity, allergies, or asthma.

The more social, economic and educational status is taken into account, therefore, the smaller the differences between breast and bottle become. A 2018 study by two American researchers even showed that the *intention* to breastfeed was itself associated with better infant incomes, whether or not the baby was actually breastfed. 'Most physical health benefits associated with breastfeeding are likely attributable to demographic characteristics, such as socioeconomic status,' they concluded. Even when researchers try to control for these social factors, bodies as diverse as WHO and BPAS have noted the problem of 'residual confounding': even within the same social group, mothers who breastfeed are likely to be more health-conscious than those who don't, which may lead them to promote healthy habits generally for their children.

In 2013, a government scheme offered low-income women in deprived areas of Yorkshire and Derbyshire shopping vouchers worth up to £200 if they breastfed their babies. Only half took up the offer, and breastfeeding rates increased by just 6 per cent. Poverty is structural: addressing it requires more than just shopping vouchers.

Breastfeeding was in the past regarded as a lowly activity, but it's now associated with higher education and affluence. Social status may influence whether or not women breastfeed, but being breastfed does not confer the benefits of higher social and economic status. That's what politics is for. Yet in 1992, the *New York Times* published an editorial on the importance of promoting breastfeeding in the 'developing' world.

A reader – a nurse and lactation consultant – responded in a letter: 'As long as children are breastfed, the holding, cuddling, and skin-to-skin contact they receive with their feedings eliminate the disparities between rich and poor.' While the intentions behind the voucher scheme shouldn't be second-guessed, this belief in the right kind of maternal nurture as a substitute for economic redistribution is widely held: I'll discuss it again in chapter 7. It's as if initiatives such as this are an attempt to fix an economic problem with a cultural tool – under the guise of public health.

The scarcity of good evidence to support breastfeeding doesn't mean there are not advantages; but these are not make-or-break and do not support the extraordinary weight of promotion. Formula milk is not actively harmful, despite statements like that of Suzanne Haynes, senior scientific adviser to the American government, who told the *New York Times* in 2006: 'Just like it's risky to smoke during pregnancy, it's risky not to breast-feed after.' It's as if, on this topic, we cannot trust plain common sense. Middle-aged friends of mine whose mothers bottle-fed them as a feminist statement seem pretty healthy to me.

The advantages of bottle-feeding – which can include economic survival, the maintenance of a career in the absence of parental leave, independence, equality with one's partner, and not suffering what is sometimes extreme pain – are not regarded as legitimate considerations. As the obstetrician Amy Tuteur notes, the heavy promotion of breastfeeding also carries risks: hospital readmission due to falling birth weight, or injury to the baby as the result of twenty-four-hour 'rooming in' (having babies stay with the mother overnight in hospital is less common in the US, but the norm in the UK). Dummies, abhorred by breastfeeding counsellors on the grounds of the fabled nipple confusion, have been shown to help prevent Sudden Infant Death Syndrome (SIDS).

If there is a place for choice in infant feeding, it is surely in the weighing up of benefits and costs. As BPAS's Clare Murphy told me: 'There is an inability to understand the context in which women make feeding decisions, whether it's about the wish to involve partners in feeding, or having a toddler to care for. Individual women might reasonably conclude that for her, any benefits that come from breastfeeding are more than offset by the advantages gained from feeding a different way. The benefits of breastfeeding are real, but they are presented as so inordinate as to preclude making another choice.'

The attention paid to breastfeeding seems almost totemic, whereas other, more clear-cut improvements to children's lives – generous funding for state schools, or reducing air pollution for example – seem less of a policy priority. That is perhaps because those improvements are collective ones: society seems keener to personalise responsibility for children's wellbeing onto individual mothers. The feeding debate is also part of the microscopic focus on the first months, when there's a good eighteen years of ups and downs ahead. Breastfeeding offers an illusory chance to wash away social inequality and vaccinate the messy, long haul of parenting with a short-term milky shot.

The paediatrician Alison Steele is supportive of breastfeeding and emphasises that rates in the UK are unnecessarily low, and yet, she says: 'I do think that if somebody chooses not to feed, or they can't do it,' then 'we shouldn't make them feel guilty about that choice'. It is a difficult balance, as she puts it, 'between promoting and supporting.'

There is a 'message that we give around breastfeeding', Steele continues, 'that it's easy, it's natural', and actually, 'it's not that easy, often, and actually it's a commitment, and a tie: that child is absolutely committed to you unless you express and use bottles, but you don't necessarily want to do that to start with'. Health professionals need to be more realistic about the down-sides: mastitis, latching on and problems with the baby's weight, Steele says. She believes in providing support and information, 'but also being sympathetic to the decisions people make, which are probably in their best interests as a collective unit', because having a mother that is 'completely exhausted, tired and depressed' is not a good state of affairs, as she is not available emotionally to her child, 'whereas if she decides to bottle-feed and feels better for it, she is much more likely to be responsive'. Doctors need to keep perspective: 'there comes a point when you're looking at a baby's weight going down and down, and you're thinking at what point do we say we're going to bail out here, because it's actually detrimental to keep on – and then seeing the baby thrive because they've gone on to formula'. We need to know 'when to say enough's enough'.

A GOLDEN AGE?

In 2019, archaeologists excavating children's graves in Bavaria dating from between 450 and 1200 BC unearthed ceramic feeding vessels containing traces of animal milk. The discovery made international news: 'Historic find suggests bottle-feeding not a modern phenomenon,' announced the *Guardian*. The surprised headlines were an indication of how much we assume babies were only breastfed in the good old days. In fact, as the historian Corin Throsby has argued, the very idea of breast-feeding as more natural or authentic than alternative methods is itself a relatively recent invention. Breastfeeding did not necessarily come naturally to women in pre-modern times: archaeologists have found lactation instructions from ancient Egypt, including one papyrus advising mothers to have their backs rubbed with oil infused with swordfish bones, or to sit cross-legged and eat sorghum bread while rubbing their genitals with a poppy plant.

History reveals huge variation in infant feeding habits, documented in treatises such as the 400-page-long *Natural and Artificial Methods of Feeding Infants and Children* by the physician

Edmund Cautley, published in 1897, and the multi-volume 1950s compendium of historical feeding practices by another doctor, Ian Wickes. There are archaeological filing cabinets full of modified animal horns and terracotta pots with long spouts. Mothers in ancient Greece deployed ceramic cups; the Romans invented glass drinking straws.

According to Roman mythology, Romulus and Remus were famously suckled by wolves, Jupiter by goats, and Pelias by horses. And throughout history, real babies have been fed by donkeys, sheep, deer, cows, camels, dogs and pigs – sometimes using containers, sometimes directly. In the late eighteenth century, the French physician Alphonse Le Roy installed goats in a Provence hospital to feed foundlings. 'Each goat,' he observed, 'enters bleating' into the ward and 'goes to hunt' its allocated infant: it 'pushes back the covering with its horns and straddles the crib to give suck'. In 1816, the German physician Conrad Zwierlein penned a (possibly tongue-in-cheek) treatise entitled *The Goat As the Best and Most Agreeable Wet-Nurse*.

Animal feeding wasn't entirely uncontroversial: a sixteenth-century English physician, Thomas Muffett, wrote in his 1584 *Healths Improvement* of Aegisthus, Clytemnestra's lover, 'who being fed in a Shepheards Cottage only with goat's milk, waxed thereupon so goatish and lecherous, that he defiled not only Agamemnon's bed, but also neighed (in a manner) at every man's wife'. (It is said, incidentally, that the nursery rhyme 'Little Miss Muffet' was written by Muffett's stepdaughter.)

Babies in the past also had to contend with artificial foods far inferior to today's formula. From the fifteenth to the eighteenth centuries, the most common concoctions were pap – bread in water or milk, and panada – bread in broth with vegetables, butter, milk, or eggs. Some infants were given honey, or even wine or beer. Not everyone approved – with good reason. King James II's son nearly died from eating pap. The seventeenth-century physician Michael Ettmüller described it as 'a viscous and crude paste more proper to binders to bind their books than for the nourishment of infants'.

Despite the extraordinary variety of practices, therefore, most religious and medical writers still advocated breastfeeding – on the grounds of health as well as morality. Yet the breast in question did not necessarily belong to the mother. Nowadays, the very rare instances of babies being fed by other women are the subject of slightly disgusted media fascination: 'The weirdness of breastfeeding someone else's baby' is one representative headline. Yet wet-nursing was once widespread: James II's son recovered after he was sent to one. Wet-nursing contracts have been found in records from ancient Egypt, Greece and Rome, and the practice continued into the early modern period among both upper- and middle-class women. The Nurse in *Romeo and Juliet* fondly jokes about weaning a three-year-old Juliet by rubbing wormwood on her 'dugs'. In his famous *Anatomy of Melancholy* (1621), the Anglican scholar Robert Burton advocated wet-nurses on the grounds that they could correct the child's 'ill-disposed temperature [temperament] which he had from his parents'.

Sometimes wet-nursing was stipulated by the father or husband. In *The Winter's Tale*, Leontes says to his wife: 'Give me the boy. I am glad you did not nurse him.' Others disapproved of the practice: in a curious didactic poem, *Paedotrophia*, the eighteenth-century French historian Scévole De Sainte-Marthe reproved mothers for sending their babies off: 'But you, perhaps, by other cares beguiled/ Wish, to the nurse's home to move the child;/ Because by his continued cries at home,/ Your sleeps are broken and your joys o'ercome.'

Jean-Jacques Rousseau abandoned his own five illegitimate children at birth at a foundling hospital. Yet he declared that wet-nursing was a 'fatal depravity' by which a 'woman sacrifices to her own convenience the joys and the duties of motherhood'. He condemned those who, 'freed from their children, devote themselves to the city'. Rousseau's naturalistic ideals influenced the French polymath Georges-Louis Leclerc's forty-four-volume *Histoire Naturelle* and its admiring portrayals of 'exotic' tribes-peoples and their devoted, breastfeeding mothers. In 1769, the French physician Joseph Raulin praised the customs of the 'savages' – Africans, Native Americans, Brazilians – for their attention to their offspring; in contrast, children of his own countrywomen were products of the 'degradation of human kind in our corrupt and civilised Europe'. Dr Raulin praised cows and goats for their wholesome diet of plants and grasses, and chastised mothers who indulged in tea, coffee and spirits. Mothers being told to be more animal-like is a frequent refrain in this book; those who did not feed their own children were told they were even inferior to beasts. Whereas today it's often work that gets in the way of breastfeeding, in the eighteenth century it was thought to be socialising: one Gillray cartoon from 1796 depicts a fashionable lady fitting in a brief feed before stepping out for the evening's entertainment. Yet this was not mere frippery: the erudite coffee-house culture of eighteenth-century London was a form of public life.

'Let mothers deign to nourish their children,' Rousseau wrote – revealing how breastfeeding was figured as both humble and virtuous – and benefits to both babies and the nation's stock will ensue: 'our manners will reform themselves; the feelings of nature will re-awaken in all hearts. The State will be re-peopled. This chief thing, this one thing, will bring everything into order.' A tract from 1695 also praised women who 'condescend' to breastfeed. The recurrent exhortation to act more like 'primitive' natural mothers both curtails women's ambitions and disparages non-elite and non-European women (the positive eugenic attitude is in evidence here too).

The notion that the rise of the modern 'career woman' has

led to a decline in breastfeeding is complicated by the fact that formula milk was developed not in the second half of the twentieth century, but in the late nineteenth. As the medical historian Jacqueline Wolf has described, in this era of urbanisation and industrialisation, as factory workers paid more attention to time, mothers put their babies on strict feeding schedules. This led them to produce less milk, fuelling the development of formula.

Can mothers really run out of milk? According to a rather lovely kink in traditional zero-sum game logic, the drinking baby stimulates milk production. The more they take, the more you have to give. An analogy is Keynesian macroeconomics: a national economy is not like a household budget, because the more you invest, the more wealth you generate. A breastfeeding mother is printing her own currency: there is a magic money tree. Yet doctors were under the false impression that 'overeducated' mothers had insufficient milk: too detached from nature, you see. But since these women were instructed to feed only at four-hourly intervals, their supply decreased accordingly.

Breastfeeding fell out of fashion over the course of the twentieth century with improvements in sanitation, and by 1975, half of new babies in the UK were bottle-fed; a full three-quarters in the US. 'If you are reluctant to nurse your child,' counselled the psychiatrist Helen Flanders Dunbar in her 1949 *Your Child's Mind and Body*, 'if it makes you tense and uncomfortable, or if you are too busy and are just doing it because you have an idea that it is your duty, do not attempt it.' The American paediatrician and author L. Emmett Holt agreed: 'A mother who cannot or does not wish to nurse, or a mother who must return to a job should not feel that she is neglecting an important duty,' he wrote in his popular 1957 childcare manual: 'a bottle mother may still be a perfect mother.' The historian of childcare, Christina Hardyment, cites another outspoken critic of breastfeeding, a certain Mrs Panton, who commented that although breastfeeding may have suited us humans in a state of nature, we don't live that way now; therefore 'let no mother condemn herself to be a common or ordinary "cow" unless she has a real desire to nurse'.

Towards the end of the twentieth century, however, the tide turned back again. These zigzagging transformations in parenting styles are not simply shifts of fashion and habit on the ground: they are also driven by agendas and lobbies. As with the publicity campaigning of Grantly Dick-Read, the promotion of breastfeeding in America was led by an influential organisation: La Leche League. The League was born, it is said, when two devout Roman Catholic mothers, Mary White and Marian Tompson, were at a Christian Family Movement picnic in a Chicago park in the summer of 1956, sitting under a tree breastfeeding their babies. As bottle-feeding was still the norm, other women came up to admire this rare scene. Along with a group of friends, they formed the League, choosing that name, apparently, in order to avoid the racy word 'breast'. Gregory White, obstetrician and husband of one of the founding mothers, came up with a solution: he was in the habit of presenting his pregnant patients with medals from a shrine in Florida dedicated to a Spanish Madonna saint, Nuestra Señora de la Leche y Buen Parto, or, loosely translated, 'Our Lady of Milk and Good Delivery'.

Mary White and Marian Tompson also had an interest in natural childbirth, prompted in part by the predilections of two physicians, White's husband, and her former teacher, and they invited Dick-Read over to be their first guest speaker. Their 1958 publication *The Womanly Art of Breastfeeding* articulated their 'maternalist' philosophy, centred on 'good mothering through breastfeeding' and a defence of traditional domestic life against the incursions of modern industrial society – a later newsletter contrasted the 'quiet order of nature' with the 'mechanized world'. I have sympathy with the critique of automation. But it should not be used to confine women in the home.

As with the natural childbirth movement, regressive feminine domesticity came to acquire an aura of progressive feminism. In 1971, a League member from Ohio wrote: 'I've been reading and hearing a lot about Women's Liberation and I think I would like to be liberated too! . . . I want to be free to, of all things, feed my baby when he is hungry . . . Yes, I want to be liberated! I want to be free! I want to be free to be a woman!' Breastfeeding was framed as an expression of 'womanly power', a way of being 'in control' – although not of one's time. The League presents bottle-feeding as a modern development: 'For thousands of years,' their website explains, 'women gave birth and nursed their babies, supported by a close-knit group of family and friends.' Yet 'artificial' feeding and wet-nursing have been commonplace for millennia.

Breastfeeding advocates rightly oppose the multinational corporations who flog unaffordable formula to women in countries where there's scant access to clean water; a situation which has contributed – outrageously – to high rates of infant mortality. Yet in the global north, the promotion of breast-feeding by governments, health officials and the culture at large is occurring at a time when infant mortality is lower, and more women are working, than ever before. It is a somewhat perverse combination.

For more affluent mothers, breastfeeding dogma is an expression of modern, middle-class intensive parenting culture which too often compromises women's career aspirations and sets up heuristic inequalities with male partners. But at least they have the resources to do it. Those women could once afford wet-nurses; now they take long maternity leaves. For the less affluent, however, it is a different story. Because breast-feeding is 'natural', because it is 'free', society does not count its economic cost for many: not being able to work. 'It's only free,' noted the journalist Hanna Rosin, 'if a woman's time is worth nothing.'

The situation is particularly extreme in the US, with its absence of paid maternity leave. The American Academy of Pediatrics recommends six months' exclusive breastfeeding, but only women with high-status jobs can take time off during the day to sit in one of those lactation rooms. Breastfeeding rates drop off sharply at three and six months, reflecting the rigid demands of the labour market. The Quartz website calculated in 2017 that for a woman making $60,000 a year pre-tax (approximately £45,000), working fifty hours per week, the cost of the average time spent breastfeeding in the first six months is $14,250 (about £10,000). Breastmilk is portrayed as a basic, animal substance, but viewed in this light it is actually a luxury good; yet since its cost is invisible, it is easier for people to judge a formula-feeding mother as if she is exercising free choice.

HIDDEN INVESTMENTS

If the real cost of breastfeeding is disavowed by modern society, its considerable cultural value is also downplayed. As its benefits tend to be articulated in terms of nutrition and health advantages, the moral pressure to breastfeed is concealed behind 'hard' scientific facts. This literalism also means that the more intangible, emotional aspects of feeding a baby become associated with breastfeeding only, when they can just as well apply to babies who are formula-fed. As pro-tolerance groups such as the Infant Feeding Alliance argue, it is of course possible for a mother to affectionately cradle her child as she gives it a bottle.

In 2008, the international press reported the results of a study by researchers at Warwick University who worked out the mechanism for how and why breastfeeding mothers experience a rush of oxytocin: the 'love', 'trust' or 'cuddle' hormone. These kinds of discoveries receive revealingly avid coverage, which shows the extent to which our culture privileges biology over learned behaviour. Whereas previous cultures were overtly moralising, we do our moralising covertly, outsourcing it to science.

Yet feeding practices vary not only through history, but also across different countries and communities. 'In humans, breast-feeding is not only a biological process,' write anthropologists Patricia Stuart-Macadam and Katherine Dettwyler, 'but also a culturally determined behaviour.' It is subject, notes another anthropologist, Vanessa Maher, to 'considerable cultural elaboration': in Baganda, Uganda, babies are weaned at one and sent to live with their uncles, to reinforce kinship bonds with the father's family. These social bonds are more important, here, than the 'natural' mother–baby bond. Margaret Mead, whose earlier work has revealed great variation in feeding habits across different settings, warned against advocating behaviour based either on 'earlier periods' or 'other cultures': that way, 'violence is done'.

The notion that both pre-modern and 'tribal' women were and are closer to nature is a myth. Many communities in the global south have long prevented babies from drinking colostrum (the sticky yellow substance that comes before the milk), and in medieval Europe puppies were put on the breast in order to get rid of it. Yet these practices are clearly 'against nature', not least because colostrum is nutritious for babies.

Historical attitudes may have been primitivist, but they were sometimes less biologically fundamentalist than our own. The physician Hugh Ashby wrote in 1922 that 'the infant possesses very little natural instinct compared with other animals'; and unlike a kitten or puppy, it 'cannot even find its way to the breast' (they can, of course). Similarly, 'we are wrong,' he warned, 'if we think that the human mother knows by instinct what is best for the child.'

By emphasising natural maternal instinct, we in the modern

West are reluctant to acknowledge both the extent to which our actions are shaped by cultural expectations, and the symbolic significances we attach to them. Yet past representations were more explicitly metaphorical. The historian Caroline Walker Bynum describes how medieval paintings associate the lactating Mary with the Eucharist: 'To medieval natural philosophers,' she writes, 'breast milk was transmuted blood.' And although we tend to think only of Mary as the primary maternal figure in Christianity, the idea of motherhood as self-sacrifice comes from Jesus too. A painting by the Italian Renaissance artist Quirizio di Giovanni da Murano depicts a beautiful, feminine Christ displaying the wound in his side high up where a nipple would be. He offers the wound between two fingers of his left hand as a symbolic gesture to mankind, as the Virgin offers her breast to the infant Christ in so many other paintings.

In our post-Freudian age, we tend also to forget the valuable insights of psychoanalysis, which – like these artistic portrayals – understood the symbolic value of breastfeeding and milk. The psychoanalyst Melanie Klein developed a theory of the 'good breast' and 'bad breast', a curious but resonant emblem of the available, generous mother on one side, and her unavailable, withholding counterpart on the other. Mothers may feel it is right to feed on demand – babies are babies, after all – but part of their growing up is learning to cope with the fact that not all demands will be satisfied; at least, not immediately. But since contemporary culture cannot countenance the reality of maternal ambivalence, it projects the bad side onto the bottle.

The way we talk about infant feeding today has no space for this kind of conscious understanding. Yet breastfeeding is still freighted with meanings that we fail publicly to acknowledge: maternal presence, care and self-sacrifice, as well as the illusory capacity to erase broader social ills such as poverty and inequality. It is time we recognised what is at stake here – both for those who pressurise women to breastfeed, and for the women who struggle either physically or financially. Exhausted, anxious, long-suffering and scrutinised, working mothers are made to carry the burden of profound and unsatisfied desires and demands – about what we lacked in our own childhoods and who we fail to look after as a society. Breastmilk is good stuff, but it can't fix all that.

6

RED MIST

I pick the kids up from school. We shop for dinner. I've forgotten my cloth bags again in the rush to be on time, and the plastic cuts white lines into my fingers on the walk home. I help the children with their homework and reading. I help my daughter practise the piano. I prepare Mexican wraps with numerous chopped vegetable fillings. It is half past seven. I have been with the children for four hours straight. I have made a point of giving them my full attention but I'm becoming distracted by the siren call of my laptop.

My husband walks in the door, and I march straight to the study/spare room/play room. He is ten minutes late – not a crime – but that was the time I had mentally allocated to the handover. There will be no handover, I think, sourly. The children are tired and their behaviour rapidly deteriorates. I need to mark a pile of papers for the next day. My husband sits down to eat his dinner. The children loiter in the study with me. My daughter starts building a 'cottage' out of magnetic tiles. Every time she finishes it, my son destroys it with a drumstick. She is sobbing and begging him to stop. I am trying to read text on my screen. My anger rises to a boil. Suddenly I snap. I grab my son and push him backwards out the door. He falls to the floor with a bang. I just wanted him out of the room. I didn't mean for him to fall. Or maybe I did. He cries. I slam the door and sit back down at my desk, my head in my hands.

* * *

It's four o clock on a Friday afternoon. I've picked the kids up in the car as we are going away for the weekend. It's sunny, which puts me in a good mood. It puts them in a hot mood. Soon we hit traffic. They start fighting over a small glass 'jewel'. *It's mine. No it's mine.* They don't yet understand that this back and forth can only spiral downwards. Soon my daughter, who is six, scratches my son's cheek. He bites her arm. They both cry. I find the sound of my children crying unbearable, like fingernails scraping down a blackboard, only the blackboard is my brain, or my heart. This is presumably by design. It is not meant to be borne; it is meant to be attended to.

I realise later that the tears actually contain a compound of emotions. The children are upset, but also angry. As in a tantrum, the crying is also a complaint, against me. How have you let this happen? I feel terribly sorry for them, but I also feel my own undercurrent of anger. And then I feel guilty. Anger and guilt are the twin motors of family strife. One feeds the other. But barrelling down the M40 at 75 miles per hour, I can't yet see all this. I just feel that this is intolerable and therefore dangerously distracting. I express my sincere wish that they stop fighting. I try to distract them. None of this works. My son is now kicking the back of my seat and hitting the side of my face with a long, bendy pencil. This is the last straw. Shut up! I shout, so loudly it makes my throat hurt. Their tears are no longer angry, just bitterly upset. I make myself relive the incident, over and over again, for the remainder of the journey.

* * *

I am cooking a meal I meant to prepare while the children were at school, but work ate up every last minute. They are hungry and start to bicker: the volume rises as I chop an onion; but I can't separate them because my fingers are covered in onion. The onion goes in the pan. I go to sort it out. The onions are burning in the pan. I go back to chop the tomatoes. The volume rises again.

It's a long two hours getting them ready for bed. It seems impossible to get to the finish line: they move half as slowly and then half as slowly again. As they get more tired, I get more impatient. I say everything five times. Can you get undressed. Can you pick up your clothes. Can you get in the bath. Can you get out of the bath. They ignore the first three times, spoken in a gently cajoling manner. They only seem to notice once I yell. Then everything goes downhill. In our flat nobody can help, but the neighbours can hear. I feel judged and wretched. I yell some more. They crack, say I'm sorry mummy I'm sorry. They climb out and stand there dripping. I crack. We all sit on the floor in a wet hug. They go to bed. I sit down and Google: 'Will yelling at my children scar them for life?'

Google finishes the sentences for me: I see that many mothers have asked the same questions before. This is mildly comforting. But I find no reliable answers to the question of whether I have crossed the line between ordinary and bad mother.

* * *

We have had quite a few dark and difficult evenings, me and the kids. Hunger and tiredness are invariably the problem – for them and for me. I only seem to remember this afterwards. Ah yes, hunger and tiredness, like every other time. And my husband working, and it being a weeknight during the witching hours of five and seven. And having a pressing yet unappealing work task of my own looming – being in work gives me a mental outlet which helps me deal with the kids, but the difficulties of combining work with childcare increases tensions. And having more than one child. It's the fighting that really gets me. I feel fury towards the aggressor and a desperate need to protect the victim: sometimes by shutting the aggressor in another room – disapproved of but occasionally necessary.

These times are not representative of my life with my children, I feel myself rushing to point out. My children are the sweetest, sunniest creatures, the light of my life; and I know I'm a good mother, though that should not need to be said. These moments are painful to recount, but I believe that we as mothers should share them. They are hedged around with silence and taboo: I am unusual among my acquaintance in almost compulsively mentioning them. We all worry about being judged, and I myself am guilty of judging others: when I see a mother speaking harshly to her child, I feel it like a wound. But just like that I've forgotten that when it's you in the hot seat, you are unreachable. When you're out of it, you can't remember it – like thinking about being ill when you're well. We are all in the same boat, yet utterly isolated in our family units and private domestic scenes, searching inadequate message-board threads, not getting the perspective we need.

I once said to a friend that I felt ambushed by my children's moods, and she replied that she feels ambushed by her own moods, and I realised she was right. As I'll describe in this chapter, when mothers get in a rage, they become their child selves, together with the relationships they had with their brothers and sisters and parents. We repudiate and reject negative aspects of ourselves, especially our immature anger and project them onto others – including our children, who then appear even more intolerable. And this is compounded by the social expectation that mothers should be mature at all times.

None of the self-reinforcing dynamics I'll describe – aggression and prohibition, fury and self-laceration – are recognised by our intolerant culture. The advice issued by parenting websites, childcare manuals, TV programmes and the media treats mothers like wayward children and fails to countenance the challenges they face. There is an unaddressed mismatch between these messages to mothers and their lived experience. This drives maternal ambivalence and anger underground, where it grows ever stronger – rebounding not only on mothers themselves but also on their children.

THROUGH THE KEYHOLE . . .

Let's look a little closer at those Mumsnet and Netmums message boards, where penitent mothers creep out under cover of night to confess their sins and seek a comforting sense of what's 'normal'. 'Feeling Guilty for shouting – is it just me??', one pregnant mum essays after a confrontation with her toddler. 'Can anyone relate? . . . I didn't even really know I was going to shout at him before I did it. I just snapped and screamed.' 'I felt so tired,' another writes; her son 'can really push and push the limits . . . I feel so guilty about losing control in this way, I mean he's only almost 3 and I'm the adult, and I made him cry. (I feel so ashamed writing that). Does it harm them?? . . . When you're on your own, it's easy to look at all the other mums and see them as so patient and perfect . . . '

An exhausted mother of a toddler and a baby relates an incident in the park: 'When I tried to put him back in buggy he went crazy kicking, wriggling, refusing. Put up with this for a while but eventually lost it a bit and I hate to say I screamed at him and pinned him to the buggy . . . Then I thought should I be worried in case someone saw me screaming at him and reports me to social services or something!' She concludes: 'Does anyone have anything reassuring to say or am I awful? . . . Their dad is great. At work all day though of course.' Another writes:

'Please be gentle with me. I couldn't hate myself much more than I already do . . . I start each row with the best intentions but when he starts I just can't control my emotions . . . It just pushes my buttons so hard . . . I don't want to be this person, I don't want him to remember these moments . . . Has anyone felt like this? . . . Any advice welcome, please don't judge!'

The same themes come up time and again: working partners, exhaustion, solitude, boredom, trying to fill long days, a toddler, a baby, exasperation, guilt. There are plenty of kind words and smileyface emojis in the responses, but also some raised eyebrows and judgement in the form of advice. 'I think you do need to see the GP and speak to your HV [health visitor],' one mum responds. 'It may be that it's your behaviour which is making him act this way.'

As for smacking, the blanket social taboo is sustained even on these semi-private forums. The issue is sometimes raised, but most often in the form of a question – sometimes 'for a friend'. 'Really honestly curious about this, does anyone still smack their children and think it's the right thing to do? If so what are your reasons?' one poster enquires. 'Please don't comment having a go at other peoples' parenting,' she elaborates; 'I just want to hear more about "stricter" parenting styles as they seem to have gone out of fashion so let's keep it respectful' – providing an indication of the kind of responses such posts usually receive. 'Plenty of people do (Not me) but I have a sort-of friend that still keeps a wooden spoon to smack her kids and another that happily admits slapping her preschooler round the legs,' one mum replies. 'Neither of these people are really friends btw. More former friends now acquaintances.' 'I think it's child abuse,' others reply; 'It is always assault. Plain and simple.'

To lay my own cards on the table, I don't think either shouting or smacking is a good idea. If I see a parent smack a child I wince. Neither is it an effective disciplining tool. But I have shouted quite a lot, and smacked a handful of times. My argument is that I don't believe that in the context of a warm, loving relationship, occasional lapses do long-term harm. But many mothers – and me included – beat themselves up worrying that it will. And although frowned upon in public, these practices are still common in private. The gap between the two is a measure of the guilt.

Smacking within 'reasonable' limits is permitted in England, Wales, the US, Canada and Australia, but outlawed in fifty-three countries around the world, including the majority of (twenty-nine) European countries (ten further members of the EU are taking steps towards a ban). Research on prevalence is hard to conduct because shame leads to underreporting, but one study published in the journal *Pediatrics* in 2010, which measured child-disciplining techniques in the US, Brazil, Chile, Egypt, India and the Philippines found that 'screaming or yelling at children was frequent; rates ranged from 70 per cent to 95 per cent'. The lead author, paediatrician Desmond Runyan, found that amongst American parents, 85 per cent punish by taking away privileges, 79 per cent use time outs, and 75 per cent yell. A quarter of American parents admitted to smacking. According to a 2003 report, *The National Study of Parents, Children and Discipline in Britain*, over half of parents in the UK smack. An NSPCC study from 2011 found that smacking is on the decline, though still common: in 2009, 41 per cent of British 18–24-year-olds said that as children they had been smacked on the bottom with a bare hand, as compared with 53 per cent in 1998. Although it remains widespread, therefore, smacking in particular is also widely condemned. 'Spanking Is Still Really Common and Still Really Bad for Kids', reported the *Atlantic* in 2018.

STOP SHOUTING!!

The secret, everyday reality revealed on those message boards and in the research studies is entirely absent from official and popular parenting advice. Contemporary parenting culture emphasises positive reinforcement and leading by example. The NHS guide *Birth to Five* does not address the question of punishment. 'You can help your child by rewarding them for behaving well, for example by praising them or giving them their favourite food for tea. If your child behaves well, tell them how pleased you are. Be specific. Say something like, "I loved the way you put your toys back in the box when I asked you! Well done!"' On tantrums, it advises parents to 'find something to distract them straight away – for example, something you can see out of the window ("Look, a cat!"). Make yourself sound as surprised and interested as you can' (I've done this myself, and hated the humiliating mendacity). Naughtiness, it continues, should be understood, not judged. 'There are many different reasons why a child might react in a super-market environment that are not necessarily "bad behaviour"', *Birth to Five* explains. 'Often the people, lights and music can cause sensory overload. Anticipate how a child might react in a supermarket environment. Prepare and chat to the child in advance, set gentle boundaries. If a tantrum occurs, hold the child closely to calm them.'

The public tantrum is a common source of parental oppro-brium: not just the tantrum itself, but the sense that it is not being well handled. In 2020, research by IPSOS Mori for the Duchess of Cambridge's Royal Foundation found that 70 per cent of parents of 0–5-year-olds say they feel judged by others. Both the child's behaviour and the way the parent manages it were the most frequently mentioned reasons for feeling judged. In my experience, those burning eyes hinder, rather than help, calm resolution.

The contextualisation of challenging behaviour is invariably offered as a reason not to punish – the child's behaviour is normal, an understandable response to circumstances and surroundings, or just a phase they are going through. Yet mothers losing their temper is never contextualised (lack of sleep, being pregnant, having no support, and so on). Advice to mothers takes the punitive rather than the positive approach: it's as if the negativity has simply been transposed onto them. It's true that children are fundamentally different to adults: they are dependent, smaller, more vulnerable, and have not learned how to regulate their emotions. Yet parenting advice often talks about children as if they were small adults – the Verywell Family website ('a modern resource that offers a realistic and friendly approach to pregnancy and parenting') asks parents: 'How would you feel if your boss yelled at you when you made a mistake?'

In a 2013 journal article, 'The pitfalls of positive parenting', the family law researcher Helen Reece cites an expert interviewed on a programme on Parentchannel.tv, 'Why Kids Misbehave': 'If you want your children to respect you, it's important that you give them respect . . . You need to, you know, listen carefully to your child, show them that you care about what they think, and then they'll act like that back to you.' Reece paraphrases the advice: 'There is a short answer to "Why Kids Misbehave": they do not.' When they appear to be misbehaving, 'it is because society has mislabelled their behaviour as naughty, they want your attention, parental demands are unreasonable, or they are feeling sad about, for example, being bullied and do not have the words to express this.'

One of the only popular parenting experts to advocate any form of punishment is Supernanny, aka Jo Frost and her TV series of the same name, which returned to US screens in 2020. Her approach has been called 'disciplinarian' by the website raisingkids.co.uk, and the programme's use of the 'naughty step' to reinforce time out has been criticised by parenting organisations and the media. 'The threat of separation from those who protect them can cause severe anxiety and psychological discomfort in a child,' psychiatrist Edward Haas told the *Washington Post* for an article on the 'dated and ineffective' time-out technique. Children who are regularly given time outs 'have learned they must conform to the views of others in order to survive, and are thus more likely to grow up feeling insecure and powerless', he said. But what if 'the views of others' is simply behaving well?

Supernanny is not actually egregiously strict. In a section on the programme's website on strategies for dealing with tantrums, a key tip is 'Stay Calm'. The secret, the site goes on to explain, is to 'a) accept and acknowledge your child's angry feelings and b) direct her towards an appropriate outlet for expressing her intense emotion' (as a thought experiment, apply Supernanny's advice here to mothers: 'When feelings are accepted, your child will feel more understood . . . When feelings are expressed, the build up of emotion inside is avoided and so explosions become less likely').

Even the Supernanny site treads very carefully around the subject of punishment: 'If your child stops behaving aggressively, give her lots of praise. If, however, she continues her inappropriate behaviour after you've given a warning, impose a clear consequence, such as the naughty step or withdrawing privileges.' All other avenues should be pursued before turning to the naughty step. 'Is there a particular toy or something triggering the situation which you could calmly remove? Or is your child tired or hungry? Before using the Naughty Step, see if you can help resolve your child's frustration and move them on to another activity.' And when Supernanny returned to American screens in 2020, the naughty step had gone. Instead, Jo Frost emphasised the need for parents to 'connect' with their children. 'These children need care, affection, love, attention:

nurture, nurture, nurture, nurture,' she says in one episode, adding: 'I need to help this family bridge the gap and really understand their children.' The psychologist Tanya Byron suggests using time out – which she defines as putting the child in another room and shutting the door for a fixed period – only for 'extreme bad behaviour' (this is not defined); but she also states on her website: 'distract, ignore but do not punish'. It seems difficult to assert a clear position on the issue.

Although time out is the mildest disciplining technique – the punishment for those who disapprove of punishment altogether – even this is eschewed by the 'therapeutic parenting' approach, developed through experience with severely abused and neglected children, yet advocated for kids in general. Instead of time out, the Inspire Training Group, which promotes therapeutic parenting, suggests 'time in'. If a boy hits his brother, don't isolate him on his own, but stay with him, recommends one of the approach's proponents, parenting trainer Rosie Jefferies. 'Give him time to cool down but make him feel supported through it, saying, "You shouldn't have hit your brother but I still love you and when you have calmed down you can go back."'

One of the most vocal opponents of punishment is the child psychologist Margot Sunderland. 'Parents should never try to persuade their child out of feeling a certain emotion,' she told the Observer. 'Even if your child is reading a situation in a completely different way to you, it is important to prove to them you are empathising.' She warns parents of the dire consequences of making a child feel shame or fear: 'it is all too easy to break a child'. She continued: 'If you ignore a crying child, tell them to shut up or put them in a room on their own, you can cause serious damage to their brains on a level that can result in severe neurosis and emotional disorders later in life.' This language, drawn from cases of extreme abuse and neglect, is not applicable to the everyday imperfect behaviour that preoccupies many good-enough mothers.

The Healthline parenting website reproduces the warning about long-term damage to the brain. 'It's normal to get frustrated with your children, especially if they are misbehaving,' the site explains. 'But the way you express this frustration and deal with the situation can have major implications on their personality development and their long-term health.' The American family therapist Sandra Dupont is similarly absolutist: 'Encouraging your child should never include a demeaning or threatening word, act, or deed, nor should it cause them to lose their dignity or self-respect.' The Ask Dr Sears site sustains the theme: 'You may have a hug-hit ratio of 100:1 in your home, but you run the risk of your child remembering and being influenced more by the one hit than the 100 hugs, especially if that hit was delivered in anger or unjustly, which happens all too often.' The zero-tolerance approach extends to shouting, too. 'Physical hitting is not the only way to cross the line into abuse,' the site goes on. 'Everything we say about physical punishment pertains to emotional/verbal punishment as well.' 'Tongue-lashing,' it concludes, 'can actually harm a child more psychologically.' Ordinary parents, you have been warned.

'Spanking naughty children increases their risk of depression and becoming hooked on illegal drugs, a new study confirms' – so reported the Mail Online in 2017. 'The researchers made the case that smacking in childhood could have the same long-term negative impact as traumatic life events, such as being sexually abused or parents getting divorced,' the article went on to report. Yet as the NHS Behind the Headlines site pointed out, 'because of the nature of this study, a cause and effect relationship hasn't been proven, no matter how plausible the link might seem'. It went on: '"Spanking naughty children . . . should be considered as bad as going through a divorce" might give the impression this is a proven fact when this is actually only the researchers' opinion.' Yet more people will have read the original article than this qualification.

'Instead of yelling at your kid every night for the shoes strewn across the floor, ask him in the morning if he can put his shoes away when he comes home,' Alan Kazdin, a professor of psychology and child psychiatry at Yale, told the *New York Times* in 2018. 'And if your child puts his shoes away, or even puts them closer to where they're supposed to be, tell him that he did a great job and then hug him.' He explained: 'You have to be effusive, so you actually have to put a big dumb smile on your face and even wave your hands in the air. Next thing is you have to say, in a very high, cheerful voice, exactly what you're praising. And then the third part is you have to touch the child and give him some kind of nonverbal praise. The silliness is a feature, not a bug. It makes the kid notice the praise that accompanies correct behavior. And that's the point.' I find such instructions not only condescendingly exacting and prescriptive, but also unnatural: remembering, when things are going well, to praise your child so demonstratively. There's also the problem of hyperinflation: if you behave like this in response to shoes 'nearly' put away, what do you do for other acts that are more meaningful?

Tanya Byron is generally very sensible in her approach, but she too recommends the fulsome praise method: 'Imagine you've got a bucketful of praise in every room of the house with a big ladle. Every time your child does something wonderful, get that ladle and use it to shower praise. "That is lovely, thank you darling . . ." or "Oh look, you're playing so nicely."' Not only does this proposal feel over-the-top, it also doesn't seem to sit right as far as the kids are concerned. If mine are playing calmly, I wouldn't interrupt them to shower praise. They would come to expect it and become confused when it wasn't there. If it ain't broke, don't fix it. A more appropriate reward is surely peaceable normality, the satisfaction of reasonable standards being met.

The NSPCC supplies a leaflet on positive parenting. It

contains rules such as 'Keep guidance simple and consistent' and 'Introduce boundaries from an early age'. This seems straightforward enough, but in the hurly-burly of family life things become less clear. My son might whack his little sister because she broke his Lego, so I'll say in a firm voice, 'hitting is not okay'. And then he does it again, and I say 'if you do that again, you won't be able to see your friend tomorrow'. But it does happen again, because he's tired and she's envious of his Lego prowess, and I let him see his friend anyway because it would be making a weirdly emphatic statement to cancel it when the situation has been long resolved.

This doesn't seem like the maintenance of clear boundaries, but I imagine this is a pattern recognisable to most parents. To be clear, I am not advocating severe treatment: my point is that parenting advice is unhelpfully ambiguous when it comes to the question of consequences, and unrealistic when it comes to real human responses to button-pressing and line-crossing. What works in a Yale professor's ideal world does not necessarily translate when your partner is late, the dinner is burning, and the kids are at each other's throats. And what is good or even necessary for the parent in this situation is simply not a consideration.

The regular mention of 'boundaries' without an explanation of what parents are supposed to do when they are crossed means the reality of family life bears little resemblance to the official, 'correct' version. Ordinary home life is a kind of Wild West, operating according to an informal, black market economy of unfulfilled ultimatums and tiredness-induced bribes – all infused with a perennial nagging sense of guilt and unease. 'Get support from friends and try any good ideas they have found helpful,' the NSPCC continues: all well and good if you feel able to own up to last night's fireworks at the school gates. 'If you are struggling and things are getting out of hand, get advice from your GP, a health visitor, or your child's teacher':

not so useful if you feel ashamed or fear suspicious cogs turning in the minds of safeguarding representatives.

As Helen Reece puts it, 'contemporary official parenting advice about disciplining children can be boiled down to "Be nice"'. She writes: 'Positive parenting is arduous if not impossible, thereby setting parents up to fail, and partly because of this onerousness, it is arguably destructive of the spontaneity of the parent–child relationship.' By proscribing the expression of inevitable feelings, society constrains mothers' behaviour to an impossible degree, and produces children who grow up with a wholly unrealistic picture of the impact of their actions on other people. And by categorising crossness, displeasure and telling off as verboten behaviour itself, society condemns mothers to wrangle lawless toddlers with only the toothless, positive side of the equation: no tools in their armoury, no backstop, no answer to the question of 'well, what then?'

And that's even before we get on to leading by example. 'When it comes to your children, role-modelling is everything,' the American psychologist and life coach Suzanne Gelb wrote in *Psychology Today*. 'Your children pay attention to everything you say and do, and they imitate your words and actions. Keep in mind how easily they are influenced. Be your best.' Sandra Dupont agrees. 'When children observe how we treat them and others, they learn how to behave,' she told the HuffPost website. For Dupont, this influence goes beyond imitation: 'a parent's interaction with their child literally impacts their child's brain development.'

As the sociologist Sharon Hays observes, the instruction to lead by example is both exhausting and unrealistic: 'if the parents' example is crucial, then such parents must constantly monitor their actions – never exhibiting any type of inappropriate behaviour lest the child make it his own.' Be your best! The corollary, Helen Reece notes, is that whenever a child misbehaves, it is the parent's behaviour that must be scrutinised and unpicked to discern the ways in which a negative model was imparted to the child.

I asked Angela Foster, a psychotherapist and former psychiatric social worker, what she thought about the parenting advice. 'I don't think these kinds of directives are very helpful,' she told me. 'To say to someone you should never be angry or shout is absurd. The whole point about a good-enough mother is that you're good *enough*. And that the child internalises this experience of something that is not perfect, but good enough. Internalising something that is meant to be perfect is quite persecutory. Because how do you live up to that?' Foster went on: 'You could argue that the perfect mother is in fact not good enough. It would be dreadful to have a mother who thinks she's done everything right all the time, because then any problem must be your making.' The imperfections then 'belong to the child. The whole thing is turned on its head.'

Mothers might believe they are being virtuous or altruistic by applying the advice, but this can go too far. Foster is concerned that actually 'this whole industry of parenting books striving for perfection invites a kind of narcissism in the mother'. She explained: 'I think there's a lot of this about at the moment; that mothers are very aware of how they're seen, which is not really where the focus needs to be.' Her concern is that 'what you worry about is whether you're doing the right thing . . . taking your cue from the book, not your child'. Foster recently edited a book entitled *Mothers Accused and Abused*, about mothers who have been accused of harming and even killing their children. The book is about 'mothers who can't be trusted', she told me, but these advice books 'seem to imply that no one can be trusted, which undermines mothers' own confidence'.

The only advice book Foster would recommend is Winnicott's *The Child, the Family, and the Outside World*, because although it is dated (it was first published in 1964), it encourages mothers to trust themselves. 'Winnicott doesn't wag his finger at his reader implying that "you must do this, or else"', Foster said. I told her my story of trying to cook dinner while the children were fighting: 'my response,' she said, 'is that it's perfectly understandable if you shout, separate them and tell them to stop hurting each other'. This is about the real, rather than the ideal: 'it's behaviour that makes you angry. It's not the end of the world. And I would think that's what most mothers would do. You can always apologise later if you think you went too far, and this ability to reflect on one's behaviour is something helpful that the child can internalise.' Mothers also 'need support, reassurance, and help: they need a break sometimes'. The Sure Start one-stop shop family support centres were very good at providing this; Foster laments the disappearance of so much of this infrastructure, even before Covid-19, which has depleted provision still further.

I understand the vital need to protect children. But contemporary parenting techniques project a vision of family life that would look airbrushed even if mothers weren't so knackered and isolated. The *National Study of Parents, Children and Discipline in Britain* found that 'young parents, and those with unsupportive partners are more likely to use physical punishment'. Conflict most often takes place on weekdays and at home, they found, tellingly. The most common times for conflict to erupt was after school or in the early evening, and 'were preceded by disobedient or demanding behaviour by the child'. These are definitely the stress points that I recognise.

One of the few scraps thrown to mothers is 'me time' – make sure you have time for yourself! There are a number of problems with this prescription. One is that for many mothers, 'me time' equals paid work – itself tiring and taxing. Then there's the fact that other mothers I know who have plenty of time to themselves while the kids are at school still find they snap in the evenings. Maybe they'd quite like to have a job: it's not always time that mothers need, but to be valued, and for domestic work to be properly shared. A long hot soak in the bath may be 'self care', but it's not really a solution. Even those windows can be hard to find, especially if partners work long hours and, say, go to the gym at weekends. Setting up a babysitting circle is administratively daunting. Plus there is something awry about shunting everything 'for yourself' onto time without the children: why not conceive of these relationships as relaxed and authentic, rather than periods to endure while maintaining scrupulous perfection?

The only other 'resource' offered to mothers is anger management advice: take a deep breath, count to ten, go into another room. Like all such techniques, they only work some of the time – namely, if you can remember to apply them in the heat of the moment. When mothers get angry, it is often because they are being provoked by children whose job it is to explore what happens when mummy is pushed to her limits, having been effectively abandoned daily by working partners and by a society that expects them to do one of the hardest jobs in the world alone. Where are the ladlefuls of praise for mothers? The lack of either understanding or effective solutions is glaring. And it's counterproductive for children, too: those mothers who think the whole day is ruined and it's all their fault tend to act even worse. I'm not denying that some – too many – children need protection from their parents; I'll explore this line between the ordinary and the problematic later on. But concern for the genuinely vulnerable is leading to anxiety and unhappiness for the worried well.

Mainstream parenting advice is such a blunt instrument that it fails to even make the important distinction between expressing anger and imposing discipline. 'Smacking looks like it works because children stop what they're doing when they get a smack,' states the Australian parenting website raising-children.au. **But smacking isn't a good choice for discipline**

– the bold is theirs. 'That's because it doesn't help children learn about self-control or appropriate behaviour.' Who nowadays is smacking because they think it's a 'good choice for discipline'? Most parents who smack are at the end of their tether. *The National Study of Parents, Children and Discipline in Britain* found that although over half of parents in Britain had used physical punishment over the previous year, 40 per cent thought it was never acceptable to smack a child, and only one in ten found physical punishment 'always' acceptable: 'most show only conditional acceptance or reject it outright'. They're not doing it as a considered policy: 77 per cent believed discipline was about 'positive parenting' strategies such as praise and encouragement. Yelling, likewise, is not a strategy; it's a release.

Most of the time, I have the techniques stored handily in my back pocket. I get down on my knees and speak calmly. I empathise with their feelings, validating their reality. I remember that most children really want to please their parents, so I sparingly deploy a frown. I say, I don't want you to do that. But on those dark, weekday evenings, I am not myself. And I am certainly not the kind of parent who is reaching for positive parenting leaflets.

THE LONG VIEW

Prior to the eighteenth century, children were considered to be small adults, regarded with affection but also strict intolerance and suspicion; even fear. 'If left to do what he wants, there is no crime he will not plunge into,' wrote Saint Augustine; born immoral, they had to be educated into being good. The historian Philippe Ariès describes how medieval children were routinely flogged, abandoned, and put to work. Indulgence was frowned upon: the Spanish Renaissance humanist Juan Luis Vives wrote in his conduct book *The Education of a Christian*

Woman: 'Mothers damn their children when they nurse them voluptuously . . . you make them depraved by treating them as delights! Afterward you cry hot tears and lament over what you have done.'

The young John and Charles Wesley, who would later become the founders of Methodism, were throttled, whipped and instructed to cry silently in order to not disturb their elders with 'odious noise'. The historian Christina Hardyment describes how a child in early modern Europe could expect regular cold baths and 'blanket tossing' to 'strengthen frail nerves'; pistols were fired near their heads to 'promote endurance'. As soon as a child could stand it was placed in a walking stool. Opiates such as laudanum were regularly administered. Changing babies' swaddling too often was thought to make them soft, whereas the modern nappy brand sees pampering as a virtue. In his popular childrearing guide, *An Essay Upon Nursing and the Management of Children*, the eighteenth-century physician William Cadogan warned against 'the mistaken care and tenderness' of the 'fond mother'. Even crying was to be not minimised, but encouraged: 'instead of being feared', wrote the nineteenth-century author and reformer Samuel Smiles, 'the practice of crying in children in want of muscular exercise is most beneficial in its effects'. The Victorian physician Thomas Bull, author of *Hints to Mothers*, wrote that 'tears were nearly always a sign of temper and should be ignored'.

I'm not suggesting that these attitudes and behaviours are ones we should emulate; yet they cast the strict disciplining of modern mothers in a contrasting light. Contemporary parenting advice has a great deal to say about respecting children, but little to say about how they should be taught to be considerate, patient, self-regulating adults. The history of childrearing is characterised by two competing traditions: the moulding of character, and the reverence of nature. We appear to have inherited only the latter tradition.

The belief in shaping and educating children was set out most famously by the seventeenth-century philosopher John Locke: 'Great care is to be had of the forming of Children's Minds,' he wrote. Young children, he believed, should be taught by 'fear and awe': 'parents being wisely ordained by Nature to love their children, are very apt, if Reason not watch their natural Affection very warily . . . to let it run into Fondness', he warned. Rousseau, on the other hand, worshipped nature. His advice to mothers enacted a shift from moral improvement to child-centred happiness.

Whereas in the seventeenth and eighteenth centuries it was philosophers and theologians who issued advice to mothers, at the end of the nineteenth, the role shifted to medical author- ities. The veneration of natural childhood was now underpinned by science. In 1888, a group of well-to-do New York mothers set up the Society for the Study of Child Nature, and the period also saw the rise of the conservative 'mother's movement' and the Child Study Movement: child-centred child rearing became professionalised. 'There is a science in bringing up children,' declared *Babyhood* magazine.

And then in the early twentieth century, the pendulum swung again. There was an interlude of cold strictness that interrupted the emphasis on maternal submissiveness that connects Rousseau and the nineteenth-century 'mother's move- ment' to today. 'Never hug and kiss them. Never let them sit in your lap,' wrote John Watson, a prominent advocate of the new 'behaviourist' school of thought, in his 1928 guide *The Psychological Care of Infant and Child*. 'If you haven't a nurse and can't leave the child, put it out in the backyard a large part of the day. Build a fence around the yard so that you are sure no harm can come to it. Do this from the time it is born . . . If your heart is too tender and you must watch the child, make yourself a peephole so that you can see it without being seen, or use a periscope.' One of the main advocates of strict rule-based parenting was the New Zealander Frederic Truby King, the founder of the Plunket society, now the Royal New Zealand Plunket Trust.

In the mid-twentieth century there was yet another 180 degree swing – this time away from disciplinarian behaviourism and back towards permissive parenting. One mother wrote: 'I was serving a new vegetable to the boys. Suddenly I realised that I expected Peter, the oldest, to clean his plate. Daniel, the middle one, didn't have to eat it but had to taste it. And little Billy, as far as I was concerned, could do whatever he wanted.' The main proponent of the permissive approach was the 1950s childrearing guru Dr Benjamin Spock – although he disliked the term. His books, which have sold tens of millions of copies worldwide, emphasised the maternal bond and the child's emotional development. Dr Spock included in his books long lists of dos and don'ts, and warned of 'parental ruination' – misdemeanours which could wreck children's future lives. As Barbara Ehrenreich and Deirdre English note in their history of parenting advice, 'permissive child rearing . . . was permissive of everyone except mother'. Yet although his approach was child-centred, Dr Spock did not entirely neglect mothers; his bestselling *Baby and Child Care*, first published in 1946, opens with the line: 'Trust yourself. You know more than you think you do.'

Even in the midst of the new tolerance towards children, there was also still tolerance for spanking. Psychologists John and Elizabeth Newson published their study *Four Year Olds in an Urban Community* in 1968; it found that 97 per cent of parents smacked their children sometimes, half 'only in anger' and half 'as a disciplinary technique'. The twentieth-century American clinical psychologist Fitzhugh Dodson wrote in his 1970 guide, *How to Parent*: 'The main purpose of spanking, although most parents don't like to admit it, is to relieve the parent's feelings of frustration. All of us need to do this from time to time when our kids get on our nerves.' Likewise, the Australian paediatrician Christopher Green wrote a bestselling guide, *Toddler Taming*, in 1984; in a section entitled 'Smacking Used Correctly' he wrote that 'it cannot be all that damaging to children. If it was, then our ancestors, right up to our parents' generation, must have been a pretty disturbed lot.'

* * *

A friend once told me that before he had children, he entertained a reassuring fantasy. He assumed that parents had a kind of natural authority over their children simply by virtue of being parents. It was only when he became a father that he realised you are constantly level-pegging with your children over who's in charge. A toddler can undermine you, infuriate you, make you live in fear of their tantrums. Parents today are on their own. They look beyond their four walls to the wider culture and there is no infrastructure to bolster them; no recourse, rules, or chain of higher command to invoke. And their sovereignty is continually undermined by those hectoring parenting experts.

Throughout history, children have been kept in line with reference to a motley crew of bogeymen, many ironically associated with Santa Claus, prior to his contemporary association with grandfatherly gift-giving: Ru-klaus (Rough Nicholas), Aschenklas (Ashy Nicholas), Pelznickel (Furry Nicholas), or Krampus, the Christmas Devil who beats naughty children with birch sticks. I'm not advocating their resurrection, but I do believe that our culture has become unhelpfully confused about the very concept of authority. Parents are encouraged to befriend their children, to empower them, and give them 'control over their lives'; they are constantly reminded that children have rights too. Instead of straightforward commands backed up by socially reinforced boundaries, adults nowadays mood-manage, cajole, and gently hint. Teachers no longer demand silence; they say: 'Can I just ask you to be a bit quieter, please . . .?'

Or they go the other way: the new strictness policies enacted in school academy chains are a late-stage response to a parenting culture that produces widespread behaviour problems. Another is the diagnostic culture that has built up around the problem of disobedience. Rather than encourage parents to be kind but firm, we medicalise bad behaviour, and exclude increasing numbers of children. In her 1954 essay, 'The Crisis in Education', Hannah Arendt made the positive case for authority: it indicates that someone is taking responsibility. The rise of permissive parenting rightly gave careful thought to the needs of children, but it was not accompanied by a clear philosophy on discipline, and this has had perverse consequences for both parents and children. The psychologist Ada Hart Arlitt observed that a child 'will never know that there are laws that govern the universe unless he knows that there are laws that govern the home'.

Parenting today is like trying to lift up a table while you are standing on it. There is no external pivot, no underpinning to bolster you in your see-saw struggles with recalcitrant infants. Into the authority vacuum has poured a proliferation of parenting programmes – *Supernanny*, but also *The House of Tiny Tearaways*, *Driving Mum and Dad Mad* and *Who Rules the Roost*. Many of these are helpful in terms of content (as is the confidential advice line Family Lives), but their very popularity is symptomatic of a gaping void in nearly every family home. Parents sit and watch other people's children receiving expert treatment once their own kids are finally tucked up in bed – but they really could have done with that help themselves, two hours ago. Having the upper hand has become deeply unfashionable, so we outsource it onto celebrities who we then watch avidly on screen: *Supernanny* is the prime example, with her bossy business suit, executive glasses, and wagging finger. The caricatured imagery illustrates our ambivalence towards the authority we culturally reject, but privately crave.

FACING REALITY

'The Good Mother,' wrote Adrienne Rich, is 'linked implicitly . . . with the repression of anger.' The psychoanalyst Wilfred Bion recommended mothers be 'anything in short, but *not* explosive'. The author and academic Jacqueline Rose comments: 'Not being explosive will do nicely as a definition of what is mostly asked of mothers, although, as any mother will testify, explosive is what she, to her utter dismay, often feels.' Rose continues, echoing many mothers' internal monologues: 'there is nobody in the world I love as much as my child, nobody in the world who makes me as angry'. It is the very demand to be 'respectable and unexplosive', she concludes, that is 'most likely to drive mothers, and by extension their infants, crazy'.

The psychiatrist and psychoanalyst John Bowlby was reluctant to admit the reality of maternal rage. 'Unfortunately,' he wrote, 'coupled with delicious loving feelings there comes all too often an admixture – I hesitate to say it – an admixture of resentment and even of hatred.' But he went further than many modern parenting experts in acknowledging it, and even he believed that 'if the general background of feeling and relationship is good, the occasional outburst or slap does little harm; it certainly has the advantage of relieving our own feelings, and perhaps also of demonstrating to our children that we have the same problems as they'.

Donald Winnicott was similarly ambivalent about maternal ambivalence: at certain points in his writings and broadcasts, the 'ordinary devoted mother' was portrayed ready, waiting, and unhurried. Yet he also wrote that being an imperfect but 'good-enough' mother teaches children essential lessons in coping with adversity. He described how, as the baby becomes a child, its idealistic vision of its mother fades, leading it to punish her for not being perfect; but this disillusionment is a necessary part of growing up.

In fact, Winnicott's sometimes surprisingly frank and accurate account of ordinary motherhood sits in stark contrast to the photo-shopped yet exacting modern image. In an extraordinary passage in his 1949 essay 'Hate in the counter-transference', Winnicott describes how the mother 'hates her infant from the word go', and lists eighteen reasons why, including that the baby is 'a danger to her body in pregnancy and at birth', 'an interference with her private life', and a 'challenge to her preoccupations'. The baby is 'ruthless, treats her as scum, an unpaid servant, a slave'; his 'excited love' is 'cupboard love, so that having got what he wants, he throws her away like orange peel'. At first, 'he doesn't know at all what she does or what she sacrifices for him and especially he cannot allow for her hate'; he is 'suspicious, refuses her good food, makes her doubt herself, but eats very well with his aunt'. After an 'awful' morning with him, she goes out and 'he smiles at a stranger who says, "Isn't he sweet?"'; 'He excites her (sexually too) and frustrates her – she must not eat him or trade in sex with him.' Despite these remarkable and perspicacious observations, Winnicott nevertheless concludes that a mother 'has to be able to tolerate hating her baby without doing anything about it'. However, his definition of not 'doing anything about it' is more capacious than our own.

Winnicott tells the story of how he and his wife had living with them, for 'three months of hell', an evacuee boy aged nine: 'the most lovable and most maddening of children'. He was disruptive and repeatedly tried to run away, behaviour which 'engendered hate' in Winnicott. 'Did I hit him? The answer is no, I never hit. But I should have had to have done so if I had not known all about my hate and if I had not let him know about it too.' These are striking observations: that violence results from parents denying their occasional and inevitable hatred of their children, and that this hatred should not be hidden from children, either.

At times of crisis, Winnicott continues, he would take the boy by force, but without any anger or blame, and put him outside the front door. There was a bell for him to ring to be let back in again, and he knew that nothing would be said about what had happened. He learned to use the bell when he had calmed down. Winnicott adds: 'The important thing is that each time, just as I put him outside the door, I told him something; I said that what had happened had made me hate him.' The boy later reported, Winnicott writes, that his 'deeply rooted relation to us has remained one of the few stable things in his life'. Winnicott wrote that he dealt with difficult situations in this way because it enabled him to tolerate them 'without losing my temper and without every now and again murdering him'.

What modern mother would feel it was acceptable to let her child know that at certain moments she hated them? I have in the past, at my wits' end, put a child outside the flat. It's not even outside the building, it's a hallway; and it was only ever for just a few minutes. But I felt terrible when I did it. And unlike Winnicott, I did it in anger, which is probably worse. It's a fascinating issue, hatred. What Winnicott understood, the psychotherapist Angela Foster told me, is that 'hate is part of normal ambivalence: we love and we hate. There are times when you might hate being a mother, and times when your child will hate you. If we own our hatred, we are less likely to project it into the child. A mother who has herself experienced good-enough mothering will trust herself to manage this.' But our society's rejection of the very existence of this normal hatred hinders, rather than helps the process.

Jacqueline Rose comments on Winnicott: 'If, for fear of what she may do, she cannot hate appropriately when hurt by her child she must fall back on masochism,' and it is this, she believes, 'that gives rise to the false theory of natural masochism in women.' Masochism is anti-feminism's secret weapon: it undermines women from the inside. And it pervades modern motherhood – because it's a way of processing negative feelings without expressing them to children. But if mothers turn the hatred and anger back on themselves in the form of self-lacerating remorse, they end up acting even more harshly. They may even take revenge on the child for putting them in a position where they feel so despicable. 'A mother who could be condemned for any defect in her offspring naturally feels ambivalent toward the child,' writes the American historian Shari Thurer, 'especially if the child wilfully disobeys (as children often do).'

In Lionel Shriver's novel *We Need to Talk about Kevin*, the narrator, Kevin's mother Eva, castigates herself repeatedly for her failings as a mother. This book is so tantalising – and such an iconic 'book group book' – because it is not clear whether Kevin's eventual act of violence is the result of his wicked nature, or Eva's fault for being a 'bad mother'. And until the final act, there's another perfectly poised ambiguity. In one scene, Kevin scrawls over Eva's beautifully wallpapered study. It is read by Eva as an act of clear malevolence, but it could just be a toddler playing up. Is Kevin an evil child, or a normal child driving his mother mad? The novel explores these issues of ambivalence and guilt but leaves them open to debate.

In reality, it's healthy for children to straightforwardly see the effects of their own actions. The psychiatrist Harold Searles wrote about the importance of responding authentically to 'being driven crazy': he tells the story of one patient, a boy whose parents denied their own anger, who began to interact only with the family dog, because at least the dog could be relied upon to provide honest responses to his provocations. I think of this story when I read parenting experts advocate distraction or blank ignoring of tantrums: I understand the importance of not rewarding them with attention, and teaching self-restraint, but I can't believe this lack of affect is really good for kids. It's an interesting paradox, this testing of boundaries: children with scrupulously serene parents never find out where the boundaries are, but at the same time, locating them needs to be a safe experience. If a good-enough mother occasionally snaps at a child, that shows the child she can't stop herself in that moment, but what surely matters is that she generally can over the long term.

The psychoanalyst Angela Joyce told me how important it is to children to have an 'emotionally alive' mother who is able to say, 'you drove me to distraction, you were so badly behaved'. She continued: 'kids have got to know that they have an impact, and often it's the stonewalling or the blank face that is really provocative, that can produce even greater acting out or naughtiness by the child: can I get a reaction out of you mum, for god's sake respond to me!' Rozsika Parker tells the story of a woman who, after being driven mad by her children fighting in the back of the car (not just me then), stopped on the hard shoulder and started yelling, beating her hands on the steering wheel. Parker writes that this outburst, while painful, 'provided her children with a truthful experience in which they recognised the reality of their mother's feelings as well as their own agency'.

Parker memorably describes what the socially unacceptable side of maternal ambivalence actually feels like: 'the moment of recoil from a much-loved body, the desire to abandon, to smash the untouched plate of food in a toddler's face, to yank a child's arm while crossing the road, scrub too hard with a facecloth, change the lock against an adolescent, or the fantasy of hurling a howling baby out of the window'. Children bring out the best in me, but also the worst – a combination the American philosopher Sarah LaChance Adams describes in

Mad Mothers as 'love and hate, anger and tenderness, pity and cruelty, satisfaction and rage'.

We hate our children at certain moments, these countercultural accounts acknowledge, because they are sometimes just really annoying; but also because they can take on a symbolic significance for us: they can suddenly become us as a child, or a sibling who used to provoke or bully us. As the psychotherapist Philippa Perry has observed, being mindful of these resonances helps us to avoid perpetuating them. Children can also become a carrier for our own taboo feelings. 'At the bottom our strongest hatred,' the psychoanalyst Melanie Klein wrote, 'is directed against the hatred within ourselves.' Klein called this process 'splitting', the counterpart to masochism, in a sense: 'We so much dread hatred in ourselves that we are driven to employ one of our strongest measures of defence by putting it onto other people – to project it.' This splitting is also surely what's going on when we judge others – on the bus, or on online message boards. I would never talk to my child like that, we think to ourselves with smug relief.

Modern mothers are meant to engage fully with their child on the child's terms, but also to suppress their own inner child. No wonder mothers feel patronised, yet simultaneously burdened with responsibility. The mother's proximity to the child 'foregrounds the child within the mother', Rozsika Parker writes. 'The sensation of losing control, of adult reticence slipping away, can induce great anxiety and panic in a mother – and sometimes shame.' Parker tells the story of a woman who was told off in a shoe shop when her children were being naughty: 'part of her rebelliously identified with the "bad children", while part of her felt humiliated and convinced she was not a proper mother, not adult or orderly enough'. I connect with my inner child in a good way while taking them on trips and adventures – this has been an unexpected pleasure. But I also used to spend a lot of time self-righteously skulking around hushed galleries, avoiding the eyes of attendants and stylish aesthetes as my baby grizzled and struggled in his sling.

I sometimes come across mothers who never seem to lose their temper – at least not in public. They appear endlessly calm – if somewhat passive-aggressive – and able to accommodate the most extreme rollercoaster moods. These women make me feel infantile myself, though it's as if they've lost touch with their inner child. And they often treat their partners like children. Back in the mid-twentieth century, health professionals argued against maternal self-sacrifice. 'The mother who devotes herself exclusively to her child may have the satisfaction of playing the martyr,' wrote the American child psychiatrist David Levy, 'but she may dangerously handicap her offspring.' The American psychiatrist Edward Strecker noted similarly that social approval directed at 'good' mothers should be treated with caution: although they were 'spoken of as "giving their lives"', in truth they demanded 'full payment in the emotional lives of their children'.

'Always be bigger, stronger, wiser and kind,' advises the Circle of Security intervention organisation. Professionals and society at large expect mothers, Jacqueline Rose writes, to 'contain all the overwhelming impulses the baby cannot contain or manage on its own behalf'. It's hard to be a perfect container with no authority. And it is often when I try to be immaculately attentive and cheerful that I end up losing it. Perfection would seem to be the opposite of explosive rage, but it is actually its flipside.

GOING TOO FAR

It's all very well understanding what's going on psychologically, you might say, but where is that boundary between normal and damaging? And if women do cross the line, what are the long-term effects? Children may push parents to their limits – but what goes beyond an acceptable response? There's a spectrum, as Rozsika Parker puts it, 'from pulling up a zip roughly to outright acts of violence'. Yet while our culture doesn't like to admit there are shades of grey, it deploys a thin-end-of-the-wedge argument to keep parents on their toes.

Few people would say that violence is acceptable. But there's something awry in society's unwillingness to even countenance that it occurs. A 2015 study by researchers at the University of British Columbia in Canada asked a group of new mothers to listen to the sound of a baby crying for ten minutes. Nearly a quarter reported unwanted thoughts of actively harming the crying infant: throwing it, yelling at it, or shaking it.

The final chapter of Adrienne Rich's *Of Woman Born* – 'Violence: The Heart of Maternal Darkness' – opens with the story of Joanne Michulski, who murdered two of her eight children in Chicago in 1974. Commenting in a letter to a local newspaper about the storm of controversy that greeted the chapter, Rich wrote that not just Michulski but mothers at large are burdened by society's 'insane expectations'. 'What woman,' she wrote, 'has not dreamed of "going over the edge," of simply letting go . . . so that she can be taken care of for once, or can simply find a way to take care of herself?' Rich's argument was that it is the way motherhood is organised in society (motherhood as 'institution') that can produce violence, rather than the experience of motherhood itself. Instead of recognising its own shortcomings, however, society labels violent women as 'psychopathological'. We have, Rich writes, 'accepted the stresses of the institution as if they were a law of nature'. Yet both the institution and the violence it provokes are, she concludes, avoidable.

Angela Foster told me that she decided to write her book on women who harm their children because 'when motherhood is idealised, there is a societal reluctance to face the reality of really harmful mothering. So those who blatantly fail to live up to the ideal are viewed as individual aberrations: they are vilified and marginalised', and in this way we protect ourselves from the problem; 'nothing changes, and we remain complicit in the perpetuation of further neglect.' Rather than just being unimaginably evil, there are reasons why these women do what they do: they are often trapped in cycles of deprivation and neglect: 'it's quite simply that you can't give what you never had. You don't have it to give. So if you never had good-enough mothering, you don't know what it is, and that in itself can be very frightening. If what you know is violence and abuse, then it's going to come out sooner or later if you're under pressure.'

Society's intolerant denial of these mothers is counterproductive both for them and their children: if a child is removed, the mother is yet again deprived and abandoned, Foster told me. Her solution is to have another child – someone to love her. She called for mothers to be cared for as well as their children, to prevent these vicious cycles. But our idealisation of motherhood is counterproductive for ordinary good-enough mothers, too: instead of relaxing with their baby, they become anxious about living up to the ideal. Since society can't countenance the real harm that does go on, it is turned into a spectre that haunts the good-enough mother in the form of exacting and punitive control.

I also spoke to the consultant child psychiatrist Stephen Scott, who specialises in the mental health and wellbeing of children and teenagers. He pointed out that children vary and some need firmer boundaries than others; but in general, 'children are pretty jolly resilient – a few episodes of shouting are fine', Scott told me. He works with some very troubled families and draws a distinction between serious abuse and the anxieties of 'ordinary' mothers. But here is one of the difficult things, he continued: 'If you ask your child: Would you like to go to bed now? Well, no thanks, they'll say; and it's often when you start shouting that they know you mean business. So then you inadvertently get rewarded for shouting because that's when they start obeying you.' Scott runs parenting classes which employ some useful strategies: 'get down to their eye level, put your hand on their shoulder and say I want you to go to bed NOW or else you'll lose your screen time tomorrow or you won't get to play Minecraft or whatever it is – that does tend to work', he says.

Physical punishment is frowned upon culturally, but 'I think the damage of smacking is rather overdone,' Scott says; 'it depends on how often, how severe, what the rest of the relationship is like. It's quite hard to disentangle, because repeated angry smackers are usually not consistent and not very loving, so it's a whole package.' Scott adds: 'What can be more dangerous than a raised voice is criticism': after age three or four, routine criticism is associated with lower self-esteem in later life. And this is about tone as well as words: 'the little rascal' can have very different meanings for children if spoken with a wry smile or through gritted teeth.

Stephen Scott's formula is 'love and limits' – the two important ingredients for well-adjusted children. Parents need to be sensitive and responsive, but firm. He referred me to the work of the developmental psychologist Diana Baumrind and her theory of the most effective parenting style, which is both authoritative (but not authoritarian) and warm. 'What is damaging is unresolved negativity – as it is in adult relationships. So it's good if you can say, look I'm really sorry I shouted at you, I'll try not to do it again; but you also get people who go overboard and say, you can have sweets and stay up late tonight – and that's actually the parent's own issue and not the child's need – it's their own guilt.' This rang true for me: when I lose my temper with the children, I always make a point of talking to them afterwards when everyone's calmed down. I say I'm sorry, and explain what I did wrong. But sometimes I feel I'm partly appeasing my conscience.

What do the studies say? In terms of attitudes to smacking, there is considerable variation amongst health professionals:

one 2008 study by researchers at Leeds General Infirmary found that paediatricians had a wide range of views on it. Sometimes the studies themselves disagree: a review of the literature published in 2003 found that the question of 'whether or not to spank children' is 'controversial among lay and professional audiences alike'; and also that studies 'often reach different and sometimes opposite conclusions'. A 2018 report, *Parental Physical Punishment: Child Outcomes and Attitudes,* published by researchers at the Public Policy Institute for Wales, concluded that 'the evidence does not definitively show that "reasonable" parental physical punishment *causes* negative outcomes', although associations have been found. 'The effects of parental physical punishment on children is a source of debate and disagreement among professionals, academics and the general public,' they note. Research on this area is also compromised by parental underreporting. Some studies – such as one published in the journal *Child Development* in 2005 – have suggested that there's a cultural dimension here: when strict behaviours such as smacking are a fact of everyday life, they may, the study says, be less harmful.

Stephen Scott recognises that different cultures have varying attitudes towards strictness as well as whether children should be 'seen and not heard'. There are studies that suggest smacking in African-American communities is more normal and there-fore less damaging – although Scott tells me these studies haven't been that well replicated. It is, he says, important to take into account what he calls 'the meaning of it' – not just the smack, but the message it communicates to the child: including the difference between smacking for discipline and smacking out of anger. Ironically, the decline of smacking in general may mean it is worse for those who still experience it: now that it's less common and more frowned upon, those children may find it more 'serious' and therefore upsetting.

I asked Scott about the issue of shame and pride: whether

it makes problematic behaviour in families more difficult to identify and remedy, and shrouds the entire public discussion about parental discipline and anger in unhelpful secrecy. He agreed: 'I think there's a huge issue about shame, particularly if you've got badly behaved kids – and shame isn't an emotion we talk about a lot,' he told me. 'If you're the primary caregiver, it's your main job: imagine if you were going to work and told you were rubbish all the time and failing and the outcome of your work is badly behaved kids – it would be awful. There's a lot of this kind of shaming going on.' Scott draws a parallel with the parent who is told by a teacher that their child has been naughty: it may bring up memories for them of when they themselves had difficulties at school. It's for this reason, he adds, that professional interventions and parenting classes should focus on outcomes for children, rather than pointing a finger at parents.

As for those cases where a line has been crossed, Scott still emphasises the importance of understanding the problem rather than denying it. 'When parents do abuse their children,' he told me, 'it's because they don't know how else to do it, they've never seen anything else. It's not intentional evil; they're tired and fed up and perhaps they didn't have a very good upbringing themselves.' It is harder when you are in a stressful situation, of course – he points to 'the three ds': 'depression, domestic violence, and drug misuse': these make it harder to be a good parent and 'hold your child in mind'. But, he concludes, 'the majority of people living in the most difficult circumstances are doing a good job'.

* * *

As I've argued in this chapter, parenting advice on misbehaviour, punishment and anger is unfair, not fit for purpose, and actively detrimental. The results are evident in those online forums. What, really, is the point of being so hard on mothers when so many are already so hard on themselves? They have been dethroned as authority figures and treated like naughty children, yet are always expected to be the impeccable adult in the room. Mothers are not supposed to discipline their children, yet they are themselves subject to the strictest forms of discipline by government edicts, advice literature and social media, which claim simply to be reinforcing what is 'natural'. As undervalued, unrewarded individuals, mothers are not invested with validation or kudos for dealing with what can be the most challenging of circumstances.

Three changes would help. First, if social norms and the advice culture were more commensurate with the ordinary ups and downs of family life, rather than establishing scrupulously high standards that mothers inevitably fail to maintain. So on discipline and punishment, the advice should engage with the reality – including that of fighting siblings. I agree with positive reinforcement, but there's a danger that it neglects the question of how to manage behaviour on the ground. And on anger, the advice should provide parents with a sense of the evidence-based context – as Stephen Scott did for me – and not rely on the usual paternalistic 'give them an inch and they'll take a mile'.

The second change is to work towards more equality between partners: too often, mothers exercise sole jurisdiction as well as being the prime nurturers; they are both cuddly haven and strict enforcer. I've seen a lot of dads ask mums if the kids are 'allowed' to have a sweet snack or to watch TV. As the dads haven't been with the kids all day, they aren't fully conversant with what's been permitted or denied, and this means she ends up being cast in the unenviable role of bad cop. Gone are the days of 'wait till your father gets home' – not that I'm advocating a return to such threats, but too little consideration is given to the fact that in a post-authority era, modern mothers lack even that recourse.

And the third solution: too many mothers are harried and stretched thin struggling to combine family with work, the subject of my final chapter; solving the one problem would ease the other. Instead of castigating mothers, we should ask instead why a loving, caring woman is acting the way she does – how can she be enabled to be the mother she wants to be, more of the time?

Discipline is about correction; righting the wrongs a child has committed. But historically, children have been symbols of a broader project of correction: the improvement of the nation. Today, that responsibility falls to mothers, who not only attempt to make good their own failings and disappointments through their children, but also become scapegoats for society at large. In an ailing world, we imagine that children can be our phoenix-like redemption, so we foist this fantasy onto the shoulders of women, instead of taking steps to heal society through collective action. It's time we gave mothers the licence and the support they need to bring up their kids imperfectly – and with joy.

7

THE JUGGLE

I have a photograph from a few weeks after my daughter was born. I am sitting on the bed. She is lying in my lap in a white babygro. I am leaning over her, typing on my laptop. On the face of it, an image of harmonious multitasking, but I remember what was in my head: a constant, nagging worry about doing both less well. Even now, the tension between work and kids is still tight. When I'm looking after them, I'm prone to sneaking off to look at my emails for a little 'break'. The emails are never very restorative. And then one of them walks in before I've finished that never-ending task, and I feel bad for staring at my screen, and bad for being cross with them for interrupting.

I know my own mother struggled to fit everything in. She was – and is – an extraordinarily patient, devoted mother. Unlike so many adults around children, she doesn't rush, or appease, or jump in. She engages with children at their own pace. Everything unfolds as it would, without being forced. It's beautiful to watch, and it's also immensely calming. But when I was young, she had her hands full combining a medical career with raising three children: late again to pick me up from school, I would hear her car keys jangling in her hand as she hurried to where I was waiting.

My mother worked in a hospital, so she had to dash from work to the school. By contrast I, and very many of my friends, work mostly from home; a pattern that has been reinforced by the pandemic. When I am late for pick-up, it's because I feel I haven't achieved enough in the day, and am trying to launch one more task into the black hole of my own self-expectations so I can walk to school with a spring of satisfaction in my step, rather than falling into the same walk-run-walk-run as yesterday, and the day before: not having quite finished what I meant to do, and not quite managing to be on time either.

I used to work in an office. But after my second maternity leave, I sailed out the door of my interesting, prestigious workplace. I wasn't alone: a whole generation of professional women are no longer there; scattered to the four corners of motherland. During my maternity leaves, I'd grown used to utilising every spare minute: engaging the baby in some overdue quality time, putting on a wash, or grabbing an hour or two on my laptop. Yet back at work, I found it baffling how some male colleagues, most of whom had not taken more than a fortnight off for their own babies' arrival, could allow themselves to indulge in blue-sky thinking during meetings, enjoying the not necessarily productive moment for what it was. While it was a relief to relax into my screen for much of the day, the atmosphere at work felt oddly lifeless compared to the undoubted drudgery, but also the raw vitality of spending time with a small human being. The life-and-death realness of childbirth and babyhood were so intense, I couldn't bear to resume the banality of sitting at a desk in near silence for seven hours a day. So long, nine-to-fivers! I thought smugly to myself as I handed in my notice.

There was another reason, too. There was something about the wrestling and wrangling involved in looking after a baby and a toddler that made me strangely intolerant of carefully structured workplace hierarchies: I wanted autonomy and self-determination. The demeaning nature of domestic labour seemed to require a more efficiently meaningful offset than my day job. If I was going to spend hours of my week wiping an infant's bottom, preparing mush and laundering muslins, that had to be combined with a purer hit of life-goal fulfilment. I craved my own projects, putting my stamp on a tangible production; partly because I'd become used to the necessary inventiveness of looking after a child, and partly because, conversely, looking after children involves slog and routine. The pram in the hallway can be an obstacle for writers and artists, but it can also spur them on to overcome it.

The transition to motherhood is accompanied by a kind of Maoist Year Zero ideology: your past – and your future too – are to be expunged and replaced by an all-consuming present: *Enjoy it while it lasts!* There is something wonderful as well as overwhelming about the first years; like swimming in waves. It is impossible to predict how life with children will pan out. But a subtle resistance greets the wish to orientate what is happening in the context of the long-term. Strategic planning about a future return to work is obscured by a blur of bottles and nappies. 'All that can wait', is the subtext of advice by semi-strangers, as professional bridges are burned or neglected by mothers high on hormones and hazy with lack of sleep. *You wouldn't want to miss a minute!*

But then fast forward a few years, and the tiny infants who took up all that time, energy and attention, who, later on, needed walking to school every day, and provided by proxy daily water-cooler catch-ups at the school gates, are now grunting their goodbyes and waving backwards over their heads as they walk in to Years 5, 6, and soon, secondary school. The room has stopped spinning, and I've been able finally to look around me, as Winnicott so eloquently described. On some days I question my confident exit those years ago. I miss the sense of shared purpose, the feeling of belonging. I have dreams about going to work that feel like going home, except with the glow of prestige. I'm not sure I want to get back in, but even if I did, I don't know if I could locate the entrance.

I have managed to forge a very creative life since then, but I've spent the last ten years obsessing about that mythical state known as work–family balance. I have persevered through bloody-minded determination, but I'm forever propping up both fronts. I have even made it back into the workplace, on my own terms, but it's less of a breeze this time around. From being the most confident of thirty-somethings, I'm now a thin-skinned middle-aged mum/freelancer, asking relative newbies how to do basic technical tasks and always feeling a bit behind on the banter.

So many women I know are in the same boat. They left their jobs when they had their first or more often their second baby and threw themselves into motherhood; but then had a slow-motion crisis when their children didn't need them as much. They say they wished someone had told them the baby madness is temporary, that you will get your life back, that you should keep irons in the fire for when you want to be in the public world again. There's the former TV documentary director who's now giving a few hours a week to a children's charity, the record company executive who's set up a website selling baby clothes, the former musician who's now a part-time instrument teacher, and a former barrister who runs yoga classes from her living room.

I'm not criticising any of these choices. Many of these women have stepped off the hamster wheel and discovered what is really important to do in the world. Yet there is something off about the fact that they end up doing lower-paid, lower-status jobs, or give their time for nothing on the PTA committee or as a neighbourhood volunteer – maybe they'd quite like to be running a charity. I support the right of any mother to do what is right for her. But there should be much more support for those mothers who do want to get back into work, whether they decide to stick with their former career or pursue a different course.

Freedom doesn't feel quite so attractive in the bleak isolation of your kitchen on a winter Tuesday morning. We may be facing a robot-driven future, but we are still brought up to believe in paid employment as the agreed model of human utility and purpose. And those who hail superfast broadband as a route to swapping the commute for a converted garden shed in Essex or Kent, or point to the Covid-era video-conferencing norm as sounding the death knell of the quaintly antiquated physical office, can be swiftly disabused of their daydreams by a solitude-scarred 'mumpreneur'. The universal basic income (UBI) is much favoured by policy wonks in think-tanks designing an automated future in which we are free to sit around doing amateur philosophy or penning that novel. But the biggest trial of UBI has already taken place, and it produced a less than ecstatic outcome: the bored, listless, depressed 1950s American housewife. The 'post-work future' already stretches before many mothers of youngish children: it's simply the rest of their lives.

Gender equality is institutionalised in our education system, but there is no point telling schoolgirls that they can do anything in life if there is a time limit on that which kicks in at around age thirty-five. Girls consistently outperform boys at school, but that advantage is erased by motherhood. Well into the twenty-first century, scores of successful women – newspaper correspondents, restaurant managers, advertising executives, all rivalling their male peers, all initially blithe and idealistic – are resetting their expectations. As the result of a traumatic birth, pyrrhic childcare competence acquired on maternity leave, or a pragmatic truce with full-time working husbands, these women's approach to aspiration is never quite the same again.

To work or not to work: according to media commentary, that is the question. Yet as with so many aspects of modern motherhood, this apparently even-handed 'choice' is an illusion. Staying at home is considered not only virtuous but also brave, challenging the expectation that fulfilment lies out in the working world. But society does not back up that moral weighting with either remuneration or respect. Looking after children full time may be considered the ethical choice, but only working outside the home has public value. And the reality is that only the very affluent can afford to leave work altogether: for all the media reference to the plucky stay-at-home mum, very few don't work at all; they just scale it back to a level that's manageable, but with reduced prospects of success.

When my son was very young I would obsess over the correct number of days to work. Three was too many, two not enough. I felt I was treading a high, narrow path between stony gulfs. A misstep to one side and I would go mad with boredom, to the other, he would be scarred by neglect. Choosing between self-annihilation and harming the person I'd die for seemed pretty impossible. But at least I had the luxury of weighing it up. Other mothers may wish to work fewer hours, but can't afford to. What is the point of clobbering working mothers with guilt if their options are limited by circumstance?

Politicians have promised or fought for the same fabled solutions for decades – more parental leave, more flexible employment patterns – but little progress seems ever to be made. Government policy and social pressure produces the worst of worlds for all: professional women are guilt-tripped into forfeiting their high-flying jobs, while women on lower incomes are hammered with a contradictory message: on the one hand, that fully engaged motherhood will improve the life chances of their children, and on the other, that they must be 'helped back into work'. As I'll argue, much more radical solutions are required – and, with changes such as the prospect of less work for all being forced upon us by pandemics and AI, perhaps some positive outcomes are finally within our grasp.

In this chapter, I'll document the enduring difficulties faced by all working mothers. I'll describe society's condemnation of those who work both inside and outside the home. I'll trace the origins of this attitude, and examine if it has any merit in terms of the impact on children. I'll explore the fascinating science of attachment theory and show how it has been distorted by those who wish to see women sent back to the kitchen. And I'll show how the demands of a previous generation of feminists can still fuel campaigns today.

NOT WORKING

There's an assumption hidden behind many of the identity politics wars of the post-postmodern age: that all the other problems have been solved, and we can now devote our attention to defending the rights of last-frontier micro-categories. In fact, we still haven't managed to resolve the most basic of tensions: that between work and family. The Office for National Statistics reported in 2019 that three-quarters of mothers now work – a record high, and up from two-thirds at the start of the millennium. But at issue is not just the number of mothers working, but the nature of the work they are doing and the challenge of organising it. So many return part time and coast along on the mummy track, getting steadily greyer and more bitter as their predominantly male colleagues who they remember looking down on as green arrivals become their senior managers.

As I mentioned in chapter 2, the cost of childcare continues to soar – in the UK, by 58 per cent in the last decade for families with one full-time and one part-time worker; wages for the majority, meanwhile, have barely risen at all. A study by the charity Coram Family and Childcare found in 2020 that 25 hours' nursery care per week for a child under two stood at £6,800 per year for an average family – the cost had increased by double the rate of inflation over the previous year. The study also found that only just over half of local authorities in England had enough childcare for full-time working parents. A study by the OECD, also in 2020, found that full-time working British mothers with two children lose half their salary to childcare (assuming they alone pay for it of course).

The US has even more inadequate childcare provision, as well as no paid parental leave. As the Center for American Progress showed in 2020, the high cost and limited availability of childcare 'disproportionately affects people of colour' as being BAME correlates to lower income: 'Black Americans are nearly twice as likely as non-Hispanic white families to make job sacrifices because of childcare challenges.' In Australia, childcare costs have rocketed 150 per cent in the last decade: mothers lose 60 cents out of every dollar they earn to childcare (again assuming it comes out of just their salary). Mothers on lower incomes there are likewise the worst affected.

Good quality childcare is also notoriously hard to find. The best nurseries often have long waiting lists, and offer only limited hours. One-to-one care is hailed as the gold standard, at least for babies, but I found the hiring (and in one excruciating case firing) process both administratively and emotionally onerous. Each and every woman who wants a nanny (and can afford one) has to put an ad on Gumtree (a good way to sell an old mattress, perhaps, but not to find someone to care for your child), sift through hundreds of replies, and then take on the weighty responsibility of being an employer. Women with insecure relationships with the Home Office are looking after other people's children off the books with barely any rights or protections. The whole process is fragmented and decentralised, with every family reinventing its own wheel, and the majority of workers operating in the dark economy.

Given the advancements we are supposed to have made as feminists and as a society, the 'motherhood penalty' remains a shameful reality. For men, having a child positively benefits their careers. They are more likely to be hired than childless men, and – incredibly – tend to be paid more after they have children. Yet the wage gap between working mothers and working fathers starts growing from the moment women finish maternity leave. By the time a first child has reached the age of twenty, way after those early years, mothers earn almost a third less per hour, on average, than similarly educated fathers, according to a 2018 Institute for Fiscal Studies (IFS) report. In the US, according to the National Women's Law Center, mothers who work full time are paid an average of $18,000 less annually than their male counterparts. At retirement, the motherhood penalty delivers a final, resounding blow: because of lower earnings and breaks taken to have and raise kids, the average pension pot for a sixty-five-year-old woman in the UK is £35,800, one-fifth of that for the average sixty-five-year-old man.

The UK research body the New Policy Institute found in 2016 that women make up 62 per cent of all low-paid employees. Over half of zero-hours workers are women. Part-time work leads to wage stagnation. 'It is remarkable,' commented the IFS's Robert Joyce on the publication of its 2018 report on the wage gap, 'that periods spent in part-time work lead to virtually no wage progression at all.' And this is to say nothing of the fact that many supposedly part-time employees actually work closer to full-time hours. The most commonly cited solution to the problems of working mothers is more flexible work opportunities. But too often, these reinforce the pay, effort and status gap between women and men.

In fact, very many 'solutions' turn out to be traps, since they may enable mothers to work, but fail to address or even exacerbate gender inequality. Campaigning for longer maternity leave? A 2015 report on the motherhood pay gap by the Geneva-based International Labour Organisation found that, around the world, 'mothers taking longer leave periods experience a longer-lasting wage penalty'. There is also a further cost to asking for part-time or flexible work: in a 2014 study of over 600 workplaces, the American sociologist Christin Munsch found that when men requested to work from home for childcare reasons, only about 3 per cent of employers said they considered him uncommitted to his job, but when a woman did the same, about 16 per cent regarded her as uncommitted.

Though the logistical challenges of being a working mother are not new, they are no less outrageous for being a dreary cliché: they are an expression of society's neglect and implicit disapproval. That disapproval registers in more active ways, too. In 2016, a study of 3,000 mothers by the Equalities and Human Rights Commission found that three out of four had suffered pregnancy or maternity discrimination, such as not being told about promotion opportunities, being denied training, or even being threatened with dismissal. In 2014, a poll of 2,000 mothers by the discrimination law firm Slater & Gordon found that half felt they weren't taken seriously when they returned to work. Forty-five per cent were offered less senior roles. A 2018 study published in the journal of the Public Library of Science (*PLOS ONE*) which surveyed the attitudes of 50,000 working mothers in eighteen countries found they experienced not just practical discrimination but also prejudice from employers.

Surveys consistently show that working mothers reduce their contracts or change occupations not because they want to, but because childcare is unaffordable and former arrangements were not child-friendly. In 2013, a survey in Australia by the CareforKids.com.au site revealed that one in three working mums felt less valued on their return. Commenting on the survey, Marian Baird, a professor of employment relations at the University of Sydney, highlighted what she termed 'lucky mother' syndrome: 'extreme gratitude for any flexibility at work and/or support from partners', and a compulsion to demonstrate that the arrangement is working, prompting them to put in extra effort to prove themselves. In 2014, researchers at Bar-Ilan University in Israel found that working mothers felt they were bad mothers when they went to work and bad workers when they came home. The mothers they surveyed spent a full quarter of their working hours worrying about family, and routinely found themselves 'catching up' on work after hours.

Despite these material and attitudinal constraints, the rhetoric of choice still prevails. In 2014, Harvard Business School conducted a survey of its graduates that found 73 per cent of men and 85 per cent of women believed that 'prioritising family over work' was the number one barrier to women's career advancement. It is extraordinary how this language of freedom and self-determination – 'prioritising' – has pervaded our thinking. Phrases like 'opting out' or 'scaling back' create the false impression of willingness to sacrifice success. 'At a certain point the belief that a woman's primary career obstacle is *herself* became conventional wisdom, for both women and men,' the *Harvard Business Review* commented. 'The very premise seems to be that women value career less than men do,' the authors concluded, 'or that mothers don't want high-profile, challenging work.' Yet when they delved into the motivations of those 'high-achieving, highly educated professional women' who did leave their jobs, they found that only a small number did so because they preferred to devote themselves exclusively to motherhood. 'The vast majority leave reluctantly and as a last resort,' they discovered, 'because they find themselves in unfulfilling roles with dim prospects for advancement.'

All this is leading to dissatisfaction and distress across the board: a 2016 survey of 6,200 mothers by the UK's Department for Education revealed that 54 per cent wanted to work fewer hours so they could care for their children, and 53 per cent of non-workers said they would prefer to work if they could arrange good quality, affordable childcare. Modern mothers' lives are 'scattered, fragmented and exhausting', as Brigid Schulte puts it in *Overwhelmed: Work, Love and Play When No One Has the Time*. In 2019, researchers analysed the data of over 6,000 participants in the UK Household Longitudinal Survey, the largest of its kind worldwide. They found that working mothers of one child are 18 per cent more stressed than their childless counterparts; that figure rises to 40 per cent for those with two. The Resolution Foundation's 2020 report 'The time of your life: Time use in London and the UK over the past 40 years' found that women are in fact spending more time on both paid work and childcare than before.

The conflict between work and motherhood often registers in informal, nuanced ways: in the myriad micro incompatibilities between having a job and a child – particularly when they are school age. As well as holidays, there are the sports days and 'open evenings' in the middle of the afternoon and World Book Day costumes – with prizes for only the home-made ones, of course. A 2015 survey of 1,000 mothers by the education communications consultancy Gerard Kelly & Partners revealed the extent to which children's social lives are organised at the school gates. 'There's a currency you earn by helping other mothers out,' one respondent said. 'You need to be able to reciprocate otherwise it feels awkward to ask.'

For those finding it almost impossibly hard to exercise their basic right to both earn and procreate, the phrase 'having it all' appears especially rich. 'Having it all' means doing what men are given on a plate unquestioned, plus hours of extra labour every week. Employers insinuate that the women are not quite cutting it at work, and the media warns them they are damaging their kids. They feel deficient at both yet, unlike men, they feel they have to be compensatingly perfect at both. When men talk about their kids in the workplace, it adds to their progressive cred, yet women carefully avoid discussing theirs: their backstage scurrying is invisible. A man's 'do not disturb' sign – he's with the *kids* – is sacredly observed, yet women will multitask themselves to death just to keep the plates in the air.

It's a long time since the 'having it all' debates of the 1990s, yet the gender imbalance is still evident in the language: I never hear the phrase 'working dad'. When Rubin Ritter, co-CEO of the German fashion retailer Zalando, announced in 2020 that he was stepping down to 'devote more time to my growing family', his decision was covered by outlets worldwide – from the BBC to Bloomberg, *El Mundo* to the *Indian Express*. 'Is a man putting his wife's career first really so extraordinary that it deserves to make international news?', asked the *Guardian*'s Arwa Mahdawi. 'Unfortunately, the short answer to that is "yes".'

SOMEONE IS MISSING . . .

In 2018, the sociologist Ann Oakley gave an interview to BBC Radio 4's *Thinking Allowed* on the reissue of her landmark 1974 study, *The Sociology of Housework*, which found that most women disliked housework, and all women did more than men. But even in 2018, she reported, that division of labour had changed very little. I spoke to Kitty Jones, a researcher at the Centre for Family Research at Cambridge. She told me that most families think they divide up chores equally, but if you break down tasks using the neatly termed 'who does what' scale, stay-at-home mothers do way more than fathers; in families where both parents work, mothers still do much more; and in the few families with stay-at-home fathers, the housework balance is more or less equal – there is not a big swing towards the dads.

The ONS found in 2016 that women do nearly 60 per cent more unpaid (domestic) work than men. A study published in 2019 by University College London found that fewer than 7 per cent of couples split the domestic load equally. The Resolution Foundation's report 'The time of your life' found in the same year that 'mothers did the lion's share of housework and childcare': they spent on average 2 hours 21 minutes per day cooking, cleaning and doing other 'core' domestic jobs, while the average for fathers was 57 minutes. Mums spent more than double the time as dads on 'physical' childcare such as feeding and bathing their kids. Both women and men did more childcare than before, but 'the gender gap in childcare time is not shrinking as we observe a shift towards more time-intensive, child-centred parenting, particularly among parents in managerial and professional occupations,' commented research director Svetlana Speight.

The Covid-19 'lockdowns' in 2020 laid bare the shocking gender disparity in domestic life. A University of London study found that mothers spent more than twice the amount of time as fathers home-schooling their kids, and an ONS study found that mums provided two-thirds more childcare than dads. It is no surprise that one mother told researchers: 'I feel like a 1950s housewife.' In a survey conducted by the *New York Times*, almost half the men interviewed thought they were doing the bulk of home-schooling, 'but only 3 per cent of women agreed that this was the case'. There was also a marked drop in the number of academic papers submitted by women, while submissions by male academics increased. For me and many women I know, the lockdowns did not change life very much: we were still working from home while juggling kids, albeit more than usual. Our reality was in fact validated. Yet it was a very novel situation for most men, and their unwillingness to share the new load revealed not only existing imbalances, but also an ingrained resistance to equality.

This imbalance is a well-hidden reality in even the most liberal, open-minded relationships. In 2014, an American study of over a thousand families where both mother and father were medically trained and highly motivated at that – they'd all received career development awards from the US National Institutes of Health – found that the mothers spent on average an extra 8.5 hours a week looking after children and doing housework tasks such as cooking and cleaning compared with their partners, even when they did exactly the same job. 'One might expect that within a highly educated Generation X population there would be a relatively even distribution of domestic labor,' commented one of the study's authors, Reshma Jagsi of the University of Michigan. 'But what we found was that there still seems to be a difference in the expectations at home for men and women, even for those with very busy jobs, even today.' In the light of the study, Brendan Burchell, a sociologist at Cambridge, added in an interview with the *Telegraph* that women tend to double up work tasks: 'If a man is looking after the children they might sit down and watch TV together but a woman is more likely to be doing the ironing at the same time.'

Once again, the gap is also there amongst millennials. The researcher Kitty Jones told me that equality in parenting appears to have plateaued since around 2014. 'There's a clear sign that dads are more involved than in previous generations, but in the general population mums are still doing more,' she said. 'There's progress, but there's not equality in any sense, in terms of contributions.' In 2015, a survey by the site workingmums.co.uk of more than 2,000 working mothers showed a decline in the number of couples who would consider taking advantage of the much-touted shared parental leave – although this could be because the system is badly designed. 'The image of the "new man" is still largely a myth,' the survey concluded. In 2019, the ONS found that almost three in ten mothers with a child aged fourteen or under said that they had reduced their working hours for childcare reasons, compared to one in twenty fathers.

Even amongst younger families, therefore, we seem to have settled on the model of full-time working dad and part-time working mum. When Harvard Business School surveyed the attitudes of its (enlightened, educated) graduates, they found that a dispiriting two-thirds of millennial men 'still expect that their partners will handle the majority of child care'. A 2017 paper presented to the American Council on Contemporary Families found that in 1994, 83 per cent of young men rejected the idea that the male-breadwinner family was the best model, but by 2014, that had fallen to 55 per cent. 'Stuck between a traditional past and an egalitarian future, the millennial man is an amalgam of contradictory values, happy to work alongside women and live in a dual-earner household, but hesitant to do his share of the housework,' the twenty-three-year-old journalist Patrick Greenfield told the *Guardian* in 2016. While the baby carrier has been partially rehabilitated as a male accessory, rubber gloves have not.

In gay families, there is often more equality, says the family researcher Susan Golombok, but even here there can be some traditional gender-role patterning. Interestingly, the few studies that have been done show that gay couples (and gender non-binary couples) generally start out dividing childcare and housework more equitably, but if one partner takes on the role of primary earner, disparities can then develop – showing how it is patriarchy, rather than sexism pure and simple, that accounts for the unfair division of labour in parenthood.

In the 1970s and '80s, some pioneering men who supported the Women's Liberation Movement did look after children, sometimes more than their partners. Look back even further to the seventeenth century, and rather improbably, Puritan men were closely involved with raising their children. Now, however, not only are full-time and even part-time dads still a small minority, they are culturally satirised. Screen depictions of dads taking on the role of primary caregiver are either played for laughs (*Incredibles 2*, *Motherland*), viewed as the product of circumstance (the mother's death in *Sleepless in Seattle*) or end in disaster (Joe Miller in *Broadchurch* becomes a killer).

Kitty Jones, whose own research is on stay-at-home fathers, told me that although studies have revealed no difference in parenting quality compared with mothers, all the men she spoke to felt their role was stigmatised: they were exposed to negative stereotypes and comments; asked if they were babysitting, for example. Many felt they were portrayed as not coping, or as 'wet'. Some were also overtly praised, told: "'you're the most incredible person'", revealing the approbation bonus men receive – although ridiculed and patronised, they are also heroes starting from zero, whereas women are simply meeting expectations.

Even if men do their fair share of actual childcare, that's only the tip of the iceberg, the visible work that obscures a whole world of meal-planning and instrument-practice hassling and PE-kit washing and the plotting of complex chains of play-date reciprocity. This is what the French cartoonist Emma has termed the mental load – a concept that has resonated widely. It's as if we've spent so much effort trying to achieve parity in the workplace that we've forgotten about parity in the home. As the journalist Sally Howard shows in *Home Stretch*, this asymmetry is perpetuated by a combination of practice and shame. Practice makes perfect, but this creates a regressive illusion of intrinsic competence. The kind of parenting that produces secure and happy kids is not a natural elixir granted only to mothers: this is a misperception generated by the childcare gap between parents. It's not surprising that dads are often worse at reading their kids' signals if their regular parenting time is limited to a bedtime story.

The proficiency gap opens up from day one – a process also described by Rebecca Asher in *Shattered: Modern Motherhood and the Illusion of Equality* – and is a self-reinforcing monopoly. Before you know it, it's just mum who remembers that the reading diaries need filling out and who keeps track of their five-a-day. Mothers can become sulky maternal gatekeepers, a bit fixated on those box-ticking targets, and dads can be a helpful corrective: Hang loose! Eat pizza! Watch TV! But the relaxation of rules is invariably on his watch, and he burns through the valuable reward tokens, devaluing their currency.

Until recently, when my husband and I made one of our periodic efforts to rebalance, I had all the mums' numbers in my phone and the supermarket delivery shopping list saved on my account. 'It's easier if I do it,' I would snap – for the thousandth time. Women tend to *delegate* tasks to their partners because they've internalised the jobs list. This can also lead to resentment on the part of dads, who feel they lack an equal say in family plans.

The shame bit is that not carrying out all these household and social maintenance tasks rebounds disproportionately on the mother, who is framed as an inconsiderate slattern. 'I know there's tea and biscuits in the cupboard in case the in-laws pop round, and that a birthday card and stamps have been bought for my partner's cousin's son,' Howard writes. 'Because it's me – not their blood relation – who will be judged.' The tactful concealment of this imbalance is yet another second- or third-order task added to the list: many women – particularly if they consider themselves progressive – are embarrassed to have fallen into such conventional stereotypes.

The domestic discrepancy is a hidden disgrace, therefore, but its evolution is subtle and passive-consensual, and the fault is structural, not individual. 'Often men and women collude in maintaining these social norms,' Brendan Burchell commented in the light of that study of married doctors: 'Some women see it as a matter of pride that they are sacrificing their careers for their children.' Others derive satisfaction from the fact that it's to them the kids run when they need a hug. Many men, for their part, are not clamouring to spend more time looking after children because they have the power to avoid something that is often difficult and boring. And it's not just their own kids: the preponderance of women in child-minding, nursery care and primary school teaching – relatively (and outrageously) low-status, low-paid jobs – is so commonplace it is barely remarked upon.

I know from experience that it requires will on both sides and conscious, continued work to resist these dynamics within couples. Too often, the mother takes out her bitter frustrations about constantly having to negotiate her on-off, cobbled-together, meandering career on her full-time-working, steady upwards-trajectory-climbing, straightforwardly successful partner. The last thing that a mother needs is another child, but she treats him like one anyway, because he lacks expertise in sibling conflict resolution or headlice treatment. And in his tired, well-meaning confusion, it's the last thing he needs, too.

DAMNED IF YOU DO

'Stay-at-home mothers "have the most worthwhile lives"', announces the *Telegraph*. 'Decline of the stay-at-home mother', sighs the *Daily Mail*. 'Sorry Working Moms, Daycare Is Bad For Your Kid' reads the headline of one 2015 blog: 'As a society, we really ought to be more concerned about the welfare of young children than grown women.' In 2010, the international media reported a study by researchers at University College London which appeared to show that children of working mothers were more obese (an NHS 'behind the headlines' report pointed out that the study did not measure diet or physical exercise, so inferring a causal relationship was not legitimate). Yet the *Mail* reported: 'Latchkey kids have more freedom to eat sugary snacks and spend solitary afternoons slumped in front of the TV.' The guilt that so many working mothers feel is the consequence not only of a perception that they are constantly failing both kids and colleagues, but also of an active prejudice on the part of the wider culture.

Low-income mothers are demonised in the media (I'm thinking of the insult 'pram face'), but high-income mothers receive harsh treatment, too. As Helen McCarthy notes in *Double Lives: A History of Working Motherhood*, only mothers who work because they have to can be considered 'good' – and even then it's a stretch. Only 'bad' mothers work because they want to. Yet there's a covertly classist prejudice in the assumption that lower-paid women only work for money, not enjoyment, or that they more often want to look after their kids full time.

With declining newspaper circulations, it's important not to overstate the influence of the media; but its messages are propagated online, and are fuelled by conservative attitudes, such as that of the child psychologist Penelope Leach, who – while she worked herself and has always denied traducing working mothers per se – has disparaged both the quality of daycare settings and the concept of daycare itself. This led to the impression, articulated by one reviewer of her 1994 book *Children First*, that 'to be a working mother is to be somehow derelict'.

The particularly compulsive attention paid to professional mothers is partly reflective of the narrow demographic of journalists themselves, but it is also the result of the broader misogynistic notion that mothers just can't 'have it all'. Coexisting with the disproportionate focus is an irritated dismissal of the tribulations of this privileged group: since they are comparatively well off, the argument goes, they surely do not deserve further attention. Have a nanny? Then you must be one of those spoiled women who think they're above changing a nappy: too busy stabbing your male colleagues in the back with a stiletto heel, and so on.

These women may enjoy relatively high social status, but the fact that they often bear the brunt of media disapproval is rarely highlighted in the debate. Our squeamishness about matters of class and status means that these hidden cultural attitudes and their effect on mothers are not properly analysed. And this is a problem, I argue, because the pressure on the most career-successful women to give up their jobs has far-reaching consequences for the cause of feminism in general: if we undermine these women, we undermine all women's ability to attain equality with men in the workplace. There's a word for being motivated to work by choice: ambition. As Anne-Marie Slaughter put it in her 2012 *Atlantic* article, headlined 'Why women are still not having it all': 'We are the women who could be leading.'

Media dislike of professional mothers is especially unfair given that this group is subject to the widest pay inequality with men. The motherhood penalty affects different demographics differently: although women with the lowest incomes find themselves treated worst overall, those in higher-paid jobs experience the biggest gap between their status and that of their male peers. The 2018 IFS report showed that the gender wage gap has narrowed for the less well-educated – from 28 per cent to 18 per cent for those educated to GCSE level. But the wage gap has not fallen at all in the last quarter century for the highest-educated women. The IFS's Robert Joyce explains that 'this is particularly related to the fact that they lose out so badly from working part-time'.

Department for Education figures from 2014 indicate that women in the top income bracket are leaving the workplace – 'in droves', as the *Telegraph* has it – to look after their children. The writer and academic Shani Orgad notes in *Heading Home: Motherhood, Work, and the Failed Promise of Equality* that 20 per cent of stay-at-home mothers in the UK are university-educated. In the US, a quarter have college degrees.

More than half a century ago, Betty Friedan asked why 'did so many American women, with the ability and education to discover and create, go back home again?' For Friedan, the answer lay in the feminine mystique, the religion of domesticity and wifely attractiveness that bound mothers to the home. Today, there is a taboo around even asking that question, because those women are largely no longer imprisoned in the domestic sphere; they have apparently returned there voluntarily. In *Minus Nine to One: The Diary of an Honest Mum*, Jools

Oliver wrote that she 'was never really a career girl': 'Who was I kidding? I wanted the babies, the baking and the roses round the door.' I believe women should be able to choose the life they want, as long as that choice is genuinely free; but too often, the rhetoric of freedom conceals both practical constraints and outdated cultural values.

THE BACKSTORY

There's a prevailing cultural assumption that mothers in history were automatically devoted to their babies and that the rot set in when they started to go out to work. However, the historical record reveals this morality tale to be largely false. Prior to the twentieth century, children were sent out to wet-nurses not just for breastfeeding, but up to the age of two or three; rendered immobile through swaddling; parked in prams in the street or outside shops; watched by older children or neighbours; and later on, put to work. 'I have not willingly suffered them to be brought up near me,' wrote the Renaissance writer Michel de Montaigne about his own poor progeny. In *Common Sense in the Nursery*, the nineteenth-century American author Marion Harland disparaged those overattentive mothers whose 'whole soul is wrapped up' in the little 'cherub'. Model mothers, she wrote, echoing some of the attitudes I cited in the previous chapter, 'are not those in whom the maternal instinct is cultivated to an abnormal excrescence'. I'm not suggesting these practices and approaches were beneficial for children, but they shed a forgiving light on the guilt and high self-expectations of modern mothers.

There was a contradictory strain running counter to these attitudes, expressed in Victorian sentimentality towards mothers and children: the poet and author Lydia Sigourney advocated assiduous love and care in her 1838 *Letters to Mothers*, counselling them that 'every irritable feeling should . . . be restrained'. But such sentiments coexisted with harsher, brisker attitudes.

The idea that motherhood is a woman's sole rightful vocation can be traced once again back to the ideas of Rousseau and his followers. Rousseau recommended that babies be 'freed' from the 'tyranny' of swaddling clothes: this 'imprisonment of French children', he wrote, 'means liberty for the nurse', but 'a true mother is never at liberty'. Yet if elite mothers in eighteenth- and nineteenth-century Europe were subjected to the cult of motherhood – which they often ignored – for poor women the emphasis was on economic productivity, harder to ignore: hence the workhouse. Four million women and girls were in paid work in Victorian Britain. The idea that mothers only started 'going out to work' in the second half of the twentieth century, therefore, is a myth.

Equally mistaken is the idea that only mothers in the late twentieth century onwards have found it taxing to be the full-time companions of infants. In her 1901 childcare manual *The Mind of a Child*, Ennis Richmond deplored parents who indulge their little ones, becoming slaves to their every whim and giving great credence to their point of view as if 'they were not just immature beings, but of value in themselves'. For her own part, she could 'only stand an hour or two of being on all fours, rumpled and dragged at, and deafened'. From Peg Bracken's *I Hate to Cook* to Jean Kerr's *Please Don't Eat the Daisies*, mid-twentieth-century domestic satirists documented their plight with self-deprecating mirth. Even Penelope Leach quotes an example from a widely read women's liberation magazine that describes the full-time care of very young children as 'like spending all day, every day, in the exclusive company of an incontinent mental defective'.

In *The Rise and Fall of the British Nanny*, Jonathan Gathorne-Hardy describes how, until the mid-twentieth century, nannies had dominion over children in all but the poorest households. Ayahs were common in the colonies. Home help and live-in childcare was ubiquitous in a way that would be unthinkable for all but the most affluent today. As Adrienne Rich put it as long ago as 1976, women are now 'expected to fill both the part of the Victorian Lady of Leisure, the Angel in the House, and also of the Victorian cook, scullery maid, laundress, governess, and nurse'.

Female members of the Bloomsbury Group relied heavily on domestic staff, a sometimes fraught arrangement documented by the historian Alison Light. It is true that the relationship was fundamentally unequal, but there is a kind of double standard in the way it is represented today: those women could write avant-garde books, but not wash their own pants. The same criticism is never applied to Lytton Strachey or John Maynard Keynes. I'm not arguing that creative or professional achievements should be built on the backs of other women doing the dirty work, a situation deeply rooted in Britain's class system and colonial past, but the fact is that modern mothers are expected to do it all, yet that observation is rarely made for fear of appearing to endorse domestic servitude.

Our culture's hostility towards 'privileged' mothers who have cleaners was thrown into unusually stark relief during the 2020 coronavirus lockdowns. Admittedly, some (mainly white) women were rather unforgivably asking their (mainly non-white or eastern European) cleaners to put themselves at risk by travelling on public transport to their homes. The *Guardian* journalist Owen Jones suggested on Twitter that families should simply impose a cleaning rota, as his own family had when he was growing up. This triggered a huge social media row. Mothers objected to being told by a man how to keep their homes clean, especially when they had to home-school their kids, cook three meals a day, maintain a habitable living environment and, in many cases, also work from home. 'Just get your husbands to do the washing up,' was the typical response of some Generation Z-ers, as if patriarchy didn't exist. And many responses revealed that it is still considered the woman's job to either do the cleaning herself or employ someone else to do it: the comedian Mark

Steel tweeted sarcastically in defence of Jones: 'It's a basic right of women, to get other poor women to risk their lives for them so they can keep the fucking sideboard dusted.'

It is not surprising that so many books and articles about contemporary domestic life are illustrated with retro images of the 1950s housewife: our own age shares with that one the preponderance of over-qualified women doing housework, alone. I am not suggesting that children should be farmed out to wet-nurses, sent up chimneys, or looked after by low-paid or immigrant women – many of whom have left their own children behind in their countries of origin. But there is rank injustice for all women in the way things are currently set up, perpetuated by the fact that men do so little domestic work, in their own homes or other peoples'. Women who trained for illustrious careers end up scrubbing their bathrooms for nothing, and lower-status women end up scrubbing other people's bathrooms for a pittance while their own children receive substandard childcare. In these public debates, one group of women is pitted against another, while men avoid doing the dirty work, and society washes its hands.

ATTACHMENT

In 1950, the World Health Organisation commissioned John Bowlby to write a report on the psychological health of the children who had been made homeless, orphaned, or separated from their parents during the Second World War. Even before the war, Bowlby had emphasised the importance of a present and proficient mother: 'the emotional bond between child and mother is the basis for all further social development,' he wrote in 1939; and prolonged separations cause children to feel 'deserted and betrayed'. His report was published in 1952 with international publicity; in it he concluded that the young child 'should experience a warm, intimate, and continuous relationship with his mother (or permanent mother substitute)' and that if this is not provided, the child is liable to develop significant and irreversible mental health problems.

As well as examining the war's impact on children, Bowlby was also influenced by the study of animals; specifically, a branch of zoology developed by the ornithologists Konrad Lorenz and Nikolaas Tinbergen called ethology. Ethology is the study of behaviours that animals have evolved to protect them from danger. Through a process known as imprinting, a duckling or gosling will avoid predators by staying close to its mother, a behaviour ethologists believe is biologically programmed to ensure the survival of the species. Bowlby was also in close contact with the American animal psychologist Harry Harlow, who studied the effect of maternal deprivation on monkeys. Bowlby believed that humans were subject to the same basic mechanisms as animals, and that if a mother was absent during the crucial early period of her child's development then this would spell trouble later on.

Bowlby was critical of working mothers: 'In days gone by when higher education was closed to them,' he wrote, 'there was less conflict between the claims of family and career.' In an analysis of why families fail, he listed 'fulltime employment of mother' on a par with the imprisonment or death of a parent and 'social calamity' including war and famine. A baby, he argued, should have 'constant attention night and day, seven days a week and 365 days a year'. The consequences of not doing so were grave: 'What occurs in the earliest months and years can have deep and long-lasting effects.' In 1958, the American magazine *Ladies' Home Journal* ran a forum on the question: 'Should mothers of young children work?' Bowlby was one of the participants. 'To deprive a small child of his mother's companionship is as bad as depriving him of vitamins,' he wrote. To put a child under three in daycare, he believed, was tantamount to serious neglect.

At the same time, it is important to remember that Bowlby was in some ways more lenient towards women who wanted or needed time off than we are in the twenty-first century. 'The absolute need of infants and toddlers for the continuous care of their mothers will be borne in on all those who read this book,' he wrote in his 1953 *Child Care and the Growth of Love*, 'and some will exclaim, "Can I then never leave my child?"' Admitting that 'far more knowledge is required before a proper answer can be given', Bowlby advised that 'the holiday whilst granny looks after the baby, which so many mothers and fathers pine for, is best kept to a week or ten days'. Even while his phraseology – 'best kept' – comes across as a little patronising, many modern readers will read this passage with a double take: 'a week or ten days'! Most of my mum friends feel bad going away for a weekend.

Although Bowlby's ideas were somewhat constraining, therefore, later in life he would acknowledge that he had overstated the dire consequences of maternal separation. But in the post-war period, politicians and policy-makers keen to ensure employment for returning servicemen used Bowlby's research suggesting that children in orphanages did less well (unsurprisingly) than children in the families to argue that mothers – many of whom had been employed during the war – should now stay home with their children. Lessons of extreme neglect were employed, therefore, to curtail the ambitions of newly emancipated women. The war effort had been necessary, the *Ladies' Home Journal* article reported, but now women were going out to work 'by choice'. But was this the right choice, they asked.

The 1950s is a curious paradox: it is held up as the golden age of feminine domesticity, yet women had plainly shown they could succeed at traditionally male occupations. We should really regard the image of the Fifties housewife as a kind of PR: an attempt at the time to impose an egregious mythical ideal on a rather different reality. Yet today we seem unaware of that reality and only hark back to the ideal.

Attachment theory, developed by Bowlby in the late 1960s, has stood the test of time. It describes how a child, when it is alarmed or frightened, will seek out one of a small group of primary caregivers (known as the 'safe haven'). When it feels safe, the child will internalise the presence of one of the primary caregivers (the 'secure base'), giving it the confidence to go and explore. Depending on how responsive the child's caregiver has been, the child will develop into one of three attachment types – secure (the majority of children), insecure, and disorganised (these behaviours show up in a particular experimental context, known as the Strange Situation Procedure). Insecure attachment in turn falls into two sub-groups. There are insecure-avoidant children, whose primary caregiver has repeatedly ignored or responded angrily to the child's distress. And there are insecure-anxious children, whose primary parent has been erratic in their responses.

As the Yale developmental psychologist Diana Divecha has noted, creating a secure attachment doesn't mean responding positively to a child's every need. In fact, researchers like Divecha stress the importance of miscommunications, misunderstandings and failed interactions – these teach the child that the caregiver is able to repair mistakes and this helps them develop vital coping skills. A secure connection is not the same as a 'tight' connection. Once again, experts show that ordinary imperfection is not only inevitable; it is actually beneficial for children. Furthermore, mental health professionals are careful to stress that although the caregiver is usually the mother, this doesn't necessarily have to be the case. It is wider society that is lagging behind in the regressive claim that it really should be mum.

When I spoke to the child psychiatrist Stephen Scott about attachment, he reiterated that while Bowlby's theories may have been used by non-experts to make ordinary mothers feel guilty, his essential theory is still relevant today: 'When a child is upset or frightened or ill they seek comfort from a safe haven,' Scott explained. The key question is 'whether the adult can do the business when the chips are down'. Insecure attachment 'doesn't matter very much,' Scott continued; although they may have more hurdles to get over, these children 'seem to do just as well in life – in stability of romantic relationships, earnings and so on'.

The category that is really problematic is 'disorganised' attachment: this affects around 15 per cent of the population and is found in up to a fifth of children in deprived areas: not because those parents are any less loving or worse at parenting, but because they are under more pressure. Disorganised attachment is associated with emotional and behavioural problems later in life, but as Scott explained, even this can in many cases be remedied. He told me about a recent study he'd carried out with children who were so abused or neglected they'd been taken into care. The study found that they could still form secure attachments to their foster carers. So while it is true that the early years do make more of a difference in terms of attachments, repair and progress is still possible later on. 'You're not done for,' he said.

Bowlby's ideas – from both his early and his later career – have been highly influential not just within the medical establishment but also in public policy, parenting advice, and the media. One of Bowlby's most devoted advocates was the American psychoanalyst Margaret Ribble, whose popular *Rights of Infants*, first published in 1943, championed co-sleeping among other child-centred mothering styles. Ribble quoted a study on institutionalised children that appeared to show that 'babies in the best homes and hospitals, given the most careful attention, often drifted into [a] condition of slow dying, while infants in the poorest homes, with a good mother, often overcame the handicaps of poverty and unhygienic surroundings and became bouncing babies. It was found,' she explained, 'that the element lacking in the sterilized lives of the former class . . . was mother-love.'

Ribble also recommended prolonged breastfeeding, arguing that those unfortunate babies whose mothers were absorbed in their social lives, their professions, or artistic pursuits would come to no good. Ribble drew another analogy from nature: 'Sometimes, in the case of the cold-blooded reptiles like the dinosaur, the female laid the eggs in the sand, let the sun do the hatching, and left the infant in the hands of fate,' she wrote. 'There are some modern parents who seem to think this was a good idea; they do not wish to be burdened with the care of an infant. Particularly has breast-feeding gone out of vogue, and mothers say with spirit that they are not going to be cows. They seem even to prefer to be dinosaurs. When scientists find the unhatched dinosaur eggs in the sand near a few of the bones of the dinosaur parents,' she concluded darkly, 'they are apt to speculate what went wrong with the system.'

'NEUROPARENTING'

It is surely the case that mothers – and fathers – share some parenting techniques with our animal relatives. Yet these analogies with ducks, geese and monkeys resonate uncomfortably with a long tradition of comparing mothers to animals, and implying in fact that they should dispense with their ambitions and act a bit more like them. Towards the end of the twentieth century, this essentialist tendency joined forces with arguments drawn from neuroscience: more ameliatory discussions about child rearing were replaced by biological references to the brain as an unalterable lump of meat.

Having taken over from sociobiology and evolutionary biology, which were weaponised against feminist advances in the 1980s and 1990s, neuroscience – or at least, a popular extrapolation of what is a perfectly reasonable branch of science in itself – has been deployed to endow the old injunction to be a stay-at-home mum with hard, shiny 'evidence'. Whereas in the past that case would have been made argumentatively, with recourse to morality or religion, patriarchal commentators now simply hold their hands up and say, don't blame me, it's just nature talking.

Advocates of what became known as 'neuroparenting' argue that any trauma a baby or toddler experiences during the crucial first three years when the brain is developing most quickly – including the absence of a mother through work – will be hard-wired into its brain, resulting in emotional and cognitive problems in later life. Any attempts to remedy these, they claim, are futile.

The 'first three years' movement arose in the US during the 1990s and acquired substantial policy and media momentum. A public awareness campaign was launched – 'I Am Your Child' – featuring the actor Rob Reiner. In 1997, *Newsweek* ran a special issue on 'Your Child: From Birth to Three'. The American paediatrician Jack Shonkoff, co-editor of *From Neurons to Neighborhoods: The Science of Early Childhood Development*, worked with a public relations agency, FrameWorks, to spread the message that in the first three years of life, 'the human brain is developing the foundation upon which all future learning and function will rest, impacting academic performance, employability, and ultimately, the competitiveness of the national workforce'.

This philosophy was popularised in the UK by psychologists including Sue Gerhardt, Margot Sunderland, Penelope Leach and Aric Sigman. Two MPs, Iain Duncan Smith and Graham Allen, produced a report in 2008 emphasising that 'the greatest gift for a baby is maternal responsiveness', and that 'the more positive stimuli a baby is given, the more brain cells and synapses it will be able to develop'. Baroness Tyler, the Liberal Democrat peer, reinforced the message. 'It is parents,' she wrote, 'not teachers or government', who are 'ultimately responsible for a child's development in these early years' – the desire to offload political responsibility palpable here. In 2014, a cross-party group of MPs led by Andrea Leadsom launched the '1001 Critical Days' manifesto, which aimed to ensure that the 'crucial' and 'critical' early years, are 'placed at the heart of the policy-making process'. The then prime minister David Cameron gave a big speech on 'Life Chances'. 'Thanks to the advent of functional MRI scanners, neuroscientists and biologists say they have learnt more about how the brain works in the last 10 years than in the rest of human history put together,' he said. 'Destinies can be altered for good or ill in this window of opportunity.' The policy agenda was reinforced in the media: 'Research has for decades kept proving that, by the age of three, a child's destiny is all but sealed by how much affection, conversation, reading and explaining they have received,' wrote the columnist Polly Toynbee in 2012.

As the sociologist Jan Macvarish has noted, 'first three years' campaigners often use the phrase 'we now know' to describe how children should be parented, as if an insight into how the brain works constitutes knowledge in a way that more informal know-how doesn't. 'We now know through science that the first three years of life is the most critical time period,' Rob Reiner told the American National Governors Association in 1997. 'By age 10 your brain is cooked and there's nothing much you can do.'

Even though neuroscience is new, the conclusions which commentators draw from it often closely resemble traditional norms: the science also proves 'what we have always known'. I am certainly not denying the usefulness of neuroscience when properly applied, but too often it is misused in order to advance agendas that rebound disproportionately and unfairly on good-enough mothers who need to or have to work. The reality is that the brain is not 'set' by age three.

Stephen Scott is critical of what he calls 'neurobabble' drawing far-fetched inferences from fairly limited observations of what goes on in the brain. 'It's interesting how this trumps something more ethereal or difficult to define like happiness or sadness,' he says. 'It's as if the brain structure is real so it has more validity.' He continued: 'I'm a brain researcher, but I hate that stuff. The important thing is behaviour, and you can change people, so does it really matter if you change their brains or not?'

It is ironic that during the 1980s and 1990s, at the same time as the 'first three years' arguments were being cemented, epigenetics was revealing that our brains are more pliable than we previously thought. As the philosopher of science John Bruer notes: 'We should never forget that humans are highly adaptive and our children are remarkably resilient.' And Steve Petersen, a neuroscientist at Washington University in St Louis, told the *New York Times*: 'At a minimum, development really wants to happen. It takes very impoverished environments to interfere with development.' His advice: 'Don't raise your children in a closet, starve them, or hit them on the head with a frying pan.'

Attachment parenting, promoted most prominently by William and Martha Sears in their bestsellers, is often confused with attachment theory; it is actually crucially different. In *Attachment Parenting*, the Searses advocate seven practices they call the Baby Bs: 'birth bonding, breastfeeding, baby-wearing, bedding close to the baby, belief in the baby's cry, balance and boundaries, and beware of baby trainers'. Those who 'fail' to tick these practices off – because, say, an emergency caesarean deprives them of initial 'skin to skin contact', or they give up breastfeeding after developing mastitis – may worry that they've blown the chance of forming a good relationship with their child; an unnecessary and counterproductive anxiety.

As we've seen, a secure attachment is not about constant contact, but rather the ability to separate from the caregiver for short periods of time, safe in the knowledge that they won't disappear. The priority is not the caregiver's presence as such, but the degree to which they are attuned and sensitive to the child's signals. In fact, as Winnicott observed, one of the most important aspects of good mothering is teaching the infant the 'capacity to be alone', the title of one of his papers, in which he portrayed solitude not as neglect or abandonment but as 'a most precious possession', linked to the capacity to dream.

Advocates of attachment parenting, described by the Searses as 'common sense' parenting, cite Bowlby frequently, as well as other theories derived from ethology – and neuroscience. 'At its essence, Attachment Parenting is our biological imperative – the source of our most instinctual behaviors,' states the advocacy organisation Attachment Parenting International. 'In the last sixty years, the behaviors of attachment have been studied extensively by psychology and child development researchers, and more recently, by researchers studying the brain.' Here they imply – as do the Searses – that attachment parenting produces a secure attachment. Yet attachment parenting has only a tenuous relationship either to Bowlby's ideas or to other sophisticated notions of attachment developed since his time.

William and Martha Sears's recommendations are derived in part from observations of indigenous childrearing practices that are often assumed to be more 'natural'. Yet David Lancy, an American anthropologist who has studied how mothers play with their children through history and across different cultures, argues that Western thinkers have developed a distorted view of ideal motherhood by looking through the lens of psychology, not anthropology. For example, we in the West have decided that a particular, elite model of play is the natural norm. 'Even a cursory review of websites and parent-orientated trade publications,' he wrote in 2007, 'will yield the inescapable conclusion that good, effective parents play with their offspring from birth and continue, through adolescence, to take an interest in and manage the child's toy inventory, game and sports schedule, and choice of play- or teammates.' Failure in this vital role, he argued, supposedly 'sets one's child loose in a minefield of potentially debilitating outcomes'.

Yet, Lancy continues, if we look as anthropologists beyond these prosperous Western communities, it is evident that parents in other countries and times simply have not had the time for such exhaustive pursuits. What is universal across cultures, he stresses, is *children* playing. But 'one rarely sees adults playing with children'. He cites an analysis of 186 ethnographic studies which show 'wide variation in the amount of mother–infant play and display of affection'. In fact, it was not until the late 1940s that babycare manuals referred to playing as a maternal duty; before then it was considered harmfully overstimulating. Western habits that we regard as universal are the product of culture, not nature. We may argue – I do – that parents having the time to play with their children is a social good that we should try to enable; but that is different from enforcing it.

Although there are some constants, a meta-study of attachment behaviours across cultural contexts found significant variations in the way those behaviours manifest: for example, children brought up communally in Israeli kibbutzes are used to being separated from their mothers, but they display anxiety when left with strangers. As Ana Fernandez, a clinical psychologist who has worked in both her native Peru and the UK told me, the attachment relationship between mother and child can be enacted differently in different places: in the global north, there's an emphasis on verbal interaction, whereas in Latin America, physical cues are more important. In some cultures, maternal care is expressed through keeping a child clean and well dressed, which is less of a marker here.

Arguments derived from animal behaviour and non-Western societies alike have been used to claim that for women, anatomy is destiny, and destiny is domesticity. Yet anthropologists such as Lancy have shown that it is actually commonplace in cultures invoked by conservatives as exemplary of devoted motherhood for childcare to be shared by a group of adults – or other children. Lancy notes that 'across nearly 200 societies, 40 per cent of infants and 80 per cent of toddlers' are cared for 'primarily by someone other than their mother – most commonly, older sisters'. Another anthropologist, Sarah Blaffer Hrdy, notes that 'alloparenting', children being looked after by people other than their mother, is common amongst a diverse range of cultures; by four months of age, an infant in the Ituri rainforests of the Democratic Republic of Congo spends an average of 60 per cent of each day away from its mother, passed between a small group of caretakers. Hrdy even suggests that the efficiency of shared childcare might be the key to our evolutionary success. A study by the National Institute of Child Health and Development in the United States reviewed parenting practices in 186 non-industrial societies: mothers were the exclusive carer in only five. As the historian Sarah Knott shows, shared parenting is also common in contemporary non-white, non-affluent Western communities – as well as in Mediterranean cultures.

Attachment parenting and 'neuroparenting' emphasise maternal nurture, but they also rely on a universal, fixed view of nature. In 2015, the American political scientist Robert Putnam wrote that 'providing physical and emotional security and comfort – hugging, for example – is the human equivalent of a mother rat's licking and grooming behaviour and can make a great difference in children's lives'. Yet the relationship between nurture and nature is paradoxical in such statements: on the one hand, there is the assumption that mothers will – like most other mammals – naturally become attached to their babies. On the other, top-down government and expert advice indicates that mothers need to be persuaded into it.

Invoking science and nature in this way also provides a way

for politicians to displace responsibility for tackling complex problems of poverty and inequality onto mothers. This approach regards high-quality mothering as the engine of social mobility, rather than investment in the welfare state. Yet it also drives high-end competitive parenting: the alleviation of economic and maternal deprivation alike is elided with the enhancement of cognitive performance. As Jan Macvarish puts it, 'is a "deprived environment" a cold Romanian orphanage with no toys or pictures, inadequate food and scarce human contact, or is it a family which cannot afford the latest brain-boosting infant products or which struggles to fit in an extra bedtime story?'

* * *

One morning, the day after my daughter's seventh birthday, she woke with a temperature. I volunteered to stay home with her, as my commitments were less pressing than those of my husband. This is often the case amongst my friends, even if the dads are willing, which they very often aren't. Data from a 2014 Kaiser Family Foundation survey showed that 40 per cent of working mothers in the US take time off when their children are sick, compared to 3 per cent of fathers.

My daughter was ill, but not that ill. She was well enough to make paper-lantern animals, one of her birthday presents, and ask me regular questions about the position of eyes and ears. I could have taken the day off. I could have sat and played with her. But I carried on working. In fact I did more work that day than most other days. My daughter being off school had driven me into compensatory productivity. But I felt conflicted all day. It was a relief when it was time to pick up her brother from school. Finally, now that I had both to look after, I was able to give them my full attention. The economy of scale had been restored.

The possibility of a child's illness hangs over the working mother, revealing the lack of a structured back-up system and the fragility of her daily occupation: it can be pulled away at any time, according to the vagaries of infection, and revealed to be actually a fair-weather pursuit, not as vital as she imagined. Covid-19 has been an extreme iteration of this perennial reality. The hardest day at work is mitigated by validation, but a day spent unexpectedly at home unfolds at the languid pace of unobserved labour.

I found it hard to hear that the early years of my children's lives were the most critical. I remember some mums saying their infants were 'good company', and found it an odd phrase, as if they were at pains to prove something to be true. Or maybe it was just me that found the baby and toddler stage a bit of a challenge. I've never been very good at just sitting. I'd bundle my children onto the train to Kew gardens, where we'd schlep around a ridiculously overambitious itinerary taking in the flora of numerous tropical and temperate climatic environments, just so I could feel I was accomplishing something with the day. And then we'd tackle the return journey with their empty stomachs and full nappies, because I'd run out of wipes and had forgotten to bring along the mini Tupperware boxes of cucumber sticks and picked grapes. Commuters understandably stared daggers at me while my kids wailed in stereo.

The reality of many supposedly 'present' mothers' lives is a lot of time staring at a screen. A survey by the data company Nielsen found that this group spend even more hours on computers and smartphones than their working counterparts. And while I understand that bonds are formed early on, when children are at their most dependent and vulnerable, it is also the case that during those years it felt like the easiest time to hand my babies over to someone else. I did agonise over choosing nannies and nurseries, but sometimes I entrusted them to a stranger (vetted, of course) I'd found online. I don't think I need have worried as much as I did, as they didn't seem mind being handed over temporarily, as long as that person was warm and engaged.

It is since they have grown into individuals that I've felt I can't just palm my children off on a kindly stranger from the internet. It's ironic that finding childcare is most straightforward for younger children – the period that is most closely scrutinised. Having other people look after your kids when they are school age is much less frowned upon, but after-school and holiday childcare is practically and emotionally harder to organise. That 2015 workingmums.co.uk survey found that childcare for school-age children topped the list of mothers' concerns. Half of those polled complained that recent government initiatives to improve childcare provision for three- and four-year-olds were of no use to them. Once again, society's obsessive focus is on the early years, and then it appears to lose interest.

IS DAYCARE DAMAGING?

This question has received avid media attention over the decades. Simply posing it so repeatedly creates anxiety for many working mothers. The answer, broadly, is no, even when it's full time: in fact, it can be beneficial, though quality matters. This was the conclusion reached as long ago as 1997 by two psychologists, Tony Munton and Ann Mooney, who conducted a comprehensive survey of forty years' research into the effects on children of mothers in full-time work for the Coram Research Unit at London University's Institute of Education. 'There isn't a scrap of evidence that putting children in daycare while their mothers go to work is bad for their health or education,' commented Ian Roberts, director of the Child Health Monitoring Unit at the Institute of Child Health, when the study was released. 'On the contrary, the evidence from well-conducted and controlled trials suggests that it's very good for children.'

One of the largest studies was carried out in the 1990s by the National Institute for Child Health and Human Development in the US, which followed the development of more than 1,200 children from birth to mid-childhood. It found 'no significant differences in attachment security' between children who were in daycare and those who were at home. There were even some advantages for the children in daycare, such as improved cognitive performance. This was true even if the care 'began early in the child's life' – although again the researchers emphasised the importance of quality. Another study, led by the American psychologist Margaret Burchinal, and published in 1992, found that even full-time daycare from six months 'was not associated with increased insecure attachment'. Daycare 'did not negatively change, and sometimes enhanced, the associations between the infant–mother attachment and the mother's involvement and warmth toward her infant' during the first year of life.

I spoke to Tony Munton, co-author of the Coram report, who has worked as a scientific adviser in government evaluating policy programmes including Sure Start. 'We really ought to put to bed this notion that pre-school non-parental care is harmful,' he told me. 'We've got an absolute mountain of evidence now that says good quality pre-school experiences have a positive impact on children's development.' The 'iron triangle' of quality – established in the influential *Cost, Quality and Child Outcomes in Child Care Centers* study begun in 1993, and in research by the Education Policy Institute – are staff qualifications, ratios between children and staff, and group size; even with the same child–staff ratio, some children benefit from being in smaller groups. There's an additional reason why daycare is beneficial for children, Munton went on: 'The very fact that mothers have access to good quality affordable daycare means that they can work, and this in and of itself has a positive impact on outcomes for children. We know that one of the most important predictors of child outcomes is parents' socioeconomic status, their income. Poverty is bad for people on so many levels, and this context is no different.'

Despite the 'mountain of evidence', the studies keep coming, but they provide the same answers. A 2018 analysis by researchers at Harvard Business School found that the daughters of working mothers have better careers, higher pay and more equal relationships than those whose mothers stayed at home. The sons grew up to be more involved fathers to their own children. The Harvard study, which looked at data from twenty-nine countries, also showed the US and the UK to have some of the least helpful arrangements for mothers in the world. According to a 2016 study by Silvia Mendolia, an economics professor at Australia's University of Wollongong, which looked at British Household Panel Survey data designed to be representative of the whole population and collected between 1994 and 2006, a mother's working hours have no negative effect on teenagers' self-esteem, life satisfaction or educational prospects; the children of mothers who work full time are more likely to pursue higher education.

The science quoted in the media invariably concerns 'impacts' on children, but what about the wellbeing of mothers? Researchers at the University of Bath found in 2012 that single mothers who work are about 15 per cent less likely to be clinically depressed than those who do not. For mothers who are part of a couple, work reduces the likelihood of depression by 6 per cent. A 2012 Gallup poll in the US also found that stay-at-home mothers were more likely to be depressed. Researchers at the University of North Carolina interviewed 1,300 women over ten years from 2003–08; they found that for women going back to work there was a 26 per cent fall in the incidence of mental health problems, while those who left employment showed a 25 per cent rise. A 2014 poll of 900 mothers by Mumsnet found that a third of stay-at-home mums admitted they would prefer to have a job, and 52 per cent said staying at home was tougher than going out to work.

A MODERN PROBLEM

Work and childcare are regarded today as a zero-sum game: the phrase work–life balance seems benign, but it implies that a gain on one side entails a loss on the other (it also assumes work is not life, and 'life' is not work). Yet work is not opposed to motherhood; it underpins it. I am so much more patient with the kids when my work is going well: it's as if I have an inner reservoir of affirmation to sustain me while I sit on the floor playing Dobble.

'Work–life balance' is in fact a function of the modern, formalised 'workplace'. As Sarah Knott has shown, children in the past were taken to work with their mothers – worn on the backs of agricultural workers, or placed in a basket hung from a nail in factories. Working from home was also commonplace, for women and men: as the historian Helen McCarthy has documented, in the 1890s alone, British women were 'making matchboxes, mending sacks, stitching tennis-ball covers, pulling fur out of rabbit skins, sewing shirt-collars, finishing lace and 'attaching bristles to broom handles' – all from the comfort – or discomfort – of their own homes.

'Working mothers are not new,' observes Sarah Blaffer Hrdy. 'For most of human existence, and for millions of years before that, primate mothers have combined productive lives with reproduction.' She argues that contemporary society has just made it harder for women to combine the two: 'The factories, laboratories, and offices where women in post-industrial societies go to "forage" are even less compatible with childcare than jaguar-infested forests and distant groves of mongongo nuts reached by trekking across desert.'

In the 1980s, a 'new' solution was found to this problem of our own making: 'teleworking' enabled mothers to work from their spare room (or kitchen table). Women could thereby hang on to their hard-won careers, but they have paid a heavy price:

community, camaraderie, being part of a joint enterprise. With the decline of clubs, churches and civic institutions in the late twentieth century – and despite the best efforts of organisations in Britain such as the Women's Institute and the National Women's Register – work became the centre of social life, as well as the source of fulfilment and validation. Researchers have stressed the importance of weak ties – the kind of relationships that are regularly formed between colleagues. In 2020, many men discovered for the first time what women have known for decades – that the price of convenience (or in the case of Covid-19, necessity) is loneliness. A 2019 study by researchers at Essex University who crunched the data from the UK Household Longitudinal Survey revealed that neither working from home nor flexitime reduced mothers' stress levels.

Technology can be liberating, but it is also a tether. The 2015 Gerard Kelly survey found that 20 per cent of mothers feel the need to stay on top of work emails while on school trips to museums, say, or the zoo. A survey carried out in Ireland in 2017 by the formula milk company SMA found that half of women work during maternity leave (these commercial surveys should be taken with a pinch of salt, but they can still be illustrative of genuine social trends). In 2015, researchers from the University of Queensland found that the self-expectation to be both perfect workers and perfect mothers was exacerbated, not alleviated, by devices. The research, published in the *Journal of Child and Family Studies*, found guilt was 'crippling' for some mothers while others felt 'constant pressure to fight the clock', causing them to be impatient with their children, which tainted their time with them and intensified their guilt still further.

Mothers are often excluded from the physical workplace, therefore, with its public pleasures, yet technology enables work demands to intrude into the home. For all the supposed valuing of children, we apparently can't stand to have them around, and new technology means we don't have to. It is women who deal with their mess and their noise, out of sight and out of view. If my ten-year-old had a cold, it would make complete sense to bring him to sit at my side while I am doing some freelancing in the office. But even in a forward-looking media environment, this would feel like I was breaking protocol. My impression is that the separation is even starker now than for a previous generation: I remember accompanying my mum to work at the hospital. You can take your baby in for one big reveal at the start, but then they're bundled back behind the scenes for the remainder of their upbringing.

During the Covid-19 lockdowns there have been some entertaining moments when both male and female TV correspondents have been invaded on air by their bored or curious offspring – the hilarious collision of professional and domestic life a visible illustration of how separate these worlds have become. The virus has repeatedly broken down the façade modern society has constructed between the public world of work and the private world of children – one which mothers have had to sprint between constantly, on stage off stage and on again, often with multiple changes of clothes in a single day. I'm as much a fan of civilised adult spaces as the next sybaritic feminist, but healthy attachment would be much easier to maintain if public society actually tolerated children.

FORGOTTEN FIGHTS

The lessons of history are mixed. Looking back, we can see the origins of some of the restrictive, judgemental advice we have today. But the past also reveals liberating variations in behaviour and attitudes which were often more tolerant and free-thinking than our own. Donald Winnicott was not very keen on the idea of mothers being active in the world, seeing this as aping men: 'When a woman has a strong male identification,' he wrote, 'repressed penis envy leaves little room for maternal preoccupation'. But he was also supportive, reminding mothers that much child development simply happens by itself. 'Some people seem to think of a child as clay in the hands of a potter,' Winnicott said in one of his broadcasts. 'They feel responsible for the result ... you will feel weighed down by this,' he told his listeners; 'but think of the baby as a "going concern",' and you will then 'enjoy responding to the baby's development'.

Working mothers cowed by relentless media coverage of 'damaging daycare' could benefit from remembering the very vocal demands of a previous generation of feminist writers and activists, who argued that the liberation deficit was harmful even for children. 'The great risk our mores present for the infant,' wrote Simone de Beauvoir, 'is that the mother to whom he is tied and bound is almost always an unfulfilled woman.' The mother 'has no hold on the world or the future; she will try to compensate for her frustrations through the child'. As the American historian Kirsten Swinth has noted in *Feminism's Forgotten Fight*, the women's movement has traditionally been viewed as not that interested in the tribulations of mothers; but while some second-wavers regarded motherhood as intrinsically enslaving or boring, many fought for its inclusion in campaigns, on both sides of the Atlantic.

Letty Cottin Pogrebin, editor of the American *Ms.* magazine, argued that feminism should not be about either having it all or doing it all, but admitting that both were impossible in the current system. In 1969, the American feminist writer Alix Kates Shulman penned a much-publicised 'marriage agreement' with her husband, enshrining an equal division of housework and childcare. Four months in, their five-year-old daughter told her father: 'You know, Daddy, I used to love Mommy more than you, but now I love you both the same.' In 1970, a group of feminists took over the offices of the *Ladies' Home Journal* and a few months later published an insert calling for free childcare centres, food co-ops to reduce time spent shopping, and mass meal preparation.

The collective publishing the magazine *Up from Under* recommended women's groups follow the Black Panthers' example and set up children's breakfast programmes. One of the first four demands of the Women's Liberation Movement in 1970 was free twenty-four-hour nurseries. The US National Organisation for Women (NOW)'s Congress to Unite Women in 1969 – 'What Women Want' – declared: 'More and better child care facilities are an absolutely urgent need, to make the liberation of women real.' The 'Working Mothers Charter' produced in 1972 by Mothers in Action (a group set up to help unsupported mothers) stated: 'Adequate substitute care for babies and young children should be provided at all times necessary to enable the mother to work without undue worry.' On a more local level, there were many examples of community-run nurseries and babysitting circles: to mention just one, Bronagh Hinds, a key figure in the Northern Irish women's movement, helped establish an informal crèche, with fully trained staff, to look after her and her friends' children. The Women's Liberation Movement also experimented with communal living.

Many of these interventions are still resonant, relevant and radical today. In 1989, the American sociologist Arlie Hochschild coined an expression for the phenomenon of working women still doing most of the housework: 'the second shift'. Ten years later, she noted that many women took on an additional 'third shift' as well: this was managing the emotions that getting through your first and second shift produced – the indignation of realising that 'having it all' often just meant 'doing everything'. Then and now, society unfairly considers cleaning toilets and wiping bottoms to be humble work, and there is a prevailing belief that if it's your own child's bottom you're wiping, you do not need paying at all.

Selma James pioneered the Wages for Housework campaign: in 1972, the Women's Liberation Movement conference in Manchester read out a paper by James that set out her key demands: the right to work less; the right to have or not to have children; equal pay for all; free community-controlled nurseries and childcare – and wages for housework. James took as her model single mothers on benefits: reviled by society, these women are nevertheless given a basic wage to look after their children – the most important job in the world, we are told. James cited one of the leaders of an American campaign led by black single mothers, Johnnie Tillmon, who wrote in 1972: 'If I were president . . . I'd just issue a proclamation that "women's" work is real work. I'd start paying women a living wage for doing the work we are already doing – childraising and house-keeping' (by implication, if men pull their weight, they should get paid, too).

As a society, we have sustained a fervent investment in the maternal presence Bowlby and his followers advocated (inter-estingly, Bowlby believed that mothers should be paid, if necessary, to stay at home with young children). Yet the plight of single mothers reveals that this investment translates into pressure without support. In the absence of state help or a very robust family network, it is hard for lone parents to either work or not work (the proportion of single parents who work has risen from 45 per cent in 1997 to 70 per cent in 2019). The introduction of working and child tax credits was an attempt to tackle this – with varying impact.

The entire way in which we pay or do not pay people for doing different jobs is irrational. 'Compensation' for high-status financiers is culturally accepted, but where is the compensation for work which society supposedly values but which nobody sees, and which when done just has to be done all over again? When this earlier generation of feminists chal-lenged the iniquities of domestic labour, their interventions were fresh and original; the trouble now is that the assumption of enlightened progress has been accompanied by a largely unobserved creeping back of the conditions that prompted those earlier campaigns in the first place. The task now is to find new ways to defamiliarise and dismantle what has once again become a discriminatory status quo.

Today, if you are at home looking after children, the mostly unchallenged implication is that you will clean and tidy, too, and put a wash on, and cook dinner. A 2014 commercial survey found that the average stay-at-home mother does thirty-one hours of housework a week, not including the weekly shop. Four out of five mothers said they spent more time clearing up after their children than they spent playing with them. Two-thirds said their partners were too tired after work or at the weekends to help. But housework is the enemy of looking after children. In some ways it's easier to just be absent: children hate it if you are there, but not really present, because you're loading the dishwasher or changing sheets. 'The child is the enemy of waxed floors,' wrote Simone de Beauvoir. 'Maternal love is often lost in the reprimands and outbursts that underlie the concern for a well-kept home.' The days of waxed floors may be over, but today's Instagram-ready and shabby chic homes are no less carefully curated, albeit artfully dishevelled in a child-friendly way. 'Mothers are ideally expected to maintain an environment characterised by cheerful, warm, childish chaos,' writes Rozsika Parker. 'They are expected to tidy up *and* thrive in anarchy.'

Modern motherhood somehow manages to demean women while simultaneously raising the stakes. In her study of pre-school children and their mothers in London, the sociologist Mary Georgina Boulton found that high-powered women in particular felt they ought to play with their children and enjoy it, too: they even did it when they didn't feel like it – echoing the observations of the anthropologist David Lancy (and,

from chapter 4, those of the psychologist Martha Wolfenstein).
'I believe that caring for babies should be fun,' writes the
bestselling childrearing expert Miriam Stoppard. But the
journalist Rosalind Coward has argued that it is not just lack
of time that prevents mothers playing with their children;
it's also disinclination. Even cooking and cleaning are sometimes more attractive: 'at least you can think while you are
doing it'. Rozsika Parker suspects that all those dance lessons
and drama clubs are really about 'the escape or respite from
the command to join in and become playing children once
again': she describes watching mothers who've dropped kids
off to their after-school activities 'sink gratefully into conversation with friends – or into their own preoccupations'.
Motherhood is now framed not as self-sacrifice but as an
enjoyable, meaningful job. And if it's enjoyable, remuneration
is surely unnecessary.

A COLLECTIVE CHOICE

With the Second Wave a distant memory, and in an era shaped
by conservative politics, solutions to the reconciliation of work
and childcare are now too often regarded as individual choices:
'lean in' or stay home on your own. As the sociologists Jo Littler
and Janet Newman have argued, the figure of the mumpreneur
privatises the problem of work for each and every mother – as
well as being essentially an airbrushed version of the digital
gig economy. 'There is no justification for mutual help or social
change,' write Barbara Ehrenreich and Deirdre English, 'in an
ideology which holds each person wholly responsible for her
own condition.' In *Making Motherhood Work*, the sociologist
Caitlyn Collins argues that it's time to get beyond the concept
of 'work–life balance', as it reinforces the idea of personal choice
and leaves every mother to hammer out her own compromise
behind closed doors. Yet no woman should have to choose

between career and motherhood if she wants to have it all – or rather both.

So what of the future? Scores of books and policy papers have advocated extending and enhancing parental leave, employer flexibility and access to good quality, affordable child-care. Yet the situation never seems to improve. In fact, as I've argued, in some ways the situation is getting worse. As John Oliver puts it: 'You can't have it both ways. You can't go on and on about how much you love mothers and then fail to support legislation that makes life easier for them.' The same applies to children. If society really put its money where its mouth is, and acted on its noisy disapproval of nurseries, there would be excellent, free, one-to-one or small-group care for young kids.

Tony Munton told me that while there should be no debate now about the benefits of daycare for kids, the question that remains is how to pay for it. It costs the state around £5,000 a year to have a child in primary school, but the current average cost of a pre-school childcare place is £3,000. That makes absolutely no sense, he says, when the child–staff ratio in primary schools is about twenty to one; in nurseries, it is less than half that. So why is childcare so much cheaper? 'The reason is that we are not using quality, well-trained staff. If we want good childcare, he told me, 'it's going to cost more than £10,000 per child per year.' So the policy conundrum is how to fund that. 'I've spent most of my career as an evidence-based policy wonk listening to politicians saying, why don't we follow Sweden; childcare works brilliantly there,' he said – and indeed it does, in Sweden and in other Nordic countries – 'but there you have a population that's happy to pay 60 per cent income tax: that's how they afford it.'

Munton points out that there are other, more creative ways of funding childcare aside from taxation: some have recom-mended a kind of student loan scheme for parents; or – and

I prefer this idea – we could tax wealth rather than income, as many progressive economists have recommended. After all, good quality childcare pays for itself in the long run: in terms of those children's future employment prospects, earning potential and therefore tax revenue, and the reduced chance of being involved in the criminal justice system. 'The argument that we can't afford it,' Munton told me, 'is unjustifiable short-termism.'

The question of who is left holding the baby has a structural solution, therefore, and one that would shift the debate away from the scrutiny and punishment of mothers' behaviour. As I've argued, it is important to distinguish between the good-enough parenting of the 'worried well' and the problematic parenting that produces difficulties later in life for a relatively small proportion of children. There is of course room for improvement for all parents, and we should be aiming for more securely attached children; but this depends on more than just mothers. Really struggling parents, for their part, are simply unable to meet the standards set out in good faith by mental health professionals. There is a cognitive dissonance between policy pronouncements intended to produce healthy outcomes for children on one hand, and the removal of state services that support families on the other.

* * *

The fact that both work and family life have been organised so differently throughout history points to the possibility of a radical rethink today. With new technologies, rising unemploy-ment and the growing needs of an ageing population, work is set to change for very many of us, so why not take the oppor-tunity to finally make it possible for mothers to work without becoming thoroughly burned out? A consensus on the kind of working lives we want appears to be emerging: some time spent working together to operate effectively, keep us all sane and retain social ties, but also more time at home. During the Covid-19 crisis, which has offered an unprecedented experiment in homeworking, over half of respondents to a 2020 YouGov survey said they missed in-person conversations with colleagues, and a majority said they felt the lack of a separate work and living environment; however, a report by academics at Cardiff and Southampton universities found that 90 per cent of the workers they interviewed wanted to carry on working from home some of the time.

The workplace under late capitalism is often an unhappy place: bureaucratic, stultifying, demanding emotional investment but failing to love you back. A universal basic income is not a panacea: it is blind to economic inequality, has little to say about the unwaged work mothers are already doing, and could be used as a pretext to get rid of centrally funded state services. Shorter working hours for all, on the other hand, could solve multiple problems in one go. From trades unions to corporations to think-tanks such as the New Economics Foundation, voices across the board are advocating a four-day week. Working Monday to Friday is not a natural state of affairs but a construct, an artefact of the accommodation reached between labour and capital in the nineteenth century.

Going on maternity leave breaks apart the illusion that work has to be this way: policy architects who wish to 'think outside the box' could learn from every mother who steps off the hamster wheel. Yes, we also need to reduce the cost of living, but there is simply less real demand for full-time jobs now. Much contemporary overwork takes the form of what the anthropologist David Graeber called 'bullshit jobs' – service sector, managerial, and form-filling jobs we do to pay the mortgage, but if they disappeared, society would not suffer. With the collapse of manufacturing and a looming environmental crisis, great swathes of our work economy is a house of cards built on consumerism, dissatisfaction and debt. We should be striving for meaningful work in reasonable hours, while not losing sight of the fact that daycare is positively good for children: Tony Munton warns against a solution that aims at eliminating childcare altogether by 'liberating' parents to share it out between them.

There is in fact no shortage of innovative ideas: the 'Green New Deal for Europe' proposes a 'care income' for all those who look after other people or the planet. The 'Marshall Plan for Moms' advocates paying American mothers as a way to kickstart the post-Covid economy. Campaigning groups in the UK such as Pregnant Then Screwed have called for the self-employed, a growing group, to be given statutory shared parental leave. As well as macro state solutions, there are also community, ad hoc and local ones: businesses from First Direct to Addison Lee have experimented with at-work daycare. Intergenerational daycare centres are appearing in the US and – since 2017 – in the UK, where the old and young can be looked after together, benefiting both. Perhaps calls for a new green economy, as well as the impact of both the social care crisis and the pandemic, will prompt the reassessment we need.

I have had enough of policy solutions aimed solely at mums. It is time for holistic societal shifts that involve dads. Here, we cannot rely on a shift in attitudes alone. Unless egalitarian policies are mandated top-down by government, individual fathers' behaviour will always be judged against an outdated archetype of manly presenteeism.

The problems faced by working mothers – like so many of the aspects of modern motherhood I've discussed in this book – exist on a spectrum which runs from outright discrimination, through outdated male attitudes, through to women's own self-censorship and lowering of expectations. In order for mothers to make demands, they must throw off the internalised repression and reticence that is both archaic, and also curiously new: the sense of failure and insufficiency they feel towards their children, and their gratitude towards employers who toss them scraps of flexibility or partners 'stepping up' to do 30 per cent. For too long, the injustices of modern motherhood have been concealed by anxiety and guilt. Not any more.

CONCLUSION

If mothers really did what most NCT classes, advice books, parenting websites, online forums and media reports expect of them, they would have children in their twenties; not drink while they were trying to conceive; when pregnant they would avoid not just alcohol but caffeine and a whole host of delicious foods, and not go near any DIY materials or cleaning products. They would choose a midwife-led birthing centre and eschew anaesthesia. They'd breastfeed exclusively and on demand for at least six months. They would not sleep-train their baby. They would not work – or only very part time – during the first three years. They would pay full attention while looking after their children, playing with them assiduously and enthusiastically. They would neither lose their temper nor put them on a time out. And they would praise them for good behaviour, loudly and continuously.

This is not a credible way to live.

Mothers today are bullied and guilt-tripped into lowering their sights, reining in their ambitions, shelving their pleasures, and putting their own needs last. It's done explicitly, through guidelines; subtly, through the media and public attitudes; and practically, through structural obstacles at every step of the way. They spend a substantial portion of their waking lives depressed, exhausted and fretful, constantly juggling children's emotional needs, life admin and paid work. Mothers are expected to be responsible and controlled at all times; yet their dignity and autonomy is constantly undermined.

Above all, modern motherhood is characterised by two incompatible and unattainable ideals: the return to nature, and the pursuit of perfection. As I've argued in this book, what is regarded as 'natural' parenting is often not natural at all, but a certain set of practices characteristic of affluent families in the twenty-first-century West. And the relentless perfectionism is propelled by the illusory spectre of harm to the child. These dreams and nightmares alike are preventing motherhood from being a truly gratifying experience for both mothers and children.

As I've shown, some of the panic around attempts to impose a single 'correct' parenting style can be dispelled by appreciating how these vary across both time and space. Norwegian parents put their babies out for naps in the freezing cold: they apparently sleep better and longer. In the Polynesian Islands, infants are looked after by other children who are themselves younger than five. The Kisii people of Kenya avoid looking their babies in the eye, for fear it will cause them to grow up thinking they can control their parents. Spanish children stay up late, and Italian pre-teens drink wine with their meals. Japanese parents let seven-year-olds ride the underground by themselves.

By remembering that these variations exist, and recognising that our own moment in history is not in all respects the teleological culmination of human progress, my hope is that more mothers can, finally, give themselves permission to think critically about the norms they have been dealt.

In his highly popular childcare book *Infants and Mothers: Differences in Development*, published in 1969, the paediatrician T. Berry Brazelton divided babies into three essential types.

Some are active. Some are quiet. And some are average – a bit in-between. There is something freeing about this observation: parents can only do so much to mould their children – as the writer Nora Ephron put it, the comforting old adage was 'they never really change'.

Now, by contrast, mothers in particular are expected to do whatever they can to improve their children's life chances, however marginal the gain to the child, and however weighty the cost to her. 'The culture came to believe in the perfectibility of the child,' Ephron observes – echoing the critique of scientific determinism I have developed in this book – 'as it also came to believe in the conflicting theory that virtually everything in human nature was genetic.'

Childrearing today involves incessant rumination: about fertility, pregnancy behaviour, childbirth styles, feeding techniques, sleep routines, work patterns and childcare arrangements. As I've argued, these 'debates' are traps that misrepresent the mix-and-match muddle of parenting, corrode women's confidence, prevent them from listening to either their own needs or those of their child, divide women into camps, pit them against each other, disavow the covert privileging of child-centred options, and obscure the important ways in which the interests of mother and child are aligned.

Now that my children are older, I look back to those debates with disbelief. There is pleasure to be found down the rabbit holes, but also extravagant waste. These shibboleths absorb energy and headspace when women could be thinking about more worthwhile things. Some women don't have the time to think about them at all. I am far enough away from that early stage to know that none of it really makes a difference either way. Parenting debates are a disappointingly limited response to the (admittedly daunting) freedom and creativity of being able to bring up a baby any way you like. It's such a waste of this little utopian window.

As the child-rearing culture wars rage on, much more significant threats to children are simply out of view: poverty and inequality, cuts to essential state services, a shoddy and inadequate education system, limited life chances for children in disadvantaged families. At the same time, there is a belief that less-than-perfect mothering produces these societal problems – or that the 'right' kind of mothering is their only available solution. It's tempting to spend time thinking about parenting practices you can control rather than political decisions you cannot, but collectively, we are missing the wood for the trees.

In the twenty-first century, the UK could, as the sixth richest country in the world, and where the super-rich possess a combined fortune of £750 billion, invest in thorough research into maternal health, proper support for new mothers, a system of shared parental leave that works, good quality, free daycare, schools that are not held together by teachers' superhuman efforts and mothers' voluntary labour, school-hours employment, and formal routes back into work. We could revitalise the welfare state and build a new economy based on care for others. The question is, whether we value mothers and children enough to do it.

* * *

Our modern attempts to protect children from any and all risks are leading to unintended consequences. Children play outside less, are afraid to climb trees, and eat food from plates that have been washed in anti-microbial detergent. Some social changes – primarily road safety – are positive developments. But the same inordinate risk avoidance that restricts mothers is also creating a generation of anxious, lonely and unhappy kids.

Because instead of letting children take ordinary, instructive risks out there in the real world, kids are encouraged by the wider culture and peer pressure to spend more and more time sitting in front of screens. It's complicated: screens give hard-pressed mothers a break, and I'm all in favour of that. And of course, it may be that this is just a new moral panic. We don't yet have enough evidence. But we do know, via the critiques of technology writer James Bridle and others, that children are exposed through screens to the full blast of the consumer society, and to other even more dubious agendas. They may be cosseted in the living room, but they are sitting targets for the subtle advertising operations of multinational corporations, in-game purchases, entry-level gambling, pornography, and bot-generated horror montages slipped into YouTube compilations of *Peppa Pig*. The attempt to erase ordinary flaws and pitfalls such as dirt, scrapes and boredom exposes kids to actual harm.

Children are put in front of screens, arguably, because a lack of discipline and boundaries early on (as well as the screen use itself) has left many with an inability to self-regulate. Yet in a final irony, technology ends up imposing on children the kind of exacting micro-management and gruelling self-maintenance that mothers have laboured under all along: it's there in the inflexible school testing regimes and carefully curated social media profiles. Digital technology is – like modern parenting – unrealistic and absolutist. Mediocrity and defeat were once an accepted part of life; now they must be eliminated: 'Smile!'

Unlike many modern manifestos, therefore, this book does not locate remedies in new technology. For all its solutionist shine, technology prevents us from seeking political solutions to social problems; leaving us, instead, with only the unrelenting drive towards individual self-improvement. As well as accepting the good-enough mother, we must realise that building a better society is a shared, incremental, real-world process.

* * *

It is time to acknowledge the real cultural pressures on mothers – especially where they masquerade as false feminism. It's time to look candidly at mothers' actual lived experience and the ups and downs of their relationships with their children, illuminated by psychoanalytic insights. We must reject finally the zero-tolerance rigidity that blights motherhood, accepting failure as inevitable, and distinguish that reality from genuine problems. We need to remember forgotten feminist demands and combine these with new realities: transforming birth from trauma to miracle, instituting support structures for new mothers, reorganising work both outside and inside the home, and using scientific and historical knowledge to liberate mothers from anxiety and guilt. My message is critical, therefore, but also hopeful: that modern motherhood doesn't have to be this way.

When I had a baby, people would say, ominously, 'you just wait'. You mean it's going to get worse than this? I thought. Sometimes it was men with older children, trying to preserve their place in the hierarchy of suffering. I know the teenage years can be harder than the toddler stage; perhaps I'm in the sweet spot. But gradually, over the years, difficulty has given way to delight. Our culture's disproportionate focus on the baby stage means that later childhood is curiously neglected. Perhaps there's an ungenerous reluctance on the part of society to reveal how much can be improved upon over the long haul: the spotlight is on the beginning as make or break.

But this is what I wanted to be told, when I was struggling with a baby and a toddler: that it would get much, much better. The relationship between a mother and her child – so often vexed at first – is usually healed over time. Kids get easier, and mothers learn on the job. It's a virtuous circle. What happens, Rozsika Parker writes, is 'the building up of an image in the mother's mind of the essential goodness of her child, and her belief in herself as able to shape and raise an increasingly "good" child'.

I used to tell my child-free friends to take me aside for a quiet word if I turned into one of 'those' mothers, the former feminists who'd had their heads turned by their babies. I don't believe I've been 'turned'. I am still a feminist, and I am still far from perfect. Even in the course of writing this conclusion, I have broken off to shout at the kids for fighting. But I love them, and I love being a mother, more than I can say. Surely we can have the love, and the politics, too.

NOTES ON REFERENCES

INTRODUCTION

For Adrienne Rich's distinction between motherhood as experience and as institution, see *Of Woman Born: Motherhood as Experience and Institution* (1976). The *Vogue* interview with Serena Williams is from 10 January 2018. Simone de Beauvoir's *The Second Sex* was published in 1949. The *Guardian* article about career women returning to work is from 16 June 2013. The *Daily Mail* article on a child's first 1,000 days is from 17 August 2011.

There are now too many rich and illuminating motherhood memoirs to mention here. But, as well as Rachel Cusk's *A Life's Work: On Becoming a Mother* (2001), see in particular Kate Figes, *Life After Birth: What Even Your Friends Won't Tell You* (1998) and Anne Enright, *Making Babies: Stumbling into Motherhood* (2004). Sheila Heti, *Motherhood* (2018), Elisa Albert, *After Birth* (2015), Rivka Galchen, *Little Labours* (2015), Chris Power's 2019 story collection *Mothers*, Liz Berry's 2018 poetry collection *The Republic of Motherhood*, Nadja Spiegelman's *I'm Supposed to Protect You from All This* (2016), Clover Stroud's *My Wild and Sleepless Nights: A Mother's Story* (2020), Maggie Nelson's *The Argonauts* (2015), and Jenny Offill's *Dept. of Speculation* (2014) have all explored different aspects of motherhood and non-motherhood in fiction and non-fiction in recent years. Lara Feigel's *Free Woman: Life, Liberation and Doris Lessing* (2018) explores the surprising ways in which modern wives and mothers are still not liberated. Fay Weldon's *Puffball* (1980) and Joanna Kavenna's *The Birth of Love* (2010) are both, in different ways, compulsively realistic portrayals of both labour and motherhood under pressure. There are many others.

The NICE consultation on FASD can be found on their website (expected guideline publication date: 30 July 2021).

For more on relative risk to children, see Michael Blastland and David Spiegelhalter, *The Norm Chronicles: Stories and Numbers about Danger and Death* (2013). The study on the morality of risk perception is 'No Child Left Alone: Moral Judgments about Parents Affect Estimates of Risk to Children', *Collabra: Psychology*, 2016; see also Linda Fentiman's *Blaming Mothers: American Law and the Risks to Children's Health* (2017), and Peter Stearns's *Anxious Parents: A History of Modern Childrearing in America* (2003).

On the methodological problems with research into pregnancy, childbirth and parenting styles, I drew on Emily Oster's *Expecting Better: Why the Conventional Pregnancy Wisdom is Wrong and What You Really Need to Know* (2018), and her *Cribsheet: A Data-Driven Guide to Better, More Relaxed Parenting, from Birth to Preschool* (2019), and Linda Geddes's *Bumpology: The Myth-busting Pregnancy Book for Curious Parents-to-be* (2013).

Sarah Moss's novel *Night Waking* was published in 2011.

On the history of childrearing, see for example Jennifer Traig, *Act Natural: A Cultural History of Misadventures in Parenting* (2019), and Ann Dally, *Inventing Motherhood: The Consequences of an Ideal* (1982). On advice to parents, see Barbara Ehrenreich and Deirdre English, *For Her Own Good: 150 Years of the Experts' Advice to Women* (1978), Christina Hardyment, *Dream Babies: Childcare Advice from John Locke to Gina Ford* (1983), Fran Abrams, *Songs of Innocence:*

The Story of British Childhood (2012), and Ann Hulbert, *Raising America: Experts, Parents, and a Century of Advice About Children* (2003). In *Feminism's Forgotten Fight: The Unfinished Struggle for Work and Family* (2018), Kirsten Swinth shows that the feminist movement did campaign for mothers. Jill Lepore's *The Mansion of Happiness: A History of Life and Death* (2012) explores how fundamental life events have been framed differently across time. For past experiences of motherhood, see Sarah Knott's *Mother: An Unconventional History* (2019).

The article by EJ Dickson is from Bustle.com, 30 March 2018.

On the psychoanalytic understanding of motherhood, see to begin with Jacqueline Rose's *Mothers: An Essay on Love and Cruelty* (2018) and Rozsika Parker's *Torn in Two: Maternal Ambivalence* (1995).

1: MOTHER NATURE

On birth trauma, see the Birth Trauma Association website, and 'The prevalence of post-traumatic stress disorder in pregnancy and after birth: A systematic review and meta-analysis', *Journal of Affective Disorders*, 2017.

For the Care Quality Commission's survey of women's experiences of maternity care, see '2017 survey of women's experiences of maternity care' on the CQC website, January 2018.

On tocophobia, see 'Worldwide prevalence of tocophobia in pregnant women: systematic review and meta-analysis', *Acta Obstetricia et Gynecologica Scandinavica*, 2017. For Catriona Jones's comments, made at the British Science Festival, see 'Rise in childbirth terror disorder "fuelled by social media"', the *Guardian*, 13 September 2018. The Bournemouth study on attempts to find out the reality of childbirth is '"Is it realistic?" the portrayal of pregnancy and childbirth in the media', *BMC Pregnancy and Childbirth*, 2016.

'My parents had been missionaries in Papua New Guinea' is from the *New York Post*, 13 July 2016. The *Daily Mail* article about the birth of George was from 27 July 2013.

The NHS Digital report on the decline of epidurals is at digital.nhs. uk/data-and-information/publications/statistical/nhs-maternity-statistics/2017-18.

The Ann Oakley essay is the William Power Memorial Lecture published as: 'Who cares for women? Science versus love in midwifery today' in *Midwives Chronicle* (1989).

On maternal and infant mortality, see 'Each Baby Counts', RCOG, 2018; 'Stillbirths: Where? When? Why? How to make the data count?', *Lancet*, 2011; 'Maternal mortality', a 2019 WHO factsheet; 'Child and Infant Mortality', Our World in Data, 2019; and 'Ending Newborn Deaths', Save the Children, 2014.

For the anthropology of birth practices, see for instance the classic studies: *Childbearing: Its Social and Psychological Aspects*, edited by Stephen Richardson et al (1967), and *Newton on Birth and Women: Selected Works of Niles Newton, Both Classic and Current* (1990), Margaret Mead's *Male and Female* (1949), as well as Brigitte Jordan's *Birth in Four Cultures: A Crosscultural Investigation of Childbirth in Yucatan, Holland, Sweden, and the United States* (1978). For the 'tribal' natural childbirth archetype, see for instance healingourchildren.net.

On varying childbirth management worldwide, see 'Variations in use of childbirth interventions in 13 high-income countries: A multinational cross-sectional study', *PLOS Medicine*, 2020.

On the obstetrical dilemma hypothesis, see Holly Dunsworth's article, 'Metabolic hypothesis for human altriciality' in *Proceedings of the National Academy of Sciences*, 2012. On C-sections and babies' heads, see 'Are caesareans really making us evolve to have bigger babies?', *New Scientist*, 5 December 2016.

For the history of natural childbirth, I drew on Margarete Sandelowski's *Pain, Pleasure and American Childbirth* (1984); Jacqueline H. Wolf's *Deliver Me from Pain: Anesthesia and Birth in America* (2009); Amy Tuteur's invaluable *Push Back: Guilt in the Age of Natural Parenting* (2016), Judith Walzer Leavitt, *Brought to Bed: Childbearing in America, 1750–1950* (1988) and her article 'Birthing and Anesthesia: The Debate over Twilight Sleep', *Signs*, 1980; Christina Bobel, *The Paradox of Natural Mothering* (2001); 'Natural Childbirth in Twentieth Century England: A History of Alternative Approaches to Birth from the 1940s to the 1990s', an unpublished 2009 PhD thesis by Amanda-Jane Raphael; Randi Hutter Epstein, *Get Me Out: A History of Childbirth from the Garden of Eden to the Sperm Bank* (2010); Monica Green, *Making Women's Medicine Masculine* (2008); Katharine Park, *The Secrets of Women: Gender, Generation, and the Origins of Human Dissection* (2006); Sanjay Datta's *Childbirth and Pain Relief: An Anesthesiologist Explains Your Options* (2001); Leon Chertok's *Psychosomatic Methods in Painless Childbirth: History, Theory, and Practice* (1959); Tess Cosslet's *Women Writing Childbirth: Modern Discourses of Motherhood* (1994); Jane Sharp's *The Midwives Book, or, The Whole Art of Midwifry Discovered*, edited by Elaine Hobby (1999); Helen King's *Midwifery, Obstetrics and the Rise of Gynaecology* (2007); *Radical Midwifery: Celebrating 21 Years of ARM: An Anthology Compiled from the Archives of the ARM 1976–1997* (1997); and Jacques Gélis, *History of Childbirth: Fertility, Pregnancy and Birth in Early Modern Europe* (1991).

On Grantly Dick-Read and the history of the NCT, I explored the archive relating to his life and work and the archive of the NCT in the Wellcome Library in London. I also drew on *Post-War Mothers: Childbirth Letters to Grantly Dick-Read, 1946–1956* edited by Mary Thomas (1998), Ornella Moscucci's 'Holistic obstetrics: the origins of "natural childbirth" in Britain', *Postgraduate Medical Journal* (2003), Donald Caton's 'Who Said Childbirth Is Natural?: The Medical Mission of Grantly Dick Read', *Anesthesiology* (1996), and Tuteur's *Push Back*.

The quotations from Dick-Read can be found in his *Childbirth Without Fear* (1942), *Natural Childbirth* (1933), and *Motherhood in the Post-War World* (1944).

The Belinda Phipps quotation is from the *Telegraph*, 25 May 2008.

The Australian study of the subjectivity of labour pain is 'The meaning of labour pain: how the social environment and other contextual factors shape women's experiences', *BMC Pregnancy and Childbirth*, 2017. Clare Monagle's paper is 'Scholastic Affect: Gender, Maternity and the History of Emotions' (2020); see also Joanna Bourke's *The Story of Pain: From Prayer to Painkillers* (2017).

For the French context, see Elisabeth Badinter, *The Myth of Motherhood: An Historical View of the Maternal Instinct* (1980), and *The Conflict: How Modern Motherhood Undermines the Status of Women* (2006). For Fernand Lamaze and natural childbirth in the Soviet Union, see Paula A. Michaels, *Lamaze: An International History* (2014), and *Preparation for Birth: The Complete Guide to the Lamaze Method* edited by Beverly Savage and Diana Simkin (1987).

Ina May Gaskin's comment about the 'princess' was made to the *New York Times*, 23 May 2012.

On the risks of anaesthesia and caesareans, I drew on Geddes's *Bumpology* and Oster's *Cribsheet*. On the efficacy of pain relief techniques, see 'Pain management for women in labour: an overview of systematic reviews', Cochrane Library, 2012. On the safety of epidurals, see 'Epidural versus non epidural or no analgesia for pain management in labour', Cochrane Library, 2018. The 2011 NICE guidelines on caesarean sections were updated in 2019. On VBAC, see NHS Behind the Headlines, 'Planned caesareans "safer" for women with past history of caesarean sections', 25 September 2019. For home births, see 'The Birthplace in England Cohort Study', *British Medical Journal*, 2011.

For the implications of the Montgomery ruling, see the *BMJ*'s commentary, 'Montgomery and informed consent: where are we now?' on the *BMJ* website, 12 May 2017.

Elselijn Kingma's paper, 'Improving Our Thinking', is published in *AIMS Journal*, 2013. Alexandra Fowler Dalton's thesis is 'Moms, Midwives, and MDs: A Mixed-Methods Study of the Medicalization and Demedicalization of Childbirth', unpublished PhD thesis, Duke University, 2009.

The Birthrights and Birth Companions study on mothers with multiple disadvantages is available on the Birthrights website, entitled 'Holding it all together: Understanding how far the human rights of women facing disadvantage are respected during pregnancy, birth and postnatal care'. The Canadian study on low-income women's birth choices is 'Social disparity and the use of intrapartum epidural analgesia in a publicly funded health care system', *American Journal of Obstetrics & Gynecology*, 2010. See also 'Access to midwifery care for people of low socio-economic status: a qualitative descriptive study', *BMC Pregnancy and Childbirth*, 2019, and 'What influences birth place preferences, choices and decision-making amongst healthy women with straightforward pregnancies in the UK? A qualitative evidence synthesis using a "best fit" framework approach', *BMC Pregnancy and Childbirth*, 2017.

The *Guardian* article citing Ted Baker's comments is 'Midwives and doctors at odds over "normal" births in English hospitals', 11 December 2020.

2: TICK, TOCK

The *Newsweek* story is from 12 August 2001; the Kirstie Allsopp interview 1 June 2014; 'Geriatric pregnancy', 15 October 2018; 'Career women's baby hunger', 27 June 2003; 'Desperate to conceive?', 26 March 2014; 'Teach girls of 12 to start a family', 15 June 2016; 'Boys born to women who delay motherhood', 8 June 2018; 'Childlessness doubles', 5 December 2013; '"I couldn't have it all"', 20 April 2013; 'Why we prioritise career success', 15 November 2019; 'Career versus motherhood', 22 July 2020; 'Millennial women are delaying', 1 May 2020. 'Middle-class French mothers', 20 September 2005. 'The clock is ticking for the career woman' is from 16 March 1978. Moira Weigel's *The Labor of Love: The Invention of Dating* was published in 2016.

The 2017 survey on attitudes to prioritising children over career was conducted by the toy retailer Play Like Mum. The *Loose Women* episode was aired on ITV on 13 October 2018. Jody Day's TEDx talk is 'The Lost Tribe of Childless Women', March 2017. Jordan Peterson's 'Women at Thirty' is at www.youtube.com/watch?v=LASAIgBt-4g. The *BMJ* editorial is from 17 September 2005. 'It's kind of like issuing a warning' is from a *Newsweek* interview, 8 December 2001.

For the history of infertility and fertility treatments I drew on *The Palgrave Handbook of Infertility in History: Approaches, Contexts and Perspectives*, edited by Gayle Davis and Tracey Loughran (2017), Shari Thurer's *The Myths of Motherhood: How Culture Reinvents the Good Mother* (1994), and 'Infertility through the ages – and how IVF changed the way we think about it', *The Conversation*, 1 May 2018. Rachel Chrastil's *How to be Childless* was published in 2019.

On the facts of age-related fertility, start with data on the NHS, HFEA, BPAS, and American Society of Reproductive Medicine websites, Oster's *Expecting Better*, and Geddes's *Bumpology*. The Purdue study on perceptions of childlessness was published in the journal *Sex Roles* in 2017. Jean Twenge's article is 'How Long Can You Wait to Have a Baby?', from the *Atlantic*, July/August 2013. The 2011 study by the Centre for Longitudinal Studies is 'Age and fertility: can women wait until their early thirties to try for a first birth?', *Journal of Biosocial Science*, 2011. David Dunson's study is 'Increased infertility with age in men and women', *Obstetrics and Gynaecology*, 2004. Kenneth Rothman's study is 'Volitional Determinants and Age-related Decline in Fecundability: A General Population Prospective Cohort Study in Denmark', *Fertility and Sterility*, 2004.

The *New Republic* cover story is from 20 December 2012. 'Know What You're Doing' in the *New York Times* is from 15 October 2014. BPAS's comments on 'scaremongering' were made to the *Telegraph*, 18 May 2014. The 2015 BPAS study is 'Becoming a mother: understanding women's choices today'. The study by researchers from Aix-Marseille, 'Femmes infertiles de plus de 40 ans: loin du mythe de la femme «carriériste» et du «droit à l'enfant»' is from *Gynécologie Obstétrique Fertilité*, 2016. The study by researchers at the University of California is: 'Age shock: misperceptions of the impact of age on fertility before and after IVF in women who conceived after age 40', *Human Reproduction*, 2013.

'Elizabeth sweeps into my consulting room' is from the *Daily Mail*, 26 March 2014.

On the motherhood pay penalty, the 2006 IPPR report is 'Population Politics'. See also 'Women's Incomes Over the Lifetime', edited by Katherine Rake, 2000, and the TUC/IPPR's updated report, 'The Motherhood Pay Penalty', 2016. The Washington University researchers' recommendation to delay motherhood is from 'The Relationship between Age at First Birth and Mother's Lifetime Earnings: Evidence from Danish Data', *PLOS ONE*, 2016.

For the ONS statistics, see 'Birth characteristics in England and Wales: 2018'.

For Cora Du Bois on Alor men, see *The People of Alor; a Social-Psychological Study of an East Indian Island* (1944).

'Should women delay motherhood?' is from the *New York Times*, 8 July 2013. 'The number of older mothers has soared' is from the *Daily Mail*, 4 September 2017. The 'Egg whisperer' article is from the *Telegraph*, 6 December 2014.

The study on lottery language is 'IVF as lottery or investment: contesting metaphors in discourses of infertility', *Nursing Inquiry*, 2002. On the Israel National Bioethics Council, see 'Egg freezing for age-related fertility decline: preventive medicine or a further medicalization of reproduction? Analyzing the new Israeli policy', *Fertility and Sterility*, 2011.

Full Surrogacy Now: Feminism Against Family was published in 2019. On the Nordic model, see for example Rebecca Asher's *Shattered: Modern Motherhood and the Illusion of Equality* (2011), and Caitlyn Collins's *Making Motherhood Work: How Women Manage Careers and Caregiving* (2019).

A 'generation' of women having children on their own is from the *Daily Mail*, 15 March 2018.

3: DOWN TO EARTH WITH A BUMP

The NCT's guidelines on alcohol are at www.nct.org.uk/pregnancy/food-and-nutrition/alcohol-can-i-drink-when-im-pregnant. The latest edition of *What to Expect When You're Expecting*, by A. Eisenberg, H. E. Murkoff and S. E. Hathaway was published in 2018. For the Chief Medical Officer's advice, and the *BMJ*'s response, see www.bmj.com/company/newsroom/evidence-for-potential-harms-of-light-drinking-in-pregnancy-surprisingly-limited/, and 'Low alcohol consumption and pregnancy and childhood outcomes: time to change guidelines indicating apparently "safe" levels of alcohol during pregnancy? A systematic review and meta-analyses' *BMJ Open*, 2017. The Texas obstetrician is John Thoppil; his comments were made in 2018 in relation to the *BMJ Open* article. For domestic abuse in pregnancy, see the BMA Board of Science's report from 2007, updated in 2014.

The Hastings Center Report is 'Risk and the Pregnant Body', 2013. The Evelyn Glenn quotation is from *Mothering: Ideology, Experience, and Agency*, edited by Evelyn Nakano Glenn, Grace Chang, and Linda

Rennie Forcey (1994). The article from the American Medical Association's *Journal of Ethics* is 'Mothers Matter: Ethics and Research during Pregnancy', 2013.

On the assessment of risks in pregnancy, see *Oster's Expecting Better*, and Geddes's *Bumpology*. The large Danish study is 'The effect of different alcohol drinking patterns in early to mid-pregnancy on child's intelligence, attention and executive function', *BJOG: An International Journal of Obstetrics and Gynaecology* (2012), and the Australian study is 'Low–moderate prenatal alcohol exposure and risk to child behavioural development: a prospective cohort study', *BJOG*, 2010.

Colin Gavaghan's article is '"You Can't Handle the Truth"; Medical Paternalism and Prenatal Alcohol Use', *Journal of Medical Ethics*, 2009. For developments in pregnancy medication, see the 2017 MBRRACE report, 'Saving Lives, Improving Mothers' Care', and the MHRA and the Bill & Melinda Gates Foundation's research project, launched in 2019, on safer, effective use of medicines during pregnancy. For Zoe Williams's excellent commentary on childbearing, see her *Guardian* columns, and *What Not to Expect When You're Expecting* (2012).

The study by researchers from Bielefeld University is 'Determinants of dietary patterns and diet quality during pregnancy: a systematic review with narrative synthesis', *Public Health Nutrition*, 2017, and the Belgian study on obesity is 'Effect of Lifestyle Interventions in Obese Pregnant Women on the Neurocognitive Development and Anthropometrics of Preschool Children', *Obesity Facts*, 2020. The 2014 study on antenatal care for women on low incomes is 'Experiences, utilisation and outcomes of maternity care in England among women from different socio-economic groups: findings from the 2010 National Maternity Survey', *BJOG*, 2014.

On the history of pregnancy prohibitions, see for example Jacques Gélis's *History of Childbirth* and Badinter's *The Myth of Motherhood*. On prohibitions in cross-cultural context, see 'Food Taboos and Cultural Beliefs Influence Food Choice and Dietary Preferences among Pregnant Women in the Eastern Cape, South Africa', *Nutrients*, 2019, and 'Traditional Chinese Pregnancy Restrictions, Health Related Quality of Life and Perceived Stress Among Pregnant Women in Macao, China', *Asian Nursing Research*, 2011. Mary Douglas's *Purity and Danger: An Analysis of Concepts of Pollution and Taboo* was first published in 1966. See also Marika Seigel's *The Rhetoric of Pregnancy* (2013).

On the history of pregnancy loss, see Badinter's *The Myth of Motherhood*, Mead's *Male and Female*, and Shannon Withycombe, *Lost: Miscarriage in Nineteenth-Century America*, (2018). Julia Bueno's *The Brink of Being: Talking About Miscarriage* was published in 2019. For more on the history of pregnancy, see Ehrenreich and English, *For Her Own Good*, and Shulamith Firestone's *The Dialectic of Sex: The Case for Feminist Revolution* (1970).

4: IS IT NORMAL TO FEEL LIKE THIS?

The NCT survey of 1,012 women was carried out in 2017 as part of its 'Hidden Half' campaign.

'Postnatal depression blood test breakthrough' is from 2 July 2013. The *Telegraph* article is from 22 May 2013. Kimberly Yonkers was quoted in a 16 March 2018 article on the Seleni Institute website, as was the comment about the test being 'still in the early stages'. The Leipzig study is 'Elevated Brain Monoamine Oxidase A Binding in the Early Postpartum Period', *Archives of General Psychiatry*, 2010. 'Neurological cause found for the baby blues' is from the German news site dw.com, 25 August 2010. 'Enzyme behind baby blues found' is from the DNA India site, 17 June 2010. 'Drug that beats the "baby blues" in 48 hours' is from 21 March 2019.

The Nuffield report is 'Born into care: Newborns in care proceedings in England', October 2018.

For reluctance to take antidepressants in pregnancy, see 'Women's

Attitudes, Preferences, and Perceived Barriers to Treatment for Perinatal Depression', in *Birth: Issues in Perinatal Care*, 2009. See also 'Perinatal Antidepressant Use: Understanding Women's Preferences and Concerns', *Journal of Psychiatric Practice*, 2013.

The *Nursing Standard* study is 'Shame makes women hide post-natal depression', 1987. For partners providing 'low care', see 'Parents, partners or personality? Risk factors for post-natal depression', *Journal of Affective Disorders*, 1991. On the expectation that parenthood 'would be naturally fulfilling' see 'Maternal expectations and postpartum emotional adjustment in first-time mothers: Results of a questionnaire survey', *Journal of Psychosomatic Obstetrics and Gynaecology*, 2014. For factors including 'brooding rumination', see 'Cognitive factors and post-partum depression: What is the influence of general personality traits, rumination, maternal self-esteem, and alexithymia?', *Clinical Psychology & Psychotherapy*, 2017. The Mumsnet survey is at www.mumsnet.com/surveys/postnatal-depression; the Netmums survey at www.netmums.com/support/maternal-mental-health. For the Co-op and Red Cross survey, start with 'Shocking extent of loneliness faced by young mothers revealed', Co-op website, 2 May 2018.

For the experience of postnatal depression, see for example Natasha Mauthner, *The Darkest Days of my Life: Stories of Postpartum Depression* (2002). See also Tina Miller, *Making Sense of Motherhood* (2005). On bonding, see Figes, *Life After Birth*. The NCT survey of 1,515 parents was carried out by the polling firm Survation in 2016. The study on the benefits of sleep training is 'Infant sleep training: rest easy?', *Canadian Family Physician*, 2018. The Ask Dr Sears comments are at www.askdrsears.com/topics/health-concerns/fussy-baby/letting-baby-cry-it-out-yes-no. Penelope Leach was speaking to BBC News online, 22 April 2010. See also Oster, *Cribsheet*.

The Stern and Kruckman paper is 'Multi-disciplinary perspectives on post-partum depression: an anthropological critique', *Social Science and Medicine*, 1983. The 'reverse Cinderella' is from *What to*

Expect the First Year by Arlene Eisenberg et al, 1994. The study on PND in Pakistan is 'Frequency of postpartum depression and its association with breastfeeding: A cross-sectional survey at immunization clinics in Islamabad, Pakistan', *Journal of the Pakistan Medical Association*, 2017. The Ethiopian study is 'Postpartum depression and associated factors among mothers who gave birth in the last twelve months in Ankesha district, Awi zone, North West Ethiopia', *BMC Pregnancy and Childbirth*, 2019. For the Brazilian study, which was carried out by Tania Salem, see *Parenting in Global Perspective: Negotiating Ideologies of Kinship, Self and Politics* edited by Charlotte Faircloth et al, 2013. The study showing declining postnatal care cross-culturally is 'Postnatal care: A cross-cultural and historical perspective', *Archives of Women's Mental Health*, 2010.

On the history and representation of PND, I drew on Ehrenreich and English, *For Her Own Good*; Hardyment, *Dream Babies*; Rose, *Mothers*; Dally, *Inventing Motherhood*; and Thurer, *The Myths of Motherhood*, as well as the classics, including de Beauvoir, *The Second Sex*; Rich, *Of Woman Born*; Ann Oakley, *From Here to Maternity: Becoming a Mother* (1986); and *Women Confined: Toward a Sociology of Childbirth* (1988). Oakley's British Library recording, as part of the 'Sisterhood and After' oral history treasure trove, is at www.bl.uk/collection-items/ann-oakley-motherhood-and-depression. See also Firestone's *The Dialectic of Sex*, and Juliet Mitchell's *Women's Estate* (1978).

For Winnicott's broadcasts, see www.oxfordclinicalpsych.com/page/609/the-ordinary-devoted-mother-and-her-children-parents-and-children-bbc-196062. See also Anne Karpf, 'Constructing and Addressing the "Ordinary Devoted Mother"', *History Workshop Journal*, 2014. Rachel Cusk commented on the publication of *A Life's Work* in the *Guardian*, 21 March 2008. On maternal ambivalence, see Parker's *Torn in Two*. Juliet Hopkins's paper, 'The dangers and deprivations of too-good mothering', is in *Journal of Child Psychotherapy*, 2007. For Mauthner's comment on normality, see 'Postnatal depression:

how can midwives help?', *Midwifery*, 1997. See also Paula Nicholson's *Postnatal Depression: Facing the Paradox of Loss, Happiness and Motherhood* (2001).

5: NURTURE ON TAP

For the BBC poll on breastfeeding, see 'Breastfeeding guilt experienced by half of mothers – BBC survey', BBC website, 29 January 2019.

For the NHS guidelines on breastfeeding, see www.nhs.uk/conditions/pregnancy-and-baby/benefits-breastfeeding/. For the Baby Friendly Initiative, see www.unicef.org.uk/babyfriendly/. For the American ad campaign, see webarchive.library.unt.edu/eot2008/20081104211812/http://www.womenshealth.gov/breastfeeding/index.cfm?page=ad-council. For the posters on the dangers of formula, see www.tensteps.org/pdf/21dangers-jun2012.pdf. For the *Lancet* figures, see their 'Series on Breastfeeding 1' on the Lancet website.

The trust that referred to artificial feeding was Worcestershire Acute Hospitals NHS Trust. On national guidelines and midwives' interpretation, see 'An evaluation of midwives' knowledge of formula feeding and their role in supporting mothers who formula feed their infants', *Journal of Family Health Care*, 2010. '"The midwives aren't allowed to tell you": perceived infant feeding policy restrictions in a formula feeding culture – the Feeding Your Baby Study' is from *Midwifery*, 2014. 'UK women's experiences of breastfeeding and additional breastfeeding support: a qualitative study of Baby Café services' is from *BMC Pregnancy and Childbirth*, 2015. The RCM's updated position statement on breastfeeding is on their website, 12 June 2018.

The Tel Aviv paper is 'Biomechanics of milk extraction during breastfeeding', *PNAS*, 2014. The Danish study on feeding problems is 'Early breastfeeding problems: A mixed method study of mothers' experiences', *Sexual and Reproductive Healthcare*, 2018. For the demographics of infant feeding, see the most recent Infant Feeding Survey, from

2010: digital.nhs.uk/data-and-information/publications/statistical/ infant-feeding-survey/infant-feeding-survey-uk-2010. The NPR interview with Andrea Freeman is 'From Breastfeeding To Beyoncé, "Skimmed" Tells A New Story About Black Motherhood, NPR, 11 February 2020.

The 2018 study on factors influencing feeding decisions in areas where breastfeeding rates are low is an evaluation of the voucher incentive scheme: 'Valuing breastfeeding: a qualitative study of women's experiences of a financial incentive scheme for breastfeeding', *BMC Pregnancy and Childbirth*, 2018. 'The odds are stacked against breastfeeding' is from the *Observer*, 20 April 2019. The Nottingham study is 'The portrayal of infant feeding in British women's magazines: a qualitative and quantitative content analysis', *Journal of Public Health*, 2017. The Liverpool study is 'The emotional and practical experiences of formula-feeding mothers', *Maternal and Child Nutrition*, 2016. The Aarhus study is 'When breastfeeding is unsuc-cessful – mothers' experiences after giving up breastfeeding', *Scandinavian Journal of Caring Sciences*, 2013.

On the science of infant feeding, see Oster, *Cribsheet*; Geddes, *Bumpology*; Tuteur, *Push Back*; Joan B. Wolf, *Is Breast Best?: Taking on the breastfeeding experts and the new high stakes of motherhood* (2010); Suzanne Barston, *Bottled Up: How the Way We Feed Babies Has Come to Define Motherhood, and Why it Shouldn't* (2012); and Hanna Rosin, 'The Case Against Breastfeeding', *The Atlantic*, 1 April 2009.

For Cochrane on cup feeding, see 'Cup feeding versus other forms of supplemental enteral feeding for newborn infants unable to fully breastfeed', and on feeding on demand see 'Baby-led compared with scheduled (or mixed) breastfeeding for successful breastfeeding'. For BPAS's research on infant feeding, see www.bpas.org/get-involved/ campaigns/briefings/breastfeeding-and-formula-feeding/.

The study by Evenhouse and Reilly is 'Improved Estimates of the Benefits of Breastfeeding Using Sibling Comparisons to Reduce

Selection Bias', *Health Services Research*, 2005. The other sibling study is 'Is Breast Truly Best? Estimating the Effect of Breastfeeding on Long-term Child Wellbeing in the United States Using Sibling Comparisons', *Social Science and Medicine*, 2014. Michael Kramer's PROBIT trial was published in the *International Journal of Epidemiology* in 2014.

The study of the impact of the intention to breastfeed is 'The best of intentions: Prenatal breastfeeding intentions and infant health', *SSM Population Health*, 2018. The evaluation of the voucher scheme is 'Cluster randomised controlled trial of a financial incentive for mothers to improve breast feeding in areas with low breastfeeding rates: The NOSH study protocol', *BMJ Open*, 2016. The *New York Times* letter is quoted in 'The class dynamics of breastfeeding in the United States of America', Quartz, 23 July 2017. Suzanne Haynes is quoted in the *New York Times*, 13 June 2006.

On the history and ideology of infant feeding, see Badinter, *The Myth of Motherhood*; Hardyment, *Dream Babies*; Lepore, *The Mansion of Happiness*; Rima Apple, *Mothers and Medicine: A Social History of Infant Feeding, 1890–1950* (1987); Jacqueline Wolf, *Don't Kill Your Baby: Public Health and the Decline of Breastfeeding in the Nineteenth and Twentieth Centuries* (2001); Linda Blum, *At the Breast: Ideologies of Breastfeeding and Motherhood in the Contemporary United States* (2000); Janet Lynne Golden, *A Social History of Wet Nursing in America: From Breast to Bottle* (1996); 'A History of Infant Feeding', *Journal of Perinatal Education*, 2009; and Caroline Walker Bynum's *Holy Feast and Holy Fast: The Religious Significance of Food to Medieval Women* (1992). The *Guardian* article on the Bavarian feeding vessels is from 25 September 2019. Corin Throsby's essay 'Breast feeding: From pap to bleeding feet' was broadcast on BBC Radio 3 on 30 June 2017. 'The weirdness of breastfeeding someone else's baby' is from TheCut.com, 5 April 2017.

For oxytocin released during breastfeeding, see for example, 'Maternal plasma levels of oxytocin during breastfeeding – A systematic review', *PLOS ONE*, 2020.

On the anthropology of breastfeeding, see *Breastfeeding: Biocultural Perspectives* edited by Patricia Stuart-Macadam and Katherine Dettwyler (1995), *Anthropology of Breast-Feeding: Natural Law or Social Construct*, edited by Vanessa Maher, (1992), and Mead, *Male and Female*.

6: RED MIST

Desmond Runyan's study on disciplining techniques is 'International Variations in Harsh Child Discipline', *Pediatrics*, 2010. *The National Study of Parents, Children and Discipline in Britain* by Deborah Ghate et al was carried out by the Policy Research Bureau, the NSPCC and the National Centre for Social Research. The NSPCC study is 'Child abuse and neglect in the UK today', 2011. The *Atlantic* article is from 6 November 2018.

The *Birth to Five* guide can be found at www.nhs.uk/conditions/pregnancy-and-baby/. It has gone through a series of iterations. The Verywell Family article is 'How to Discipline Without Yelling at Kids', 23 October 2019. Helen Reece's article 'The pitfalls of positive parenting' is from *Ethics and Education*, 2013. The *Washington Post* article on time outs is from 19 November 2018. The *Supernanny* page on 'How to deal with a very angry child' is www.supernanny.co.uk/Advice/-/Parenting-Skills/-/Discipline-and-Reward/Dealing-with-a-very-angry-child.aspx. On the return of *Supernanny* to American screens, see 'What the return of "Supernanny" tells us about parenting in 2020', *Washington Post*, 26 February 2020.

For Tanya Byron's advice, see 'Little Angels: Tanya Byron's Top Parenting Tips – Tantrums, Rewards and Routines' on the eParenting site. Rosie Jefferies was talking about the Inspire Training Group and the therapeutic parenting approach to the *Irish Times*, 21 August 2018. Margot Sunderland was talking to the *Observer*, 7 November 2004 ('Science shows up Supernanny'). The Healthline article is '5 Serious Long-Term Effects of Yelling At Your Kids', from 19 April 2017. The Ask Dr Sears advice is '10 Reasons Not to Hit Your Child'.

The Mail Online article on spanking is from 10 November 2017, and the NHS Behind the Headlines commentary is from 13 November 2017.

Alan Kazdin spoke to the *New York Times* for an article entitled 'Why You Should Stop Yelling at Your Kids', 5 September 2018. The NSPCC 'Positive Parenting' leaflet is at learning.nspcc.org.uk/media/1195/positive-parenting.pdf. Suzanne Gelb's article on *Psychology Today*'s website is '10 Ways to Become the Parent Your Children Really Need', 27 June 2019. Sandra Dupont's HuffPost blog is from 12 October 2012. For Sharon Hays's comments, see *The Cultural Contradictions of Motherhood* (1996). The raisingchildren.au article is 'Smacking: what you need to know', 31 October 2019.

Angela Foster's *Mothers Accused and Abused: Addressing Complex Psychological Needs* was published in 2019. Winnicott's *The Child, the Family, and the Outside World* was first published in 1964.

On the history of child discipline and punishment, I drew primarily on Hardyment, *Dream Babies*; Ehrenreich and English, *For Her Own Good*; Hulbert, *Raising America*; Badinter, *The Myth of Motherhood*; Traig, *Act Natural*; Thurer, *The Myths of Motherhood*; John Gillis's *A World of Their Own Making: Myth, Ritual, and the Quest for Family Values* (1996); *Philippe Ariès's Centuries of Childhood: A Social History of Family Life* (French edition first published in 1960); and *Mothers and Motherhood: Readings in American History*, edited by Rima Apple and Janet Lynne Golden (1997).

On the psychoanalytic understanding of maternal ambivalence and anger, see Rose, *Mothers*, Parker, *Torn in Two*, and Lisa Baraitser's *Maternal Encounters: The Ethics of Interruption* (2008). On the idealisation of motherhood, see Rich, *Of Woman Born*; Jennifer Senior, *All Joy and No Fun: The Paradox of Modern Parenthood* (2014); Susan Douglas and Meredith Michaels, *The Mommy Myth: The Idealization of Motherhood and How It Has Undermined Women* (2004); Dally, *Inventing Motherhood*; Barbara Almond, *The Monster Within: The*

Hidden Side of Motherhood (2010); Sarah LaChance Adams, *Mad Mothers, Bad Mothers, and What a 'Good' Mother Would Do: The Ethics of Ambivalence* (2014); Judith Warner, *Perfect Madness: Motherhood in the Age of Anxiety* (2005); Susan Maushart, *The Mask of Motherhood: How Becoming a Mother Changes Everything and Why We Pretend It Doesn't* (1997); Tracey Jensen, *Parenting the Crisis: The Cultural Politics of Parent-Blame* (2018); Cathi Hanauer, *The Bitch in the House: 26 Women Tell the Truth about Sex, Solitude, Work, Motherhood, and Marriage* (2003); Diane E. Eyer, *Motherguilt: How Our Culture Blames Mothers for What's Wrong With Society* (1996); and Ruth Cain, *Privatised Motherhood: Confession and Anxiety in Neoliberal Times* (2012).

On the repetition of childhood dynamics, see Philippa Perry, *The Book You Wish Your Parents Had Read (and Your Children Will Be Glad That You Did)* (2019).

The Bowlby quotations are from *The Making and Breaking of Affectional Bonds* (1979). Winnicott's essay 'Hate in the counter-transference' was published in the *International Journal of Psycho-analysis* in 1949. For more on Winnicott, see Alison Bechdel's graphic novel memoir *Are You My Mother?* (2012). The Harold Searles story is from 'The effort to drive the other person crazy – an element in the aetiology and psychotherapy of schizophrenia', *Psychology and Psychotherapy*, 1959. For Melanie Klein's splitting, see her essay 'Love, Guilt and Reparation', first published in 1937.

For Diana Baumrind on parenting, see for example, 'Effects of author-itative parental control on child behaviour', *Child Development*, 1966.

'Paediatricians' views on smacking children as a form of discipline' is in *European Journal of Pediatrics*, 2008; 'Spanking children: the controversies, findings, and new directions' in *Clinical Psychology Review*, 2003; *Parental Physical Punishment* was produced by researchers at the Public Policy Institute for Wales. 'Physical Discipline and Children's Adjustment: Cultural Normativeness as a Moderator' was published in *Child Development* in 2005.

7: THE JUGGLE

For the ONS figures on employment, see 'Families and the labour market, UK: 2019' on the ONS website, 24 October 2019. The latest Coram Childcare Survey (2020) can be found on the Coram Family and Childcare website. The OECD report 'Is childcare affordable' is from June 2020. For the Center for American Progress report, see 'Costly and Unavailable: America Lacks Sufficient Child Care Supply for Infants and Toddlers', August 2020. The IFS report is 'Wage progression and the gender wage gap: the causal impact of hours of work', February 2018. The National Women's Law Centre data is at nwlc.org; see also 'The Wage Gap is Wider for Working Mothers', The Society for Human Resource Management website, 21 October 2019. On pensions, see 'Avoiding the motherhood penalty', a report by the financial advice firm LEBC, June 2020. The New Policy Institute report is 'Women, work and wages in the UK', October 2016. The ILO's report 'The motherhood pay gap' was published in March 2015.

Christin Munsch's study, 'Men viewed more favorably than women when seeking work–life balance', was presented to the American Sociological Association in 2014. The EHCR research 'Pregnancy and maternity discrimination research findings' is available on their website. The Slater & Gordon research is at www.slatergordon.co.uk/newsroom/. The study on discrimination and prejudice is 'Justifying gender discrimination in the workplace: The mediating role of motherhood myths', PLOS One, 2018. Marian Baird commented on the CareforKids.com.au survey in 'Working mothers still plagued by guilt', Sydney Morning Herald, 21 April 2013. The Bar-Ilan study is 'The Costs of Thinking About Work and Family: Mental Labor, Work–Family Spillover, and Gender Equality among Parents in Dual-Earner Families', Sociological Forum, 2014.

For the Harvard Business Review survey, see 'Rethink What You "Know" About High-Achieving Women', hbr.org, December 2014. The Department for Education report is 'Childcare and early years survey of parents 2014 to 2015', March 2016. Schulte's *Overwhelmed* was published in 2014. The Resolution Foundation's time use survey, 'The time of your life', is from July 2020. The analysis of the UK Household Longitudinal Survey is 'Are Flexible Work Arrangements Associated with Lower Levels of Chronic Stress-Related Biomarkers? A Study of 6025 Employees in the UK Household Longitudinal Study', *Sociology*, 2019. The Gerard Kelly survey was reported in the *Telegraph*, 3 September 2015. Arwa Mahdawi's article is from the *Guardian*, 8 December 2020.

The edition of *Thinking Allowed* was broadcast on 14 September 2020. The ONS report is 'Women shoulder the responsibility of "unpaid work"', 10 November 2016. The UCL study is 'Less than 7% of couples share housework equally', *Work, Employment and Society*, 2019. The study on lockdown division of labour was carried out by UCL Institute of Education and the IFS, entitled 'How are mothers and fathers balancing work and family under lockdown?'; it was published in May 2020. The ONS data on childcare in lockdown is 'Parenting in lockdown: Coronavirus and the effects on work-life balance', July 2020. '"I feel like a 1950s housewife"': how lockdown has exposed the gender divide' is from the *Observer*, 3 May 2020. The *New York Times* survey on home-schooling is from 6 May 2020.

The study of married doctors is 'Gender Differences in Time Spent on Parenting and Domestic Responsibilities by High-Achieving Young Physician-Researchers', *Annals of Internal Medicine*, 2014. Brendan Burchell was interviewed for the Telegraph, 4 March 2014. The work-ingmums.co.uk survey was reported on in the *Telegraph*, 22 September 2015. The Council on Contemporary Families paper is 'Are Some Millennials Rethinking the Gender Revolution? Long-Range Trends in Views of Non-Traditional Roles for Women' by Nika Fate-Dixon. Patrick Greenfield's *Guardian* article is from 21 March 2016.

On gay and non-binary parents and division of labour, see 'Lesbian women and household labor division: A systematic review of scholarly research from 2000 to 2015', *Journal of Lesbian Studies*, 2016, and 'Division of Labor Among Transgender and Gender Non-binary Parents: Association With Individual, Couple, and Children's Behavioral Outcomes', *Frontiers in Psychology*, 2020.

Kitty Jones's research on stay-at-home fathers is from her unpublished PhD thesis, 'Stay-at-home Father Families: Family Functioning and Experiences of Non-traditional Gender Roles', University of Cambridge, December 2019. For more on the role of fathers, see the work of Michael Lamb, for example: *The Role of the Father in Child Development* (2010).

On working mothers and equality with male partners, see Sally Howard, *The Home Stretch: Why It's Time to Come Clean About Who Does the Dishes* (2020); Eve Rodsky, *Fair Play: Share the Mental Load, Rebalance Your Relationship and Transform Your Life* (2019); Asher's *Shattered*; Shani Orgad, *Heading Home: Motherhood, Work, and the Failed Promise of Equality* (2018); Helen McCarthy, *Double Lives: A History of Working Motherhood* (2020); Collins, *Making Motherhood Work*; and Anne-Marie Slaughter, *Unfinished Business: Women Men Work Family* (2015).

'Stay-at-home mothers "have the most worthwhile lives"' is from the *Telegraph*, 24 September 2014; 'Decline of the stay-at-home mother' from the *Mail*, 2 March 2015; 'Sorry Working Moms, Daycare is Bad for Your Kid' is from HuffingtonPost.ca, 20 July 2015. For the obesity and working mothers study, see NHS Behind the Headlines, 'Working mothers and obese children', 26 May 2010. The review of Leach's *Children First* is from 'Still Guilty After All These Years: A Bouquet of Advice Books for the Working Mom', *New York Times*, 8 May 1994. Anne-Marie Slaughter's *Atlantic* article is from 15 August 2012. The 2014 *Telegraph* article 'Working mothers still left holding the baby . . . and the iron' is from 4 March 2014. On women leaving the workplace in droves, see 'Middle-class mothers deserting workplace to care for children', the *Telegraph*, 30 January 2014.

Betty Friedan's *The Feminine Mystique* was first published in 1963. On the history of working motherhood, see Gillis's *A World of Their Own Making*, Ehrenreich and English, *For Her Own Good*, and Rich, *Of Woman Born*. Alison Light's *Mrs Woolf and the Servants: An Intimate History of Domestic Life in Bloomsbury* was published in 2007.

On Bowlby and attachment theory, see Ann Hulbert, *Raising America: Experts, Parents, and a Century of Advice About Children* (2003), Hardyment, *Dream Babies*, and Eyer, *Motherguilt*. For Diana Divecha on the difference between attachment theory and attachment parenting, see her blog: www.developmentalscience.com, in particular her post 'What is a Secure Attachment? And Why Doesn't "Attachment Parenting" Get You There?', 3 April 2017; see also her essay 'Why Attachment Parenting Is Not the Same as Secure Attachment', Greater Good magazine (greatergood.berkeley.edu), 2 May 2018, which discusses the Sears's advocacy of attachment parenting.

On 'neuroparenting', see John Bruer, *The Myth of the First Three Years* (1999), and Jan Macvarish, *Neuroparenting: The Expert Invasion of Family Life* (2016).

For David Lancy's commentary on Western assumptions of good mothering, see 'Accounting for Variability in Mother-Child Play', *American Anthropologist*, 2007. 'Cross-Cultural Patterns of Attachment: A Meta-Analysis of the Strange Situation' was published in *Child Development*, 1988. Sarah Blaffer Hrdy's *Mother Nature: A History of Mothers, Infants, and Natural Selection* was published in 1991. See also Mead's *Male and Female* and *Understanding Children's Development* edited by Peter Smith et al (2011); for 'alloparenting', see Knott's *Mother*.

The Kaiser Family Foundation survey is 'Balancing on Shaky Ground: Women, Work and Family Health', 20 October 2014. The Nielsen study is 'Q3 2016 Local Watch Report: Stay-at-Home and Working Moms', 30 January 2017.

For Ian Roberts's comments, see 'Who's right about child care?', the

Independent, 4 February 1997. The National Institute of Child Health and Human Development's 'Study of Early Child Care' began in 1990; see also Margaret Burchinal et al, 'Early day care, infant-mother attachment, and maternal responsiveness in the infant's first year', *Early Childhood Research Quarterly*, 1992. For the 'iron triangle' of childcare quality, see 'Structural elements of quality early years provision: A review of the evidence', Education Policy Institute, August 2018.

The Harvard Business School working paper is 'Learning from Mum: Cross-National Evidence Linking Maternal Employment and Adult Children's Outcomes', *Work, Employment and Society*, 2018. Silvia Mendolia's working paper is 'Maternal Working Hours and the Well-Being of Adolescent Children', *Economics Working Papers*, University of Wollongong, Australia, 2014.

The University of Bath study on 'Lone mothers, work and depression' was produced by the Institute for Policy Research in 2012. The Gallup poll is 'Stay-at-Home Moms Report More Depression, Sadness, Anger: But low-income stay-at-home moms struggle the most', 18 May 2012.

The SMA survey on working during maternity leave was reported on in 'Why half of Irish mothers work during maternity leave', *Irish Times*, 25 April 2017. The Australian study was: 'Giving voice to working mothers: A consumer informed study to program design for working mothers', *Journal of Child and Family Studies*, 2015.

On the feminist movement's campaigns for working mothers, see for example, Swinth, *Feminism's Forgotten Fight*, and Helen Lewis, *A History of Feminism in 11 Fights* (2020).

The commercial survey on housework was for Direct Line: '90% of mums don't get enough "quality time" with children', on the SWNS Digital website, 3 April 2014.

On single mothers, see 'Under Pressure? Single parents in the UK', a report by Martina Klett-Davies for the Bertelsmann Foundation, April 2016.

For Mary Georgina Boulton's analysis, see *On Being a Mother: A Study of Women With Pre School Children* (1983). For Miriam Stoppard's comments, see *Day by Day Babycare*, 1985, and for Rosalind Coward's, see *Our Treacherous Hearts: Why Women Let Men Have Their Way* (1992).

The YouGov research on homeworking 'The new workplace. Re-imagining work after 2020' was conducted for the tech firm Okta and can be found on their website. The Cardiff and Southampton report 'Homeworking in the UK: Before and During the 2020 Lockdown', is on the WISERD website, August 2020.

CONCLUSION

Nora Ephron's *I Feel Bad About My Neck: And Other Thoughts on Being a Woman* was published in 2006.

For good advice, start with Naomi Stadlen, *What Mothers Do: Especially When It Looks Like Nothing* (2004), and Williams, *What Not to Expect When You're Expecting*.

For genuine risks to children in modern society, see Sue Palmer, *Toxic Childhood: How the Modern World is Damaging our Children* (2006).

ACKNOWLEDGEMENTS

Many researchers and practitioners gave generously of their time and expertise: obstetricians, midwives, paediatricians, psychiatrists, psychotherapists, psychologists, sociologists, statisticians, demographers, and campaigners, including David Bogod, Rebecca Brione, Danny Dorling, Ana Fernandez, Angela Foster, Susan Golombok, Eric Jauniaux, Emily Jesper-Mir, Kitty Jones, Angela Joyce, Yacoub Khalaf, Natasha Mauthner, Simon Mehigan, Tony Munton, Clare Murphy, Catharina (Rineke) Schram, Stephen Scott, Gertrude (Trudi) Seneviratne, David Spiegelhalter, Alison Steele, Philip Steer, and Kim Thomas.

Early research was carried out at the Wellcome Library, and I'm grateful to the librarians there for advising me on the collection.

This project has been a long time in the making. I would like to thank Louise Haines at Fourth Estate for her encouragement and for her excellent advice throughout. Kate Johnson was a thoughtful and sympathetic copy editor. Tracy Bohan at the Wylie Agency gave me a characteristically insightful account of what the book was about when I couldn't see the wood for the trees. She remains a loyal agent and friend.

Eleanor Birne, Isabel Davis, Chloë Houston and Siobhán Templeton read the manuscript: their suggestions improved it immeasurably. Conversations with these and other wise friends helped me turn the hurly-burly into reflection.

I was able to complete the book with the help of a generous Award for Works in Progress from the Society of Authors.

My mother Danya, who knows a thing or two about the topics I write about here, helped me ensure sections are accurate. She has also taught me about good motherhood by practising it.

I am hugely – infinitely – grateful to my husband Adam: for reading the manuscript twice, for his love and friendship, and for sharing, with a wholehearted commitment to fairness, the project of raising our two wonderful children. They had to put up with me taking time out to write about motherhood – the irony! This book is dedicated to them.

INDEX